SHAMAN'S DAUGHTER

SHAMAN'S DAUGHTER

Nan F. Salerno
Rosamond M. Vanderburgh

PRENTICE-HALL, INC.
Englewood Cliffs, N.J.

The plot and characters in this novel
are entirely fictional, and any similarities to
persons living or dead is coincidental.

Shaman's Daughter
by Nan F. Salerno and
Rosamond M. Vanderburgh

Copyright © by Nan F. Salerno and
Rosamond M. Vanderburgh
1980.

Printed in the United States of America

Prentice-Hall International, Inc., London
Prentice-Hall of Australia, Pty. Ltd., Sydney
Prentice-Hall of Canada, Ltd., Toronto
Prentice-Hall of India Private Ltd., New Delhi
Prentice-Hall of Japan, Inc., Tokyo
Prentice-Hall of Southeast Asia Pte. Ltd., Singapore
Whitehall Books Limited, Wellington, New Zealand

10 9 8 7 6 5 4 3 2 1

Library of Congress Cataloging in Publication Data

Salerno, Nan F
  Shaman's daughter

  1. Indians of North America—Fiction. I. Vander-
burgh, Rosamond M., joint author. II. Title.
PZ4.S1627Sh 1980 [PS3569.A4594] 813'.5'4 79-20280
ISBN 0-13-807768-1

CONTENTS

To all Nishnabeg,
past and present

LIST OF CHARACTERS
(approximately in the order of appearance)

Supaya Cedar
Quayo, Supaya's maternal grandmother
Jacques Cedar, Supaya's brother
Jules Cedar, shaman and Supaya's father
Kineu Bruley, Supaya's cousin and husband
Agatha Harris, schoolteacher
Reverend Nathan Harris,
        Agatha's brother and preacher on Stone Island Reserve
Aunt Theresa
Neegonas and James, Supaya's sister and brother-in-law
Jess and Kirsten Fallon, storekeeper at Two Bluffs Reserve and wife
Mr. Bonnet, storekeeper on Stone Island Reserve
Auntie Em, Quayo's cousin
Cyrus and Miriam Red Sky, Wenonga's brother and sister-in-law
Angus Red Sky and Pearline, Cyrus' son and daughter-in-law
Maud, Supaya's friend and sister-in-law
Rhea, Jules' second wife
S. M. Jackson, Indian agent on Stone Island Reserve
Wenonga Red Sky, shaman and Cyrus' brother
Hettie and Arthur Bruley, Jules' sister and brother-in-law
Keewahd'n, old storyteller
Eli Red Sky, Wenonga's son and Supaya's husband
Reverend and Amy Crowell,
        preacher on Two Bluffs Reserve and wife
Nonen, Wenonga's sister
Marie Able, Eli's girl friend
Jim Able, Eli and Marie's son

Betty, Marie's friend and Eli's girl friend
Soos and George King, Supaya's friends
Sarah King, Soos and George's daughter
Gerald and Lizzie Toomis,
    Indian agent on Two Bluffs Reserve and wife
Mary and John, Nonen's daughter and son-in-law
John and Hattie Bruley, Kineu's uncle and aunt
Wagash Cedar, Supaya's half-brother
Beedaubun, old medicine woman on Stone Island Reserve
Alma, one of Nonen's old friends who lays out the dead
Waboose Bruley, Supaya and Kineu's first son
Daniel, boat and coffin builder on Two Bluffs Reserve
Louis Hagerstrom, farmer
Annie Jones, gossip
Harry and Edna Black
Shooskonee Bruley, Supaya and Kineu's daughter
Mrs. Johnston
Caleb Sims, Sarah's husband
Louisa Hagerstrom, Louis Hagerstrom's daughter
James and Ruby, Soos and George's younger children
Victor and Hilda Fallon, Jess' brother and sister-in-law
Marietta and son Eric, Jess' sister and nephew
Frank Jones, Supaya's suitor and Annie Jones' brother-in-law
Howard Hadley, Rhea's husband
Josie, Sarah's daughter
Reverend Richards, preacher replacing Reverend Crowell
    on Two Bluffs Reserve
Ed Cassety, Shooskonee's boyfriend
Peter, Shooskonee's son
Betty, Waboose's wife
William and Natalie Brent, Indian agent
    replacing Gerald Toomis on Two Bluffs Reserve and wife
Tom and Charlie Bruley, Waboose's sons
Maggie and Theresa, Tom's daughters

PROLOGUE 1967,
Two Bluffs Reserve, Ontario

Though it was still summer, Supaya's aging bones felt the night chill. She had made up a fire in the fireplace and had fallen asleep in her rocker. Abruptly she started awake. Someone had whispered her name, touched her on the shoulder. Jess, she thought, with a surge of excitement, maybe it was Jess! Or Kineu. She squinted into the predawn dark filling her house like a pool of deep water. Was that Quayo nodding at her from the opposite chair? Jules standing in the shadow by the hearth? She sat very still and listened. But there was no sound—no knock, no step. Even the fire burned quietly, its embers sending an occasional spark up the chimney.

For weeks past her house had been full of the presences of her dead. She had sensed them about her, serene and comforting, ready to welcome her. Close to her, yet separated as by an invisible veil, they moved parallel with her in a flowing timelessness, their soft voices piercing her heart.

She stirred up the fire, raising a shower of ascending sparks, and reached for another log. As she lifted it, a sudden pain flamed across her chest, shocking in its intensity, bringing her to her knees on the hearth. Her breath choked back, she gripped the rough wood and waited. Slowly the pain lessened and she cautiously raised her head. Her body was damp, her legs trembled. But she knew now that it was time to go. She must not wait any longer.

She took the steps one at a time, grasping the rail and pulling herself along. Reaching the top she nearly collapsed and was momentarily bewildered, thinking herself in the loft of her father's log house on Stone Island. Again she waited, and when her head cleared, she went into her bedroom and opened her old trunk.

Moving as quickly as she dared without rousing a fierce, final pain, she lifted out garments she had not worn since leaving her father's house so many years before. Needing no light, Supaya dressed herself, putting on her long black skirt and the blouse with the quill embroidery on the neck and shoulders. On her feet she put the still supple beaded moccasins Quayo had made for her. Bracing herself on the edge of the trunk, she knelt down and, reaching in with both hands, raised high a necklace. Remembering herself as a child standing before her father as he solemnly placed the necklace around her neck, Supaya lowered it over her head. Lovingly she touched the smooth bear claws and pressed the blue stone pendant to her breast. Closing her eyes, she rocked back and forth, humming softly to herself. But her song broke off when a sharp pain suddenly bent her forward. She must hurry. Reaching into the trunk again, she touched a bundle of hair, hair she had cut from her own head one dreadful day while Soos had silently watched. That she could now leave. She touched a postcard with a torn corner, other cards—Christmas cards from a small English town—and several fragile letters, their smudged and faded words recounting simply what still was cause for sorrow. Those too she could leave.

Then her fingers closed over the cool, smooth surface of a gold pocket watch with chain and fob attached. For one precious second she laid it against her cheek; then, opening her medicine bag, she placed the watch and chain inside. Picking up a delicate bead necklace with a dried-skin amulet, she put that also into the bag. Finally her searching fingers grasped the small stone figure of a sitting bear. Holding it in both hands, Supaya bowed her forehead against it and murmured, "Grandfather, help me, one last time! Help me finish what I must do!" She put the stone bear into the bag, drew the drawstrings tight, and went downstairs.

Going down was easier. She opened wide the front door and looked out toward the east. Ground mist hung low over the field, obscuring the woods. Above, pale stars glistened in the gray dawn sky. The damp air cooled her head and helped steady her. Leaving the door open, she went back through the house to the lean-to. Facing the dark shadow of herself in the mirror, she unpinned her thick gray braid, letting it hang down her back.

Raising her arms made her dizzy with pain, and she leaned against the wash bench until the faintness passed. Gathering her strength, she remembered another morning long ago, another room, dark like this one, the touch of her grandmother's ashy fingers marking her cheeks. But this morning, unlike on that other, she was not afraid. She was not alone. And she knew where she was going.

Opening the back door, she stepped out into the gray dawn.

PART ONE
1897–1901

CHAPTER ONE
Summer, 1897, Stone Island, Ontario

Supaya hesitated on the threshold and glanced back over her shoulder at her grandmother, her motionless figure barely discernible in the dark room. Drawing courage from her resolute silence, Supaya quietly latched the door and paused to look about and listen. The still, predawn air was heavy with dampness, and she drew her grandmother's shawl more closely about her head. Nothing stirred. The whole world seemed lost in deep sleep. Never before had she gone out so early, but she must avoid the eyes of Reverend Harris, and those who would tell him. Two years before, when she was ten, he had seen her going in the first light of sun and had turned her about and scolded her grandmother, saying visions were not to be found by fasting in the woods but by sitting in church. Her grandmother had listened, eyes fixed on a point beyond him, her blank expression masking what she felt for this plump man in black who had turned her elder granddaughter, Neegonas, away from the ways of her people. Since then Supaya had risen well before dawn to kneel before her grandmother and have her cheeks marked with charcoal from the cold fire. Each time she had stayed on the hill longer, waiting to be blessed by a vision, but each time she had returned empty. This morning her grandmother's hands had gripped her shoulders. She had put her face close to Supaya's, her old eyes shiny in the dark. "This time," she whispered, "this time you will be blessed." Then she had leaned back in her chair and closed her eyes.

Supaya moved swiftly away from the log house into the

woods that stretched unbroken for miles to the north of the island. She followed no path, only her own sense of direction and feel for the land where she had lived all her life. Often she had gone through the woods and climbed the steep, rocky slope that rose high above the trees to the little pocket among the boulders, her own secret place, where, hidden from view, she could gaze up at the vast sky and at the most distant rim of the world where lake and sky met. She had never spoken of it to anyone, not even to Kineu. Under the trees, darkness was almost a solid through which she pushed her way, bent forward, eyes straining to pierce the gloom, arms raised before her face. She half walked, half ran, twisting away from low branches that scratched her legs and snagged her clothes. Firs and cedars, deeper black than the night, loomed up, receded. She heard an animal plunge away from her, its crashing movement sharp in the silence. She tripped, caught herself, was showered with heavy drops of moisture shaken from branches as she passed. Breathless, she stopped, bracing herself against a tree trunk until, in the darkness, the earth steadied beneath her feet. "This time," her grandmother had said. Supaya hoped fervently that she was right. If only she had her grandmother's heart! If only she would be found worthy!

Above her a bird called; another answered faintly, and she knew she must hurry to reach the hilltop before dawn. As the trees thinned out, she moved faster and was soon climbing the slope, slipping on the damp, loose stones that rattled under her steps. She felt for footholds and climbed over and around boulders, pulling herself steadily upward. Gasping for breath, she paused and, tilting back her head, saw the rocky summit silhouetted against the paling night sky and knew she had come too far. Skidding and sliding, she scrambled to her left and down and found the small pocket hidden between the boulders. She sank down on the patch of earth, dizziness momentarily overcoming her. Her pulse throbbed; her forehead was clammy. She had eaten nothing since midday the day before, and felt an empty, nauseating fear. Perhaps she should go back! Perhaps, like her older sister, Neegonas, she shouldn't try at all! Who knew what might happen! A terrible grinning manito might come to shake her senseless or fling her down the hill and break her bones like poor Waboose, who hopped around the reserve on puny legs and never lifted her eyes. Yet Jacques, her brother, had fasted many times, had dreamed and been greatly blessed. And her grandmother, who cared for her, had wrapped her in the strength of

4

her own shawl and given tobacco for her to offer. Regaining courage, she looked up and saw the stars glittering in their last brilliance
before dawn and low in the west, the glowing sickle of the moon,
hazy and faintly orange. She stood up and leaned against the huge
rock, her hands resting on its cold surface. A faint wind cooled her
forehead. Gazing upward, she felt her spirit drawn up into the
boundless magnitude of the sky, into that majestic, eternal serenity
stretching above the earth whose vastness diminished her world,
made herself less than a speck. She became bodiless, drunk with
space, enraptured with the immensity of the heavens, pierced by its
awful beauty. Swiftly she took tobacco from a small pouch and,
stretching out her arms, made an offering to the east where already
night had faded, to the south, to the west where now only one horn
of the moon shone above the distant edge of the lake, and to the
north. Head flung back, she turned round and round to the four
points of heaven as the paling stars swung above her and repeated
the prayer her grandmother had taught her.

> "Oh Great Spirit, hear me! The moon and stars are
> yours! The sun that brings us life is yours! The winds
> that blow are your breath! All the earth, even the
> smallest stone, you have made!
>
> "All birds, beasts, people are yours! See me here! I am
> yours! Without you, I am nothing. Great One, help
> me! Accept my offering! Show me the path that I
> must follow! Teach me where to set my foot!
>
> "Mighty Father of all, I bow before you, weak and empty!
> Help me! Breathe upon me! Make me strong! Make
> me worthy!"

Supaya closed her eyes. Unaware of herself, she slumped down on
the earth. She was floating, moving effortlessly over a green
meadow where sunlight sparkled in a meandering stream. There
were women, talking and laughing together, picking berries and
sweet grass. All were dressed for a festival, their clothes embroidered with quills in the most glowing colors and intricate patterns
Supaya had ever seen. She moved among them and put out her
hand to them, but they didn't see her. She thought one of the
women was her mother, but when Supaya spoke to her, the woman
smiled and moved on with her friend. Then clouds covered the sun
and all the women faded with the sunlight. The meadow became a
dark forest filled with weird hootings and harsh cries. Frightened,
Supaya began to run, but the earth swerved up, the path vanished

in thick undergrowth, and branches pressed suffocatingly about her. Her feet were too heavy to lift and she cowered down against the earth. Abruptly the branches above her parted. A huge bear loomed over her, his massive body ringed with light, his eyes glowing like coals of fire. He swung his head and showed his sharp, powerful teeth. His raised paws dripped red. Supaya opened her mouth but could not scream. She tried to raise her arms to shield herself, but a terrible numbness overcame her. The bear grew larger and larger until her weak sight could no longer encompass him, and she lost all consciousness. Then slowly her spirit revived and she awakened. Like a returning wave, her strength washed over her. A profound serenity filled her being. She saw that the bear was beckoning to her, and she followed effortlessly where he led, his radiant form illuminating the way. They emerged from the forest into a meadow where wild grasses rippled in a pale sunlight. The bear stopped by a tangle of bushes heavy with berries. Supaya saw then that his paws dripped with berry juice and understood that she was to eat the berries. They were juicy and deliciously sweet to her parched throat. As she ate, the bear's radiance grew brighter, more intense, blinding her eyes. Confusion overcame her. She covered her eyes, tried to turn from the light. Abruptly, she came fully awake.

The sky above the hollow was a thin, pale blue, its color washed out by the brilliant sunlight that glanced off the boulders and shone on her where she lay on the ground. Dazed, she sat up, a memory of sweetness in her mouth. Suddenly she remembered. She had dreamed! She had been blessed with a vision! Exultant, she breathed in the fresh morning air and gazed at the world around her. Never, she thought, had a morning been so beautiful. Below her the steep hillside still lay in shadow, its tumbled rocks like the humped backs of sleeping beasts. Beyond, the deep green of the woods extended unbroken to the waters of Georgian Bay, each pointed treetop distinct in the clear early light. And beyond the trees stretched the boundless water like a great bowl of gleaming silver, its far edge lost in a misty blue that melted, imperceptibly, into the blue of the sky. High above her a lone hawk floated, riding invisible currents, while over the lake gulls' wings flashed white as they circled about, weaving an endless pattern.

Spurred by her elation, Supaya made a wild, reckless descent, leaping and sliding over the rocks. She raced through the woods, now dimly lit by shafts of sunlight slanting through the trees.

Touched by light, the ground fog slowly rose, curled, and faded away.

Supaya came out of the woods near the end of the garden. Smoke was rising from the stack in the lean-to roof. The back door opened and Jacques stepped out, carrying a pail. At nineteen, he was taller than his father but lanky, without his father's breadth. He stood for a moment, yawning and running his hand through his tousled black hair, then started toward the pump. Supaya ran toward him across the garden, leaping the rows of cabbages, potatoes and beans. Eyes shining, she exclaimed, "Jacques! I had a vision! I must tell Grandma and Father!"

She dashed through the door into the lean-to. Her father, his broad, muscular shoulders hunched, was leaning over the washbasin, splashing his face and hair. He held out his hand for the towel lying on the bench. Supaya snatched it up and handed it to him, biting her lip to hold in her excitement, impatient for him to look at her, to speak to her.

Jules toweled his face and head vigorously and took his time in speaking. His actions were always considered, deliberate, according to his nature and his profession as a shaman. Yet this deliberateness, Supaya knew, was deceptive. Powerfully built as he was, with massive shoulders and arms that in appearance matched his manner, he was more agile than most young men and could move with startling swiftness when he chose. This latent power gave him an air of mystery, of unpredictability that enhanced the respect with which he was regarded by all members of his band. And by his family as well. Though he often joked with her and Jacques and told them stories in the long winter evenings, some part of him remained aloof, closed off like a secret room where, since the death of his wife, no one had been admitted or would dare enter. For as long as she could remember, Supaya had been conscious of this reserve in her father. It had taught her respect and caution.

Jules, a handsome, square-faced man with pronounced cheekbones, took great care with his appearance. Carefully he combed his thick black hair, smoothing it back with a strong, well-shaped hand. He looked at Supaya through the mirror, amusement in his dark eyes.

"Good morning, Daughter. You were up early today."

"Yes, Father, I was."

Jules' amusement deepened. He turned to Jacques, just en-

7

tering with the pail of water. "Jacques, your sister was up early this morning. Perhaps she was eager to hoe the potatoes."

Jacques' long, bony face broke into a wide grin. "Or pull weeds. That's the job she likes best."

Supaya tilted her chin at them pertly and turned away. She filled a large enameled pot with water from the pail and set it on the cast-iron stove.

"I can see she has nothing of importance to say," went on her father.

Quayo, hearing Jules' remark, exclaimed, "Shame! Can't you see the child will burst if you don't let her speak. Come, Supaya, tell us."

Eagerly Supaya turned, ready to share her experience with the three people she most loved. They all looked at her, smiling, waiting for her to speak: her brother, comically protective of her, but a young man with thoughts and hopes of his own; her father, whose humor she understood but whose depth of sadness eluded her; and her grandmother, the flame of life still bright in her eyes, upright despite the years on her back. Facing them, Supaya suddenly perceived each one in his own, individual, private separateness. All at once she understood why one who had dreamed never blurted out the dream, understood the impropriety of such a blunt and personal revelation; and so, almost embarrassed by what she had intended to say, said simply, "I went to the hill before the sun rose. My offering was accepted. I dreamed. I dreamed of the Great Bear."

There was an impressed silence. They gazed at her, marveling, and she felt their pride and happiness.

Her father said softly, "Ah! That is good. Very good."

Her grandmother came forward and kissed her on the forehead.

"At first," said Supaya, her constraint lessening, "I was frightened, but then I wasn't."

Jacques patted her awkwardly on the shoulder with his big hand. "I knew you would be brave. Now let's eat. I'm hungry."

"You are always hungry," declared Quayo. "We will have nothing left to store in the root cellar the way you eat!"

Jacques caught Quayo round the waist and swung her about. "Well, we have to celebrate Suppy's dream, don't we?"

Supaya poured four mugs of green tea, got out some leftover scone, and set it all out on the wooden table. Besides Jules' straight chair with arms and Quayo's rocker, both sitting near the fireplace, there were four armless chairs, all of wooden frames with double-woven splint seats, all chairs that Jules had made. There were shelves on the wall holding tins of flour, sugar, and tea, and pegs in the wall for holding clothes. A bed for Quayo stood against the far wall, opposite the fireplace, near a steep flight of steps leading to the loft where Supaya slept and where food was stored. Curtained off from the main room was the bedroom Jules shared with his son.

Going into this room, Jules opened his trunk and returned carrying a necklace of small gray stones with a large, flat, translucent blue stone at the center. On either side of the blue stone was a single curved bear claw. Solemnly, with both hands, Jules held it up before Supaya. "This was given to me by my father. It has great power. Now I give it to you."

Awestruck, Supaya bowed her head and her father placed the necklace around her neck. When she looked up at him, her "Thank you, Father," faded away, for she saw that while he passed his hand lovingly over her head and gazed deeply into her eyes, he was seeing through her or beyond her, something or someone else.

As they drank their tea, there was little conversation. Her father and brother spoke of where they would fish that morning; her grandmother cupped her steaming mug in both hands and leaned her gray head over it as if to warm her sharp nose. Supaya, after her fast, was hungrier than Jacques and consumed her tea and dry scone with relish. She looked down proudly at the necklace, touching the cool, smooth surface of the blue stone. It gleamed softly and struck off an inner point of light like a tiny star. She was surprised by her father's gift. When Jacques had dreamed, Jules had given him a fine hunting knife of proved power, but as a girl, she had expected nothing.

After her father and Jacques left to go fishing, Quayo said, "Come, Suppy, sit down in front of me and I will comb your hair. It's snarled."

Supaya brought the comb from the wash bench in the lean-to and sat down on the floor, leaning back against her grandmother's knees. She liked the feel of the comb pulling through her long hair and the touch of her grandmother's hands smoothing and stroking it back.

"Grandma, tell me again about my mother. What was she like?"

"Ah," said Quayo, smiling. Quayo was the last of her family.

Small but wiry and strong, she had outlived brothers, sisters, husband, and five children. Fiercely proud, she had taken only one husband, finding no suitor who could rival the one she lost. Her face, though lined by many sorrows, was animated by an eagerness for life, and she delighted to speak of her lost daughter, to make her live again for Supaya. "Your mother was a dutiful, loving daughter. She was always content and was kind to the old people. They would say, 'Here comes Shooskonee, bringing us food again.' She had a gift for life. Her garden was always the finest, her bread the best. Her hands were clever. Her quill embroidery was something to be proud of. Your father, who could have had any girl on the reserve, chose her, and she was a good mother to your sister Neegonas and to Jacques. She was very sad to leave you, newly come into the world."

Supaya listened with pleasure, but she was remembering her dream. "Did she wear her hair straight back, without a part, in a knot on her neck?"

"She did. She had long, glossy . . ."

"And did she have a dress with a square neck and quill embroidery on the shoulders?"

Quayo didn't answer immediately. Supaya felt her grandmother's sudden attention in her silence and the arrested movement of her hands, and heard the question in her voice when she answered, "She did."

Supaya twisted around to look up at Quayo. "I saw her, Grandma." Quayo took Supaya's face in both her hands and looked at her searchingly. "I am sure I did. She was laughing and happy."

"She thinks of you and loves you, Suppy," said Quayo. "Some day you will see her again." Then, briskly, "Now turn around and hold still while I make a part."

Supaya turned and held still, feeling the tooth of the comb draw a line across the middle of her head and the pull of her grandmother's fingers as she swiftly braided one side. Supaya ventured one more question, tinged with mischief, knowing the reaction it would provoke. "Grandma, is it truly a good thing to have dreamed of the Great Bear?"

"Supaya!" Her grandmother gathered the other half of her hair in one hand and pulled her head sharply round. Her old eyes narrowed sternly and she solemnly held up one hand. "Ah! Ah! Do not question! You have been very blessed. You have been given one of the most powerful spirits for your guardian. Never forget your dream! Remember it always! If ever you need help, you can ask Him, your Grandfather."

"I will remember, Grandma."

"Come, now. Enough talk. Let me finish. I have preserving to do and you must hoe the garden."

Supaya followed her grandmother into the kitchen. Quayo put more wood in the stove and got out a large kettle. For the first time Supaya saw how small and frail her grandmother was. The house itself had grown smaller since she had left it, only hours earlier. Everything was altered, for she had dreamed, had seen beyond these walls. Now she saw with older eyes.

She fetched the hoe from the barn and began chopping at the weeds, breaking up the hardened earth around the half-grown vegetables as she had seen Quayo do. There was much work to be done before her father and Jacques returned with their catch.

CHAPTER TWO

Buttoning her jacket against the chilly, mid-September breeze, Supaya hurried along the dirt road toward the schoolhouse. Skipping a step or two, she could feel the blue stone of her necklace bounce against her chest. She had worn it ever since her father had placed it around her neck and had promised herself never to take it off. It was her dearest possession, an object of awe and veneration, carrying as it did the love of her father and grandfather and a great mystical power through which she could draw closer to her guardian spirit. It warmed her soul as the sun was even now warming her back.

The day was fine for drying squash and beans. She was late because she had stayed to help cut and spread them out, knowing her grandmother would fret if the work were not done. Finally, "Go now," Quayo had insisted. "I will finish. You must learn what you can for your own use."

Kineu, she knew, would have waited for her at the crossroads. He never cared if he was late for school. Sometimes Supaya thought Kineu didn't care whether he learned to read and figure the white way or not, even though he learned faster than she did. But she cared. She had watched Mr. Bonnet, in shirtsleeves and suspenders, leaning on the counter of the general store, adding up their purchases. He jabbed his pencil at each figure in the column, then looked unsmilingly at her over the rims of his eyeglasses and announced the total in a voice that made Supaya wonder if what her grandmother claimed were true: that he charged them more than the figures really came to. She determined that one day she would be able to tell. Besides, there were magazines and books with pictures that stirred her curiosity, pictures of white girls in strange wide hats with ribbons, walking on beaches, holding hoops or strings attached to balls floating above them. When she asked Miss Harris what they were doing, the answer always was, "Now when you can read, you won't have to ask such questions."

Rounding the bend, Supaya saw Kineu at a distance, tossing his knife at a fence post, and she quickened her step. For her, everything quickened in Kineu's presence. The very day itself expanded, for his liveliness and enthusiasm made their wildest projects seem possible. For him all difficulties melted away. Today they were to go fishing. Supaya was eager to sell some fish to make money in order to buy her grandmother a new shawl.

Catching sight of her, Kineu came to meet her. Tall and slim, he walked with the springy step of a runner. His features, still boyish, were finely cut, his nose straight, his mouth modeled with a natural sweetness. Supaya always thought of him as moving in sunlight.

"I have the boat, Suppy," said Kineu, falling in with her step. "We can take it all day if we want."

"Then we can go right after school. No, first I must go home and tell Grandma. Then we can go."

"We can go now."

"Now," said Supaya, "we must go to school."

Kineu was silent. Head down, he concentrated on kicking a stone ahead of him. Supaya glanced at him sideways, knowing he was disappointed, that he would rather do anything than go to school, that school didn't matter to him as it did to her. It upset her when they disagreed. Her Aunt Hettie, Kineu's mother, often shook her head over them. "Those two! Like an old man and an old woman, they think alike. What next!" But about school they did not think alike. Finally she said insistently, "We must learn."

Kineu stopped and faced her, his eyebrows straight and serious. "Why? Books don't catch fish."

Supaya frowned, at a loss to explain Mr. Bonnet's figures, the mysterious lure of books, the elusive world of little girls in big hats. Baffled but stubborn, she said, "I must," and hung her head.

Kineu, unable to cause her pain, began walking again. "All right. We go after school. We can meet at North Point. I have a net set out there." He pretended not to see her happy, grateful smile.

The schoolhouse, built according to government regulations by the Ojibwa themselves, was a one-story rectangular building with the door at one end, rooms for the teacher to live in at the other, and windows along both sides of the single large classroom. It was a plain, solid building, an extension in board and brick of the character of their teacher, Miss Agatha Harris, unimaginative but practical and dedicated to good hard work. Steps—convenient for the posing of class photographs—led to the door where Miss Harris would stand and ring a hand bell as part of her effort to instill in her students a respect for time, marking off the moment before which they were "on time" and after which they were "late." To all such efforts they remained impervious. Those who were not smitten by strange, sudden illnesses or detained by work that "had" to be done, came when they comfortably could, arriving by two's and three's during the course of the morning. Between turning to the blackboard, chalk in hand, and turning back, Agatha would find her class had changed, increased, rearranged itself. Yet from the oldest to the youngest, their faces showed such uniform bland innocence that it was impossible for her to scold them. She believed it was deliberate, this refusal to conform to time, a stubbornness of character, and she included in her morning prayers a special plea for help in dealing with this perverse, pagan trait.

Sophia Cedar and Kenneth Bruley appeared as if by magic in the middle of a lesson. The younger children, in a group at the front, were copying the alphabet while she put addition problems on the blackboard for the older ones. She turned and there they were, in their seats at the back, as calmly attentive as if they had been there for hours.

Agatha's normally pale cheeks flushed with irritation. She had not even heard the door open and shut; a small detail, but it made her feel all these children slipped through her hands as they pleased, no matter how she strove to organize them. She was utterly baffled by what she conceived to be the Indians' total lack of discipline. For four years now since, at twenty-one, she had come to Stone Island, Agatha had determinedly struggled to change it, yet could see no improvement. She refrained from speaking to Sophia and Kenneth's families because these two late-comers were her best students. Kenneth was bright; he simply treated schoolwork as an unimportant game which he wasn't much interested in playing. Sophia Cedar was bright also, and in her Agatha sensed a drive to learn that set her apart from the others and made her progress a

14

source of particular satisfaction. If only the girl's grandmother were stricter with her.

Agatha, telling herself she must be patient, tried to ignore her irritation and a growing headache. She had skinned her straight, light brown hair back too tightly. Her scalp felt taut. For one absurd moment she yearned to undo it and shake it down around her shoulders, to loosen the high collar that seemed to constrict her throat. Abruptly she became aware of rows of solemn, fathomless dark eyes, all fixed on her, and she came stiffly to attention, tapping the board with her chalk.

"Sophia Cedar, come to the front and do these problems. The rest of you do them in your notebooks. Then we'll go over them together."

Reluctantly, Supaya went to the blackboard. She wished Miss Harris had called on Kineu instead. He never minded being watched while he worked.

The class bent their heads and began, sneaking looks now and then at Supaya's answers. Miss Harris walked between the rows, observing her students' work. A slim young woman in a tight bodice and long skirt, she bent over their notebooks with them, smiling encouragingly, tapping a finger at doubtful answers, raising her eyebrows at others.

Supaya was almost finished when the door opened and Reverend Harris walked in. It was his pleasure to visit the schoolroom occasionally, believing it to be rightly part of his domain. He often found his young sister too soft in her attitude toward these children, and frequently had to strengthen her discipline. At sight of his stout, aggressive figure, the class immediately grew wary and bent their heads lower, elbows angled out defensively on their desks.

"Class, say good morning to Reverend Harris." The class responded in a monotone, and Agatha smiled to turn it into a welcome. Though it pained her to admit it, her brother's presence sometimes made her uncomfortable. But this morning his appearance steadied her. His absolute self-assurance simplified her problems, drew a sharp, clear line between right and wrong.

Not for years had Reverend Harris smiled spontaneously or looked with gentle affection at any living creature. The onerous demands of his calling did not allow for it. His sense of heavy responsibility permitted no more than a benign skepticism. He strolled between the desks, nodded at the tops of bent heads, his hands stroking his lapels as if smoothing down dull, black feathers. "Doing

15

sums, I see. Good. Good. And your letters. Commendable, very commendable." He had fallen into the habit of repetition under the impression that saying a word twice made it more understandable. He approached the front of the room, his pale eye busy noting uncombed hair, a dirty shirt, empty seats. His glance flicked over the blackboard. "I see Miss Cedar is leading the . . ." He broke off, stared for one horrified moment at Supaya, then raised an arm as if to ward off what he saw. His stunned silence and dramatic stance caught everyone's attention. All heads raised. Even the two youngest, Anna and Marie, who had been slyly poking each other, stopped to watch.

"Nathan," asked Agatha, startled into using his given name in public, "what is it? What's wrong?"

Reverend Harris' face twitched with the anger that swelled within him. His voice was hollow with outrage. "How dare she wear those pagan stones? How dare she! Why have you allowed it? What kind of example is she setting for these children?"

Momentarily confused, Agatha pressed her hand against her throat. Then she saw Supaya's necklace, the gleaming blue stone and the sharp bear claws, startling against the faded print dress. "Oh but . . . she only just . . . I mean, she had her back . . ."

"There is no excuse! No excuse!" the preacher exclaimed furiously, staring at Supaya, who had backed up against the blackboard.

"No! No, of course not!" agreed his sister miserably.

"Responsibility such as ours demands constant vigilance! Constant! Now, Miss, what do you mean by adorning yourself in such a manner? Well? Speak when you are spoken to!"

Speechless at being the focus of such anger, Supaya stared back, wide-eyed, too frightened to look away.

"Ha!" He pointed a finger at her. "She understands well enough! The devil has easy work here! But we will defeat him! Take off that heathen charm! Remove it! Give it to me!" He held out his hand imperiously.

Aghast at his demand, Supaya clasped the blue stone against her chest and backed away. She was conscious of Miss Harris gesturing nervously, of the tense stillness of the class, of the bars of sunlight falling across the desk tops, of Kineu, who had risen, silently opened the door and was waiting, his hand on the doorknob.

"You dare defy me!" Reverend Harris' voice rose in pitch. "You are a child of the devil! You defy the word of the Lord!" He was suddenly beside himself with rage at this child, at her grandmother and her father, all stubbornly practicing their pagan religion and doctoring behind his back, all refusing to bend to his will, all undermining the authority of the church. "Give it to me!" he demanded, biting off his words. "Right now!" And his outstretched hand made a swift grab for her.

But not swift enough. Sensing his action, Supaya dodged past him, ran down the aisle and through the door, past Kineu, who slammed it shut behind them. Together they fled down the steps and ran without pausing until they were far from the schoolhouse.

"Come on!" Kineu was standing on a rock, his back to the lake. They had come through the woods to the shore, and he had been pitching stones, waiting for her to recover. Supaya sat on the beach, hugging her knees and sulking. I will never go back, she thought. How I hate him! That she wanted to go to school made it worse. But she would not take off her necklace, not even for school.

"Come on, Suppy!" Kineu called again.

She raised her head and saw him balanced on a rock, smiling at her, his hair shiny black in the sun, behind him the light blue sky, the deeper blue lake. Poised thus, arms out, he seemed to her enviably free and light, as though he could fly away. She looked at him wistfully, but didn't move.

Suddenly he slipped and fell, arms thrashing. "Ow, ow! My leg! Ow!"

Instantly Supaya was on her feet, running to him. "Kineu! Are you hurt? Oh, let me see!" But as she leaned over him, he stopped yelling and grinned up at her.

"Oh, Kineu!" She stood up and looked at him sideways, but in a moment she laughed too, unable to resist his smile.

"Come on! We can go fishing now! We'll have time to sell some!"

They raced along the shore to where the rowboat was drawn up on the shingle. Above the waterline, near the trees, was a small storage shack. There they left their shoes and together pushed the boat into the water.

The lake was icy cold and so clear that along the shore the sun shone into it, lighting up the stones on the bottom that seemed to ripple under the water. White gulls with black-tipped wings dipped in the sky above them, outriders of a flock that was circling another, larger fishing boat farther out on the lake.

"I row first, then you, while I haul in the net." Kineu braced

17

his feet and pulled strongly on the oars. The wind was biting fresh over the water and Supaya sat with her feet up on the seat to warm and dry in the sun.

"Better than school?" asked Kineu, teasing.

Supaya made a face at him. "Only if your net has been lucky and caught many fish."

Near the mouth of an inlet Supaya took over the oars. The water here was choppy and the boat bucked sideways in the current.

"Start on this side," said Kineu, and Supaya rowed to one end of the net floats that were bobbing up and down in a crooked line across the inlet mouth. Leaning over the side, Kineu began hauling the linen net up and into the boat. Caught by their gills in the net, fish came up shimmering through the water, suckers, white fish, and lake trout. Some hung dead, but most flipped and arced their bodies violently as they came over the side, showering water in all directions.

"Hey, hey!" cried Kineu, disengaging a trout, "that's a big one! And another!" Every pull on the net brought up more. Kineu worked skillfully and rapidly, using a stick to kill the live fish by a blow on the head. Water dripped from his arms, soaked his shirt and pants, and sloshed in the bottom of the boat. When the net was all in Kineu sank down on the seat, breathless, and surveyed the pile of fish, their sides iridescent in the sunshine.

"We got a good haul, Suppy!" he exclaimed jubilantly. "We never caught so many at one time before! We should get good money for these. Two, three times more like this and I will have plenty for my gun."

"And I can get Grandma a shawl!" Ever since the day of Supaya's vision when Quayo had given her her own shawl, Supaya had wanted to get her a new one. She had already seen just the one she wanted on a shelf in Mr. Bonnet's store.

"Your necklace brought us luck, Suppy," said Kineu.

In the excitement of hauling in the net, Supaya had forgotten Reverend Harris and her own fright and anger. Now she pulled vigorously on the oars, heading for a small island out in the lake, half a mile beyond Stone Island. She no longer worried, confident that when she told her father what had happened, he would know what to do.

They reached the island and tied up at a small jetty built out from the rocky beach. The water sparkled and lapped gently against the poles driven into the lake bottom. Children playing along the shore called out excitedly and came running. Two women appeared, coming from houses set well back in a clearing. The children crowded along the jetty, curious to see what Kineu and Supaya had brought. Kineu lifted up two large fish, a whitefish and a trout, for the women to see, then laid them down on the wooden planking.

The women admired the fish, and the older woman, who was stout and talkative, sent one of the children racing back to her house. She smiled down at Supaya. "You are Jules Cedar's girl, I know. He has given you his eyes. He is a fine doctor, a good man. He cured my son when he was a baby and very sick. He is strong now, but a no-good. Wants to play all the time." She laughed and tousled the hair of a boy standing beside her. "Here," she said, counting out some coins from a little bag the child had brought from the house. "When you have more fish, come back. We have a big hunger here."

As Kineu untied the boat and pushed off, she called out, "Old Aunt Theresa lives round the point. She would be happy for some fish."

The point extended into the lake like a crooked arm, forming a small, sheltered bay. Stunted, wind-bent pines grew far out on it, fighting for a hold among the boulders. Behind them were slender larches and cedar groves, forming a windbreak for the small frame house that sat back from the beach. At one side was a partially cleared area where a garden barely survived among the weeds. Beyond were a few old apple trees, their branches heavy with apples.

Kineu ran the boat up onto the beach, its bottom grating on the stones. Smoke rose from behind the house and from the smokestack, but no one appeared.

"We should go to the door. She may be asleep."

The front door stood ajar, and from the step they could see into the room, empty except for a bed, a small wooden table, and two straight chairs. Across the room, another door opened into the lean-to. They heard the creak of a rocking chair. Supaya knocked on the doorframe. There was no answer and the rocking continued. "She must be hard of hearing," said Supaya, entering and calling loudly, "Aunt Theresa! Aunt Theresa!"

Supaya need not have feared startling Aunt Theresa. When they entered the lean-to, her eyes were on them. She was an old,

19

old woman, beyond surprises. She seemed to have been expecting them, and her face, despite its deep wrinkles and sunken cheeks, expressed an almost youthful anticipation. "*Ahnee*," she said, nodding. "*ahnee*. Come in, children come in. I have some bread out in the fire. If you bring it in, we can eat. My old legs are tired."

In the backyard a fire smoldered under an old broken drying frame. Kneeling, Supaya raked through the ashes and charred wood with a branched stick and pulled out two loaves crusted with ashes and bits of wood. She whipped the loaves with a switch and then, using a stick so as not to burn her fingers, knocked off the cracked crust. She rolled the hot loaves into a fold of her skirt and carried them inside.

"Open that box there," said Aunt Theresa, as pleased as a child at a party. "We will have meat and tea." Kineu cut the bread and got dried meat from the tin. Supaya poured tea from an old pot heated on the iron box stove.

"Aunt Theresa," said Kineu, "we have fish. Would you like some?"

Aunt Theresa looked at him keenly, then pointed at the bread. "Eat," she urged, "eat."

"I think she is deaf," said Supaya. "You hang some fish to dry and I'll pick apples."

Kineu nodded, and Aunt Theresa, drinking her tea and rocking, smiled at them slyly like an old conspirator.

When they finished eating, Kineu repaired the drying frame, setting in firmly the slender branches that slanted up on two sides to the center pole that was held parallel to the ground, and retying the basswood fiber ties that held the cross branches in place like the skeleton of a tent. He gutted the fish on the beach, sloshed them in the water, and cut a slit along each side of their spines so they could be hung lengthwise over the poles, first flesh side out, then skin side out, until they were dried. As Kineu slit and hung the fish over the cross poles of the frame, Supaya took an old splint basket and went out to the apple trees that stood knee-deep in weeds. A squirrel, who had been carrying off apples one by one, sprang away, flicking his tail and scolding.

Aunt Theresa came to the door and watched them work, nodding her head and mumbling to herself. When Supaya brought back the basket filled with apples, Aunt Theresa picked out a large one, rubbed it against her skirt and presented it to Supaya. "Good little woman," she said, chose another, rubbed it, and handed it to Kineu. "Good little man."

Eating their apples, Supaya and Kineu walked along the curving shore out toward the point, where the beach narrowed and finally disappeared altogether, the land falling steeply into the lake.

"Look," exclaimed Supaya, pointing, "you can see the hill above the trees!" To the east, Stone Island, bathed in the late afternoon sun seemed to hover in the crystal air. Supaya, squinting against the sunlight reflecting off the water, gazed at it, rapt, as if she were again standing on its summit.

Kineu understood. Beginning at the age of seven, he had gone out in search of a vision, and one morning when he was ten, on the far side of the same hill, after a three-day fast, he had dreamed. He would never forget the splendor of that morning, that place, or the elation he had experienced. Since then he had walked with pride, at home in his world. He knew Supaya's guardian was the Great Bear, as his was the Eagle. He crouched down at the water's edge, idly flipping stones, liking the feel of their cold, grainy surfaces. One caught his attention.

"Suppy! Look! Look what I found!" He held out on his palm a curiously shaped stone, rounded and lumpish, like the body of a sitting bear.

Supaya leaned over it, awed. It was sitting, slumped a bit to one side, and there was its head, its snout and tiny rounded ears. "Kineu!" she breathed, "a bear!" Their eyes met, hers filled with wonder. Suddenly all the events of the day became significant: they had led her to this, this sign. She was almost frightened, as if the Great Bear had reached out and touched her.

"Here," said Kineu softly. "It is yours to keep."

Slowly Supaya reached out for it. It was cold and heavy and had dried to a pale gray with rings of darker gray circling it. She held it on her palm, them closed her fingers over it and put it in the pocket of her skirt.

That evening Supaya told her father what had happened at school. Jacques sat cross-legged by the hearth, breaking small branches and sticking them into the flames that crackled and gave welcome warmth on a fall evening. Her grandmother and father had drawn their chairs close. The rest of the room was in shadows. Above them, Joe Crow, her father's pet, paced back and forth on a ceiling beam, cocking his eye at them and making soft croaking

21

noises. As Quayo listened to Supaya, her mouth drew tight. She had opposed Reverend Harris since Supaya's sister, Neegonas, had abandoned the old ways. She rarely attended Sunday service, excusing her absence by saying she was too old. Supaya was always amused to see how feeble her grandmother became whenever the preacher called.

Jules listened impassively, his eyes fixed on the flames. When she finished speaking, there was a deep silence until Joe Crow suddenly swooped down onto Jules' shoulder and pecked delicately at his shirt button. When Jules turned his gaze on Supaya, she saw the anger in his eyes.

"You did well to leave. I would not have you go back to that school."

"Pah!" exclaimed Quayo, unable to keep silent longer. "That white woman knows nothing! What is she good for? Nothing!"

"It is also good for him that the preacher did not strike you or take your necklace," continued Jules, ignoring Quayo's interruption. "He does not understand that we know nothing of his devil, just as he knows nothing of the One who watches over us. But you will come with me to service on Sunday so he will know that we are not afraid of his devil or of him."

"Father," said Jacques, "if she does not go to school, the agent will send her away to a government school, especially since Mother . . . ." His voice trailed away at a sharp glance from his father. "Oh no!" exclaimed Supaya, alarmed. She leaned toward her father beseechingly. "Father, please don't let them send me away! Please!" Knowing his dislike of tears, she blinked hard and kept her eyes steadily on his.

Jules regarded Supaya thoughtfully. He saw her fear and her effort at self-control. "But the necklace—you will then take it off?"

His question startled Supaya. She stared at him, then sank back on her heels. Stubbornly, she said quietly, "No, Father, I will not."

"Ah," said Jules, deep satisfaction in his voice. After a moment's silence, he spoke again, straight-faced. "Then I see what you must do. You must wear your necklace under your blouse. That will be one more thing the preacher will not know."

His sudden change of tone surprised them all. Jacques looked up and laughed; Quayo threw up her hands, smiling and nodding. Joe Crow, reacting to their mirth, stretched his head forward and cawed.

As they all watched, Supaya solemnly lifted the blue stone and the bear claws and slipped them under the neck of her blouse. Then they all laughed together.

That Sunday Reverend Harris faced his Indian congregation and preached to them on the sinfulness of pagan adornment. Stones, feathers, claws, teeth, all were an abomination unto the Lord and were not to be endured. He spoke of the wicked, rebellious hearts beating beneath their Sunday shirts and dresses, of the sinfulness of the old men holding their good black hats on their knees and the old women in their shawls who persisted in their heathen customs. He threatened them with eternal hell's fire if they did not bend themselves to the yoke of the Lord and do His bidding.

His audience listened placidly, attentive and noncommital, sitting on benches they themselves had made, in the spare, unadorned church they had built. But when Mrs. Harris, plump and tightly corseted, struck the opening bars of the closing hymn and led the singing, they joined in enthusiastically, enjoying a good sing. If the sermon was directed specifically at the Cedar family, sitting upright in a back row, no one in the congregation appeared to be aware of it.

A week later on the steps of the general store, Agatha Harris almost collided with Jules Cedar. She had been hurrying with her head down and stopped just short of running into him.

"Oh, pardon me, Mr. Cedar. I wasn't looking where I was going." He stood on the step above her, his face shaded by the wide brim of his black felt hat. He nodded politely and stepped to one side as if to go on his way.

"Mr. Cedar." He turned, and she felt the impact of his full attention. Immediately she was thrown into confusion. "Mr. Cedar, I've wanted to speak to you for some time . . . well, that is . . . since last week . . ." She stopped, overcome with embarrassment. He waited silently for her to continue, his dark eyes on hers. Their penetration, their knowingness scattered her wits. She felt he understood precisely her agitation.

"I mean . . . your daughter, Sophia, has been absent a whole week." She hesitated. He offered no comment. "I hope she hasn't been ill." He still said nothing, but his eyes, seeing every aspect of her face and person, grew softer and darker, and she began to babble. "Well . . . she . . . she must come. That is . . . it's the law . . . as I'm sure you know . . . not that I . . ." She stopped again, her burning cheeks betraying her response to his masculinity. If only someone, anyone, would come by, would interrupt them! But no one did. In her need to cover her embarrassment, Agatha blurted out, "I hope she'll come back next week!"

At that Jules' eyes widened slightly and the faint smile at the corner of his mouth deepened. He tilted his head toward her and said with quiet emphasis, "Thank you, Miss Harris. Supaya will come." Touching his hat brim, Jules walked away.

Agatha looked after him, her cheeks still warm. If, sometimes, during the years that followed, there was a suggestive contour under the neck of Supaya's dress, Agatha Harris was careful not to notice.

CHAPTER THREE

Above the treetops all across Stone Island Reserve thin columns of smoke rose into the still, clear air of an autumn morning. Behind every home, fires burned under drying frames hung with split fish and strips of meat. Hides were stretched out for scraping and tanning. Garden vegetables were stored away in log-lined root cellars or were drying in the sun before being wrapped in birchbark to be stored for winter use.

In the garden, now gone to seed, Jules and Jacques were digging the last of the potatoes. Supaya worked along behind the men, gathering the potatoes into a basket and carrying them to the root cellar. All morning her body had felt tired, listless. Stooping made her head swim and her stomach cramp. She straightened up, and after another brief twist of pain, felt a wetness between her legs. Abandoning the basket, she stepped quickly across the dug-up garden and entered the house, giving Quayo, who was sitting outside the back door, a sidelong glance as she passed.

Quayo was stringing apple sections to be hung for drying, but she noticed Supaya's strange look and how she avoided passing near the apples. Putting aside her work, she went in and found Supaya waiting for her near the front door.

"Grandmother, what you told me would happen, that soon I would become a woman, has begun. I must go into the woods."

Hearing the tremor in her voice, Quayo touched her gently on the arm and reassured her. "Do not fear. It is natural that girls grow into women. You wait here. I'll get Neegonas. We'll make you a shelter."

Supaya's sister Neegonas and her husband lived in their own log house a short distance down the road. Neegonas had one child, a boy of three, and was pregnant again. A short woman, inclined to stoutness, she was of a generally jolly disposition now that she had her own home in which to do as she pleased.

When Quayo returned with Neegonas, Supaya fell in behind them and they crossed the field at a distance from Jules and Jacques and headed toward the woods. Supaya turned her head so as not to contaminate her father and brother by even a glance and followed the two women into the woods until they were well beyond sight or sound of the house.

"I think it was about here that I came," said Neegonas, and remembering, giggled and patted her swelling belly. "We'll have to find you a husband soon, Suppy. Or maybe now he will find you."

Supaya said nothing. She was uneasy and vexed by her sister's teasing. She had never been close to Neegonas and wished she and her grandmother could have built her shelter by themselves.

"Do not tease her, Neegonas. She is not like you. Here, this is a good place. Go and cut some branches." A large downed fir lay at an angle across a rockfall. Branches slanted across one side of the trunk and over the rocks would form a kind of cave with the rock at the back. "Suppy, you cut some cedar."

Neegonas swung her axe resentfully. She had never pleased her grandmother, who had always ordered her about, made her chase after Jacques and tend the baby, Supaya, after their mother died. No one thought of her. She had been made motherless too. She brought the branches and placed them at a slant, thrusting their cut ends into the earth. "I suppose you think Kineu won't come after her now? And all the others?" she asked, intending to hurt.

Quayo was on her knees, spreading cedar boughs on the ground inside the shelter. She looked up at Neegonas sternly. "Think what you say. She is your sister."

Supaya stood apart, her back to them, shoulders drooping, head bent. Neegonas felt a touch of shame. "I will bring a blanket and some food," she said, and went back the way they had come.

"Supaya," said Quayo, "come. Sit inside."

Supaya stooped under the branches and sat down on the cedar boughs, her back against the rock.

"See, you have room to lie down."

"Yes, Grandma." Supaya said nothing more for fear she would cry.

When Neegonas returned she brought an old blanket which they spread as a covering over the branches. She handed Supaya a box with some dried meat and scone in it. "You will be hungry later."

Supaya held it on her lap, self-conscious and awkward. "Thank you, Neegonas," she murmured, not raising her eyes.

Neegonas straightened up. Her back ached and she was impatient to return home.

"I'll bring you another blanket and water before dark," said Quayo. "Now we must go."

For a long time Supaya sat without moving, the box still on her lap. The impulse to cry had passed; now she felt only a strange emptiness. She looked down at herself. She could see nothing different, yet her body was changing, whether she wished it or not, mysteriously, by itself. She had been so happy, so content, in the pleasant, unchanging "now." Life might change for others, but hers had been secure and uncomplicated. Now she too was being swept along as Neegonas had been, as her mother, as, so long ago, her grandmother . . . reluctant and unready.

She put the tin box down and moved as far back under the branches as she could, wanting to hide herself. She took the stone bear from her leather pouch, cupped it in both hands, and addressed it silently. Oh, Grandfather! Help me! Make me strong enough to become a woman!

She spent all day leaning against the rock, watching the angle of light change where it fell on the ground before the opening. Ants toiled up and down a crevice in the rock. A squirrel carrying a nut in his mouth ducked under the branches, cocked a startled eye at her, and raced out. When the light began to fade, Quayo returned.

"Come," said Quayo, urging her out. "Stand up and put on your jacket. Drink this tea and eat. Then you will feel better. Here is a blanket to wrap up in."

The tea warmed Supaya and made her realize how hungry she was. She ate some of Neegonas' dried meat and bread. "Grandma, could you bring me some work to do tomorrow? It is hard to sit doing nothing all day."

"Yes, Suppy, I . . ." Quayo broke off and listened. They heard voices and laughter. Then three young men came into view,

27

carrying fishing lines and strings of perch and sunfish. The first one noticed the women, stopped, and said something to the other two, who turned their heads.

Supaya stared at the ground. Quayo stepped in front of her and regarded them sternly; she knew them all since they were children. As they hesitated, she raised her arm and pointed in the direction of their homes. They exchanged glances and sly grins, then moved quickly out of sight.

"Now," said Quayo, "we will make up a fire." Together they cleared a space and laid a fire. Soon the pungent odor of burning wood and leaves hung in the damp, dusky air. The cracking, leaping fire was reassuring, and Supaya knelt down close to it, knowing that her grandmother would return home, the fire would burn low, and she would be alone.

Quayo, looking at her across the flames, saw the fear in her eyes and understood. Supaya had heard women telling tales, Neegonas among them, of their times in the woods, how young men, daring each other, had broken the law and taken them against their will. Quayo got to her feet. Light was almost gone, and her old eyes no longer saw well in the dark. "I will go now. Do not be afraid. Stay in your shelter. Jacques will guard you."

Supaya watched her grandmother go, then crawled under the branches and curled up in her blanket, lying so she could see the glow of the fire. In one hand she held the stone bear close to her cheek. Once during the night, she roused. The fire had died. A heavy ground fog filled the woods. The only sound was the quiet drip of moisture from the trees.

Morning light came slowly in the woods. Supaya, waking early as usual, lay snug in her blanket until the fog, struck by sunlight, slowly began to lift and fade away. She was sitting cross-legged eating bread when her grandmother came.

Quayo was out of breath. "*Ahnee*, Granddaughter! You see, I pant for your sake! You give my old legs exercise."

Supaya laughed and hugged her grandmother. One night was safely past. With the coming of daylight, her fears seemed foolish, especially now that Quayo was come and they sat together drinking hot tea sweetened, as a treat, with maple syrup. Supaya's spirits rose and she asked eagerly, "What did you bring for me to do?"

From her basket Quayo took out a bundle of old clothes, scissors, needle, and thread. "Here, cut these up and sew them together. You'll soon need a new cover for your bed."

Left again by herself, Supaya began cutting up the clothes. Some she recognized as her old dresses, handed down from Neegonas or her grandmother, or as her father's or Jacques' old shirts. Others were strange, and she knew they had been sent to the reserve by white people. She worked contentedly, making neat stacks according to color and pattern, cutting away the worn parts. She worked steadily all morning and afternoon, the sun warming her back and lighting up the brilliant red and yellow leaves that lay in drifts against the dull brown leaves of past years. Now and then she heard the chatter of a squirrel, the hard drumming of a woodpecker, the strident call of jays, or a rustling in the underbrush that was suddenly stilled, surprised by her presence. Once a small, brown-patterned snake, scarcely discernible amid the leaves slid into view, pulled back its head to consider her briefly, then glided away. She stopped to eat and to drink some water and, thinking she heard whispering voices, climbed onto the rockfall and stood for a time above her shelter, looking in all directions. But she saw no one, and coming down, began sewing the patches together.

That evening, after the deep orange sun had disappeared behind the darkening trees, her grandmother returned, bringing food and water. Together they made up the fire and Quayo rested beside it before going home. She was pleased with Supaya's work.

"Ah, Granddaughter, you will have it half pieced when you come home."

Now that night had come again, Supaya was once more filled with dread, remembering the voices she was sure she'd heard. The time when she could go home seemed very far off. "I wish . . ." she began, then stopped, ashamed of her lack of courage. She saw Quayo's old eyes, bright in the firelight, watching her, waiting for her to continue. Supaya smiled and shook her head. "Nothing, Grandma."

But Quayo understood. She stroked Supaya's hair and said to encourage her, "Your father misses you. He has already gathered the rocks for your steam bath."

When her grandmother had gone, Supaya put more wood on the fire, crawled under the shelter, wrapped herself in the blanket, and fell asleep.

She was startled awake by the sounds of drunken voices and bodies crashing through the underbrush. Alarmed, she moved as far back from the opening as she could, pressing herself against the rock. In the dark, she could see nothing except the glowing embers of the fire, but she could hear movement, exclamations, low laughter.

"There! That's her fire. I told you."

"You sure no one's guarding?" A second voice.

"Ah! You're crazy! Give me the bottle!"

"Shut up!" A third voice.

"But her father's a doctor! And that old woman might be a witch!"

"I told you, shut up!"

There was a scuffle, grunts, a thud, then ominous quiet. Supaya scarcely breathed. Tense, she listened for the faintest sound, stared wide-eyed into the dark to catch the slightest movement. Where was Jacques? Had he heard? Was he near? Suddenly a shadow passed between her and the fire. A tipsy voice spoke.

"Come on out, Supaya! Let's be friends. Come on, let's have a little fun!"

"Come on, we know you're there. We'll see if you're a woman yet!" Laughter, and another shadow crossed in front of the fire, blocking out its glow.

"Hell, we'll make you a woman!"

"Maybe you want us to drag you out!"

Then Supaya remembered the scissors. Stealthily she felt for them in the dark. Touching the cold metal, her fingers closed around the handles and she held the scissors raised, poised to strike like a knife.

"Yeh! Drag her out! What're we waiting for!"

Branches were shoved aside from above her. A solid, breathing body lunged forward. Hands grabbed for her. With a strength born of fear and defiance, Supaya slashed out with the scissors. Instantly there was an agonized yell. The hands fell away as the man reared violently back and crashed off into the brush.

At the same moment there was another yell and the crack of a fist against bone. Supaya was on her feet, ready to run, as another body, arms flailing, sprawled backward onto the fire.

"Yiiiiii!" Screaming, he rolled over, thrashing his arms and legs. Supaya, horrified, saw Jacques, his face briefly illumined by the firelight, fall on him and beat him furiously. Suddenly out of the dark a third man flung himself toward Jacques' back. Supaya saw the glint of a knife and screamed a warning as another man leaped forward and grabbed the arm holding the knife. Under his impact, they all crashed down together, kicking and twisting. The burned man squirmed from under, and getting to his feet, rushed off. The others struggled, hands reaching for the wildly jabbing knife. It arced downward, there was a sharp cry, then a yelp of pain as Jacques caught the knifer's arm and twisted it viciously. The knife fell, the last man grabbed it up, and and for a moment all three were still, panting for breath, Jacques holding his attacker against him from behind.

Keeping his hold, Jacques spun him around and thrusting his face close, said softly but distinctly, "Next time . . . I kill you." Contemptuously he thrust him away. The man stumbled backward, caught his balance, and paused, calculating his chances. But he was uneasily aware that the other, unknown man who had his knife was somewhere in the dark, waiting. With a snarl of disgust, he turned and ran.

The fire was scattered. The woods were unusually still as if even the trees were listening, waiting. Jacques, his face grim, swept the embers together and added wood. As the fire took hold, he saw beyond the flames Supaya's hand at her side, still clutching the scissors, its points dark and wet. Without looking up at her, he said quietly, "You are a brave . . . woman. Are you all right?"

In a few deadly minutes Supaya had become a stranger to herself, but she managed, through numb lips, to answer, "Yes." Then added, in a whisper, "Thank you, Jacques."

Jacques stood up, careful to turn his back to Supaya, and said, "Kineu, I owe you my life."

Then the other man stepped forward out of the dark. Unlike Jacques, he looked directly at Supaya, and she saw with a shock that it was Kineu. But he was not the gay, laughing Kineu she knew, not the boy she had grown up with, gone fishing and hunting with, shared secrets with. Seen across the flickering firelight, he was as much a stranger to her as she now was to herself. His eyes were narrow and angry, his mouth tight and hard. Blood ran down from his slashed cheek. He stood silent, staring at her, his hand still murderously clenching the knife.

"Kineu," said Jacques, striving to divert his gaze, "Kineu, they won't come back now." He laid his hand on Kineu's arm. "Come, let's repair the shelter." He moved to pick up the branches. "Lie down, Suppy."

Supaya closed her eyes for a moment, shutting out Kineu's bleeding face. Then, dazed, she lay down against the rock and wrapped herself in the blanket, pulling it forward to hood her face.

The scissors she kept beside her. Gradually she relaxed. She could hear Jacques and Kineu moving about, rebuilding the shelter. With the rock at her back and the branches above, Supaya felt once more enclosed, protected. She fell asleep listening to the murmur of their voices.

Two days later Quayo fetched her home. They went together to the barn, where Supaya undressed and wrapped a blanket around herself, then to a small lodge made of curved saplings covered with blankets.

"It is all ready," said Quayo. "Your father heated the stones and I brought water from the spring. The steam will make you clean."

Supaya lifted the flap and stooped inside. She handed the blanket back to Quayo and lowered the flap. Naked except for her blue stone necklace, she knelt down on the cedar boughs which had been spread beside the white hot stones piled to one side. They had been sprinkled with water from a basin and steam filled the small interior. It filled her lungs and made her eyes sting. But the penetrating, moist heat warmed her to the bone and relaxed her muscles. Breaking off some tops from the cedar boughs, she flicked more water onto the stones, then stretched out her arms and rubbed them with the aromatic leaves. Their scratchiness made her damp skin tingle and come alive as if, like the snake, she was shedding her old skin for new. She arched her back and rubbed it, then her neck and chest and saw, almost with surprise, that her breasts were round and full. Turning sideways on her hip, she extended one leg and languidly rubbed the cedar over the curve of hip and thigh. For the first time she recognized the beauty and grace of her body and apprehended all at once its possibilities. She looked upon it in wonder, as on a strange, new possession, all the more remarkable in that others might desire it. Suddenly she felt a stir of pride, a new energy. Kneeling back on her heels, she looked down at the symmetry of her body and touching the blue stone that lay cradled between her pointed breasts, she whispered, "Thank you, Grandfather, for helping me become a woman."

That evening the family sat by the fireplace, eating popped corn and drinking tea. Quayo, in her rocker, sat closest to the fire, a shawl about her shoulders. Jules puffed on his pipe and stroked Joe Crow's glistening black feathers. The bird perched firmly on Jules' knee but his bright eye was fixed on Jacques, who now and again tossed him a grain of corn which he caught expertly and swallowed with a satisfied gulp.

Supaya, handing round the corn and keeping the tea cups filled, was conscious of her changed position in the family and of their eyes upon her, full of love and quiet pride. She felt a shy but giddy happiness and smiled irrepressibly at the slightest remark. And they, fondly amused, laughed with her as if they all shared a delightful secret.

"Today," remarked Jules in an offhand manner, "I heard from the wind in the trees that it is no longer safe to go into the woods." He paused, face solemn, eyebrows slightly raised. "I hear there is a terrible beast there who spits fire and strikes with claws of steel. It must be so, for I saw at the store one man whose back was burned and another whose arm had been slit from elbow to wrist. One must be very careful of angering such a fierce beast, eh, Joe?"

Joe Crow cocked his head wisely and chuckled, "Awk, awk, awk," and they all laughed. Later, from her bed in the loft, Supaya gazed out at the moonless, windy night. All were asleep, and the house was quiet. The fire had burned out and Joe Crow, full of corn, had gone to roost on a beam. Secure once more in her home, Supaya was content, but her happiness was tempered by the sober realization that no more could she rely utterly on father, grandmother, and brother to care for her, or follow their directions with no thought of her own. Now she must assume responsibilities, behave like the young woman she had become. Thinking of her grandmother, strong in spirit but frail in body, and of her widowed father whose loneliness she only now was beginning to appreciate, Supaya was filled with gratitude and a great resolve. She would work harder. She would show them how much they had taught her, and try to care for them as they had cared for her. She would make them proud of her.

And then she thought of Kineu. She had asked Jacques about him, and he had told her Kineu was well, that his face was healing. Tomorrow she would see for herself. She had known Jacques would protect her; he was her brother and nearly twenty, but Kineu . . . She remembered his face as he had looked at her that night across the fire, and smiled to herself in the dark. She was changed; he must also have changed. No longer did she feel empty. The Great Spirit, wise in all things, had blessed her with a great contentment. She lay back and fell asleep almost at once, eager for the morning.

CHAPTER FOUR

During the night a heavy fog rolled in from Lake Huron, blanketing all the west side of Stone Island, an isolating, silencing fog that chilled the bones of the old people. Supaya made up the fire in the stove, and her grandmother stood by it holding out her arthritic hands. She fretted about her cousin, Emilia.

"Auntie Em will be hungry. There is no one to make up her fire."

"I will go, Grandma. Here, drink your tea."

"But the fog is bad."

"It won't last," said Jules. "The sun will eat it up and give us a fine day for hunting." He and Jacques were leaving to check their traps and go hunting. The garden had done well that year. The root cellar was well stocked with vegetables and the loft with dried fruit. But although many fish and much meat—raccoon, rabbit, and deer—had been dried, there was not enough meat to carry them through the long winter.

"Maybe I'll bring you a good fat porcupine, Grandma," said Jacques.

"Then I will make you a fine stew, Grandson. May you be blessed in the hunt."

By the time Supaya started for Auntie Em's, the sun had risen above the trees, its glowing face as pale as the moon's. But the fog had begun to lift, moving slowly in ghostly, tattered clouds. Supaya, holding a pot of soup in one arm, walked along the road where the fence posts and trees, dripping moisture, appeared, then disappeared, and the stone church, the preacher's house, and the schoolhouse seemed to waver and shift about. Passing the schoolhouse, its row of windows pale yellow squares, Supaya felt a twinge of regret and was glad that Miss Harris, should she glance out a window, would not see her going by. Supaya was now fifteen and had not returned to school. She had completed the fifth reader and had done so well that Miss Harris had asked her to help teach the beginners their letters. But though she wanted to learn everything Miss Harris could teach her, she wanted even more to learn all that Quayo knew. Already Supaya did most of the cooking and preserving and all of the sewing. And Quayo had taught her how to make birchbark boxes and do quill embroidery, for which she now had such skill that she'd been able to sell them to Mr. Bonnet. She could add now as well as he, and one by one she had read all the books Miss Harris had on the shelf in her bedroom. Most of all, she wanted to learn how to heal. Quayo was teaching her what she knew of herbal medicine, and she was learning more from other old women who gave her recipes in exchange for food or a quill box of unusual design. Auntie Em knew little medicine, but she was older than Quayo and lived alone. Supaya often took her food, made up her fire, cleaned her house.

Auntie Em lived beyond Mr. Bonnet's store, and as Supaya approached the store and dock area, she saw that the trim little lake steamer had arrived and was docked alongside the government wharf, the lines of its steel-plated prow and smokestack softened by the shifting fog, heavier over the water. She heard raised voices and the thuds of crates and barrels being trundled down the gangplank and over the hollow-sounding boards of the wharf. The double doors of the general store were propped wide open. Mist swirled and gleamed in the pale light slanting out across the porch. Mr. Bonnet, in a long apron, his shirt sleeves tucked up, waved his arms and shouted directions. White men with faces permanently reddened from raw weather and wearing knitted caps, heavy jackets, and boots went back and forth between wharf and store, rolling barrels, carrying boxes or burlap bags slung over their shoulders. Several Indian men lounged on the porch rail that dripped moisture, their black hats set low on their heads, watching, perhaps waiting for the mailbags to be opened. Few passengers arrived this late in the year, but two Indian women, carrying carpetbags, and a small child stood to one side, waiting patiently for a friend or relative.

Supaya, hurrying past and thinking to avoid the path of a

man carrying a barrel on his back, dodged behind him and ran directly into another man who appeared unexpectedly out of the mist. She cried out as her hold on the pot slipped. They both grabbed for it, their heads almost colliding, and caught it together.

"Well, well!" The man laughed and straightened up, the pot held between them. "A double catch! My lucky day!"

Supaya had seen a few white men—Mr. Jackson, the Indian agent, Mr. Bonnet, the sailors—but never one like this. Unaware that she was staring, she stared. His black suit was stylishly fitted. The brim of his hat curved smartly over curly hair and brows nearly as black as her own. His fancy vest was a brocade and adorned by a gold watch chain. As he smiled down at her, Supaya was struck by the solid, physical force of him, but most of all she was startled by his vividly blue eyes, by their intense directness.

Jess Fallon was used to coquettish glances, but open amazement was new to him. He was surprised by the beauty of this girl, the high, smooth brow, wide cheekbones, and large, slanted dark eyes. The unconscious wonder in her expression, in her soft, slightly parted lips, touched him, stirring in him a sudden wish to detain her, to come to know her.

Realizing she was staring, Supaya started to back away and only then saw that his hands covered hers as together they held the pot. Overwhelmed with embarrassment, she lowered her head and gave a tug on the pot.

Instantly he removed his hands. "Excuse me, ma'm," he said, and she heard the laughter in his voice. "Could I carry it for you?"

Without raising her eyes, Supaya shook her head and walked rapidly away.

Auntie Em's little one-room frame house was surrounded by trees on three sides but faced the rocky shoreline and caught the full force of whatever weather swept in off the lake. She was awake when Supaya knocked but still in bed, trying to keep warm under an old quilt. The fire in the small iron box stove was out, and the room was cold.

"*Ahnee*, Auntie Em." Auntie Em made an effort to sit up. "No, no. Stay there until I have made up the fire. Grandma sent you some soup."

"Ah, you are so good to me, so good!" She lay back and

watched as Supaya made up the fire, brought in a supply of wood and a pail of fresh water from the pump.

"Now, Auntie Em, would you like to sit in your rocking chair? I'll comb your hair. Then you can have some hot soup. Here, let me help you up." Because she had broken her hip the previous winter, Auntie Em limped and moved with difficulty. She leaned on Supaya and settled gingerly into her chair near the stove. When she had washed and had her hair combed, Supaya ladled out the soup.

"Please, sit down. Sit!" Auntie Em insisted as she began to eat. She smiled slyly at Supaya. Several of her teeth were missing, and the gaps gave her wrinkled brown face a mischievous, impish expression. "You are a fine young woman. When will you marry, eh? Do not shake your head. I hear things," Auntie Em assured her, nodding, "I hear!" She ate carefully, her bony old hand trembling as it raised the spoon.

At her words, Supaya thought instantly of Kineu, the image closest to her heart, the secret motivation for all she did. Since becoming a woman, she was not allowed to be alone with him, and he had stopped school the year before she did. But they saw each other often in the company of their families. Kineu often came home from hunting or fishing with Jacques. Kineu was no longer a boy, his father, Arthur, said, but a man, since he could now wield an axe like a man. Kineu's powers as a hunter and fisherman were well known throughout the reserve, it being rumored that his blessings gave him a knowledge of the likeliest places to set his nets and place his traps. His guardian was said to guide his aim, so accurate was he with knife and gun. He was most at home, Supaya knew, when hunting or fishing, most happy and alive when free to lie back on the earth and watch the clouds move, or to climb a hill and gaze across the treetops, or to pit his skill against that of an animal or the treacherousness of winter. He would be gone sometimes for days on a hunt, but always when he returned, he brought something for Supaya, often a porcupine so she might have the quills. At the fall fair he won all the races, being blessed with swiftness, though he laughed and seemed to care no more about winning than he had about learning to read. Nothing delighted Supaya more than hearing him praised, but she tried to hide her pride in him as she did her pleasure whenever he teased her, dropping her eyes whenever she caught him staring at her.

"Ah! You smile," said Auntie Em suddenly. "You think of him," she added knowingly and with satisfaction.

"Auntie Em, your bowl is empty. Do you want more soup?"

"I know what young women think," she insisted. "I remember well."

"Auntie Em, do you want more soup?"

"No, no more. All the same, I know . . ."

"Here, Auntie Em, let me tuck your shawl around you."

"You are kind to an old woman," said Auntie Em. "I will not forget what you do for me."

Supaya bent and kissed her soft cheek. "Jacques will come later and cut more wood for your fire."

On her way home, Supaya saw that the steamer had loaded mail and passengers for its return trip and gone. The sun had burned away the fog, making the air warmer and luminous. Mist still glimmered far out on the lake. Crates were stacked on the ground in front of the store. Mr. Bonnet's son, a thin young man with the washed-out hair and pallid skin of his father, was carrying them inside one at a time. Mr. Bonnet himself stood on the porch talking to the man in the black suit, who stood with elbows out, fingers hooked in his vest pockets, nodding affably as Mr. Bonnet spoke.

At the sight of him, Supaya felt a mixture of embarrassment and irritation. She should not have run into him or been rude and tongue-tied when he offered to help her. But also he had caused her to stare at him like a foolish, brazen girl and, worse, he had been amused. She saw his head turn in her direction as he caught sight of her. Determined to maintain her dignity, she passed coolly by, skirting the crates and looking straight ahead as though no one there were worth her notice.

But he turned so as to keep her in view, admiring her carriage, the sheen of her long, braided hair, the proud angle of her chin. He listened to Mr. Bonnet, but his eyes followed Supaya until she was out of sight.

In late afternoon, when the sun hung low and blood red in a pale, cloudless sky, Jacques burst into the kitchen where Quayo was mixing bread and Supaya was sewing beads on a new pair of moccasins.

"Grandma, Suppy! Come! Father shot a bear!"

Both women dropped their work and rushed out after him. Jacques had gotten a porcupine and three beavers in his traps, but they were almost forgotten in the excitement over the bear, rarely found on their island. It was a large black bear, its pelt thick for winter and its body rich in fat. Before skinning it, Jules cut off its paws, feet, and head. The head he stuck on a stick driven into the ground near the fire. Supaya ran to the house and fetched red yarn which she wound decoratively about its head and ears. Quayo brought a pouch of choice tobacco which Jules sprinkled on the fire before the bear. As the fire crackled and the smoke curled up and around the bear's snout, Jules offered up their thanks.

"Great Bear, you have blessed us. You have guided us in
the hunt. You have given us yourself that we may
live.

"Great Bear, we, your brothers, thank you. May our
offering give you pleasure."

Then he and Jacques skinned the body, putting aside the heart and liver which Quayo carried into the kitchen and put in a pot to be cooked. Daylight was fading fast, so they hung the porcupine and the beavers by their hind feet from a tree, leaving their skinning for the next day.

They were eating fish and fried scone when there was a knock at the front door. Cyrus Red Sky and his wife Miriam stood on the doorstep.

"We have come for the doctor," said Cyrus.

"Come in," invited Jules, "come in and sit down. Jacques, bring chairs. Quayo, some tea."

Jacques brought the chairs near the fireplace, then knelt by the hearth and made up the fire. Miriam sat down as though her legs would no longer hold her and gripped the ends of her shawl in tight fists. Cyrus, a large, heavy man, moved with dignified restraint to a chair, sat down, and carefully placed the large bundle he carried on the floor beside him. Neither spoke, but there was pain in their eyes; their silence was tense with worry that all could feel. Not until the tea had been served did they speak.

"My son Angus, my firstborn, is sick. You are a good doctor. We want you to make him well again."

"What is wrong with him?" asked Jules.

"His throat is tight. He cannot swallow. His body hurts. His skin is hot."

"Oh!" exclaimed Miriam, leaning forward and clasping her hands. "He is on fire!" Having broken her silence, she was unable to restrain her tears. Her husband turned and looked at her, whereupon she sat back and drew her shawl about her head.

"I will come," said Jules. "Tomorrow evening."

"I am glad. We will have a sweat lodge ready for you. These things I have brought now." Cyrus picked up the bundle and, unwrapping it, took out a plug of tobacco which he presented to Jules and then a new blanket. Having given his gifts, he stood up. "We will go now."

Next morning light was slow in coming. A gray sky had drawn down close over the land and the lake, turning the water to cold metal. Jules, preoccupied with preparations for the curing ceremony, withdrew into himself. He spoke to no one. He tasted no food. Taking a special birchbark container sealed with resin, he walked far into the woods to a spring that bubbled up at the base of a slope. On such a still, gray day he could hear the murmur of its voice before he came upon the small, marshy pool it formed from a source that never completely froze over. Here Jules knelt on the wet, grassy margin and leaned forward, head bowed, arms extended out over the clear water that rippled up from the center and spread in widening circles. Swaying, he chanted softly. From the edge of the pool he scraped up mud and drew two smears across his forehead. Taking some of his own tobacco from his pouch and some that Cyrus had given him, he sprinkled both on the water and prayed.

"Oh Great Manitou, who gives us water that we may live,
hear me! Accept my offering! Grant my spirit
strength to drive out evil!

"Great Manitou, let your water soothe one who is sick!
Accept this, his offering! Refresh his soul!

"Oh Great Wolf, my Grandfather, give your power also
to this medicine, that it may carry your strength
through his body! Renew his life!"

Holding the bark pail to the lip of the spring, Jules filled it, then rose and returned home. When he came out of the woods, Quayo was gathering up the bones of the bear and those of the beavers—Jacques had skinned them and stripped their flesh—and she was putting them into a bag to be hung from a tree that they might again be of use to the bear and the beavers. Supaya was pulling the quills from the porcupine. Jules passed them all without a word or glance and entered the house.

Using his own special bowls, he made a mixture of dried herbs from his own collection, slippery elm bark and checkerberry leaves, moistened it with the spring water and made a paste. This he covered and put to one side along with the container of water, a small wooden drum covered with stretched hide, and his otter skin medicine bag. Then he undressed except for a loincloth, wrapped himself in a blanket, and sat down cross-legged on the floor of his room, pulling the blanket down over his face.

Pulling quills was careful, tedious work. Pulling each quill out by its tip, Supaya sorted them according to their length, placing to one side those over three inches long and thus too coarse for fine embroidery. Quayo helped Supaya finish while Jacques turned over the strips of meat drying on the frame and kept the fire smoking. As Supaya was tying the quills into bundles, Kineu appeared, his gun in one hand, a large fat porcupine in the other.

"*Ahnee*, Aunt."

"Welcome, Nephew."

"I see you've been lucky," said Jacques.

"Yes. This porcupine put himself in my path, begged me to shoot him."

"Why, Nephew, why?" asked Quayo.

"Well," said Kineu with a serious face, but looking sideways at Supaya, "news has spread of wonderful embroidery being done here, of an artist of such skill that any porcupine would be honored to be put to such use."

Jacques and Quayo laughed.

"Here?" Supaya looked around. "I know no one of such skill here."

"Ah, I was mistaken then." Kineu turned to go.

"Wait, Nephew, wait. I will take him since no one else wants him," said Quayo.

"Such a poor porcupine. I cannot think who would want him," said Supaya. "He must be sick."

"All the same," said Quayo, holding the porcupine over the fire, "I will just singe his nose and eyes so his soul will be at rest."

Kineu, standing near Supaya, noticed the backs of her fingers, scratched and bleeding from pulling quills. He took the singed porcupine from Quayo and, sitting down beside Supaya, pulled the quills himself.

Quayo spoke of the cure to be held that evening at the Red Skys'. As she talked, Supaya stole long glances at Kineu. His thick, black hair sprang back from his forehead and lay in shaggy ends against his neck. His lashes were long as a girl's, and his mouth, in repose, had such sweetness that she yearned to touch his face. At

41

that moment, he raised his head and looked at her. Caught out, she blushed and dropped her eyes, hearing with pleasure Quayo assuring him that they would see him that evening at the curing ceremony.

By evening the wind had risen and was moving the slate-bellied clouds swiftly across the leaden sky. It churned up the lake, dashed the waves into spray against the rocks, and bent the pines, singing through their branches a song of coming winter. Jules strode ahead by himself, wrapped in his blanket, his medicine bag hanging from his belt. Quayo, Supaya, and Jacques followed, the women bending their shawled heads against the sharp wind. Jacques, carrying the birch container of spring water and the drum, walked with dignity as the doctor's helper, proudly, head up, his long hair flying in the wind.

Behind the Red Skys' house a sweat lodge had been erected, covered with pieces of canvas and a blanket. Near it blazed a fire, its flames wind-whipped. As Jules approached, Cyrus, using the crossed ends of two tied sticks, lifted fist-sized rocks from the flames and carried them, one at a time, into the lodge, putting them in a pile to one side of the cedar branches covering the ground. Jules, indifferent to the sharp air, spread out his arms, putting back his blanket, which Cyrus received and held for him. Jules stooped and entered the lodge, lowering the flap behind him. With a cedar whisk, he flicked water from a pail onto the hot, hissing stones until steam filled the lodge, enveloping, warming, and purifying his body.

Jacques and the women went inside the house. Only the fire in the fireplace illuminated the room. Its beamed ceiling and corners were lost in shadows. Relatives and friends had already gathered, sitting on the floor in rows along the sides and ends of the room. Some stood, their backs against the walls. Unmoving and silent, like dark-robed statues they waited, filling the room with a portentous expectancy. The firelight gleamed in their steady, meditative eyes, threw into light and shadow their grave, strong-boned faces. Only when a newcomer entered did they move, nodding their heads in silent greeting.

As in the center of a stage, the patient, a boy of sixteen, lay on a woven mat of cedar bark in the middle of the floor. His face, turned from the fire, was in shadow. But all could see the labored rise and fall of his chest and hear the shudder of his breathing. His mother sat near him, head bowed, hands tightly clasped. High on the stairs leading to the loft her two younger children sat close together, their eyes wide and solemn. Jacques waited near the door for Jules. Quayo and Supaya joined those along the side. More people arrived, among them Hettie, Jules' sister, her husband Arthur, and Kineu. Kineu quickly picked out Supaya. Edging his way through, he reached her side, and they sat down together on the floor, their backs against the bottom stairstep.

After that no one else came. As the waiting was prolonged, the tension increased. No one spoke. No one moved. Only the patient stirred, turning his head restlessly.

Suddenly a draft of cold air swept into the room. Jules entered. Instantly all eyes turned to him, held by the dynamic, compelling power of his presence. He stood with his fierce intense gaze fixed on the patient, oblivious of the rows of people in the shadowed room.

Moving swiftly, he jerked back his head, threw off his blanket, and taking up the drum, gave it one slap, an ominous, opening note. A deep thrill ran through the watchers. Raptly they followed every move. Leaning forward, knees bent, Jules moved slowly toward the patient, lifting his feet in time to the rhythm he tapped out on the drum. He began to chant, his voice at first so faint and deep that the listeners couldn't tell when it began but felt it like a song that had risen from deep inside themselves. Four times he circled the patient, his gaze concentrated on him. Gradually the tempo of his drumming increased to a continuous, insistent beat, and his chanting grew louder. As he circled about, firelight glistened on his bare back, arms, and chest and flashed on his beaded apron. Suddenly he fell to his knees by the patient and with one swift gesture threw back the quilt. He drew from his medicine bag a handful of earth, and gently rolling the boy to one side, spread it under his back. Then with head tilted back and eyes closed, Jules resumed his chant, drumming with both hands on the drum held between his knees. His voice rose from deep in his chest, resounding, vibrating, filling the room with his supplication. The audience, entranced, swayed with the rhythm, following every modulation of his voice.

After one long, tremulous note, he abruptly stopped. He put aside the drum and laid his hand on Angus' forehead. He took from his bag a box of mixed herbs and stirred them into a bowl of the spring water. He dipped his fingers in it and bathed Angus' head and throat, stroking firmly up and down. The boy responded with a kind of groaning sigh. Lifting Angus' head, Jules held the bowl to his lips. At first the water trickled down the side of his chin, but Jules persisted. Finally, the boy's lips moved, he made a faint effort to swallow, painfully, several times.

A low sigh rose from the audience; there was a stirring among them. Miriam raised her head, the beginning of hope in her eyes. Kineu inched closer to Supaya, pressing his shoulder and arm against hers. Her eyes fixed on her father, she pretended not to notice but was careful not to move away.

Jules set aside the spring water and opened a box containing the paste. He rubbed it on the boy's chest in rhythmical, circular movements, then on his arm and leg muscles, massaging and flexing them. Gently he rolled him over face down, stretched his arms beyond his head, and rubbed the paste into the muscles of his back. The aromatic smell of checkerberry filled the room. Rolling Angus onto his back again Jules once more gave him the herbal water to drink. This time Angus weakly opened his eyes.

"Drink," said Jules, and Angus drank. "Now sleep and be healed," said Jules, covering the boy with the quilt. Angus' eyes stayed open, gazing vaguely upward. Jules began to chant again, softly, accenting the rhythm with a beat on his drum. Slowly, Angus' eyes closed, his head tilted to one side, and he slept.

Jules rose and increased the tempo of his drumming, singing softly but confidently, stepping in time to his beat. He sang at Angus' left side, then at his feet, at his right side, and finally at his head. His audience moved with his rhythm, their dark faces flushed in the firelight, their eyes glowing. As he circled round and round, his enlarged shadow slid across the beams, shot up into dark corners, came tamely back to his measured step. Finally he stopped at Angus' head, sank to his knees, lowered his head, and extended his arms over the boy. A pulsing silence filled the room. Moisture glistened on Jules' broad, curved back. His powerfully muscled arms vibrated, merging the power of the watchers with his own, concentrating all the tension, focusing it, stretching it, holding it taut, suspended.

Suddenly, just before the breaking point, his muscles went slack. His body sagged. He stood up, arms hanging wearily. Jacques stepped forward, holding up the blanket. Jules wrapped himself in it, covering his head, and quietly left the house. Quayo, Supaya, and Jacques, carrying the drum and container of water, followed him. Only then did the guests rise and, nodding at Cyrus and Miriam, silently depart.

All the next day Jules stayed in his room, resting and fasting, drinking only water from the spring. At dusk, on his way back to his patient, he saw that the wind still blew from the west, a good portent for Angus' recovery.

Angus was awake when Jules and Jacques arrived. Unobtrusively, Jacques placed the drum and water near the pallet and went to sit with Cyrus and Miriam. Jules felt Angus' forehead and again bathed his head, neck, and chest with spring water and held his head while he drank the herbal water. Then from his medicine bag Jules took a small bundle of birchbark, unwrapped it, and took out a piece of dried *weekan* root.

"Chew this slowly until it is all gone."

Obediently, Angus began chewing as Jules drummed and danced, chanting a low but vigorous song, turning in tight circles as he described a larger circle about the patient. As he danced there was a knock on the door. Before Cyrus could reach it, the door opened and Reverend Harris stepped inside.

"I heard . . ." he began, and stopped, staring amazed at Jules, now still as stone, at Angus, looking up wide-eyed, at Cyrus and Miriam. Anger rose like a blush in his face. "What is going . . . how dare you carry on these pagan rites!" Furious, he turned to Cyrus. "I have forbidden this! Your son needs a doctor, not a quack!"

Sullenly Cyrus thrust his hands into his pants pockets and said nothing. Miriam, frightened, lowered her eyes and clasped her hands nervously together. Jules glanced at Jacques, who picked up the drum and birch box and brought Jules his blanket. They moved quietly toward the door, but Reverend Harris, infuriated by such lack of response, burst out at Jules.

"You! You defy me! You defy God's word, time and again! You and your whole family!" He raised an angry fist. "You are undermining my work here, and for that you will feel God's wrath! You will burn in hell for this!" He made a move to seize the drum and birch pail from Jacques, exclaiming, "I'll burn these heathen . . ." But Jules swiftly thrust out his arm in front of Jacques, and leaned toward the preacher, his face threatening, his eyes narrowed. "It is you who should beware!"

Reverend Harris jerked back. "Don't you dare touch me!"

Jules' lips curled with contempt. "You understand nothing!" He spat out his words. "You are cold, empty! Leave this house! Go back to your god and pray for him to enlighten you!"

Stunned, his mouth dry, Reverend Harris looked to Cyrus, to Miriam, but they stared at the floor. Struggling for self-control, he could find no words, no way to oppose Jules' bitter scorn. Baffled, he turned and rushed out of the house.

Miriam raised her head, looked from her husband to Jules, neither of whom moved or spoke. Full of distress for her son, she beseeched Jules to continue. "Please! We beg you! Continue!"

"Not now," said Jules, turning away. "For now I am done. I will come again tomorrow."

The next evening, Angus was propped up on one elbow, drinking broth. Jules gave him more root to chew. Then he burned tobacco in the fireplace and sang a song of thanks to the Great Manitou and to his guardian, the Great Wolf. When he finished, he broke his fast, eating the dried meat and bread Miriam brought him.

"You have made my son well," said Cyrus. "We will have a celebration."

For the next several days Miriam and her sister-in-law busied themselves preparing for the feast. They made fruit pies, venison stew, and corn soup. Cyrus killed a pig, scalded it, scraped off the bristles, and cut it into large pieces for Miriam to roast in the oven. They borrowed an extra table and extra chairs. And on the day itself, the women heated quarts of berries in maple syrup and baked bread and fried scone.

The day was ideal for a feast: the air crisp and cold, invigorating for playing ball, the sky a fragile, cloudless blue with no hint of bad weather. The intense reds and yellows of maple and birch flamed against the deep green of fir and cedar.

Walking along the road with Jacques behind their father and grandmother, Supaya breathed deeply the tingling, exhilarating air and felt so happy with her world, so buoyant, that she wanted to spin in circles.

"What are you smiling at?" asked Jacques.

"Ah!" exclaimed Supaya, flinging out her arms. "At the beautiful world! At you! At everybody!"

Jacques laughed. "I know. You like going to a party because you like seeing Kineu."

"And you," teased Supaya, "like seeing Maud!"

"Oh ho! I'll get you for that!" cried Jacques, chasing her.

Supaya sprinted ahead, caught her father's arm, and danced along in front of him. "Save me!" she cried, laughing, "save me!"

Jules smiled and put an arm about her shoulders. "You are saved!"

Peering over her father's shoulder at Jacques, Supaya made a face.

46

"Be careful," warned Jacques. "You'll be caught when you don't expect it!"

At the crossroads they met several other families, and all walked on together. As they approached Cyrus' house, they could hear voices and smell the tantalizing aromas of roast pork and bread mingled with that of burning wood. Men stood around a large, outside fire, smoking their pipes and talking. They raised their hands in greeting to the newcomers. Children raced about, dodging their elders, dashing into the house and out again. A white spotted dog, his tongue lolling, chased after them, confused by their shifts in direction. By the door a group of young women had gathered. They watched Jules approach with sly, admiring glances.

He was greeted formally at the door as the guest of honor. "Welcome to our home," said Cyrus, ushering him inside. "Please sit here by the fire," said Miriam.

Quite aware of the young women's admiration, Jules entered with an easy dignity and accepted a chair. Relatives and friends stood back, leaving a small space around him for the payment of gifts. Cyrus and Miriam brought him another blanket, a large tin of tobacco, a sack of flour, and a quilt with a pieced design and red yarn ties. Angus, who was still resting on his cedar mat in the corner, came shyly forward. He carried a new pair of winter moccasins decorated with beadwork, and these he held out to Jules.

"Please accept these. I hope they will ease your path."

"I will wear them with pleasure," said Jules.

After the payment, formalities were forgotten. Guests crowded around the tables, helping themselves to the food, urged by Miriam to fill their bowls again and again. Women went back and forth, replenishing the food in the bowls and stirring the pots that steamed on the kitchen stove.

Supaya joined the group of young women standing outside. They were laughing and talking among themselves while watching the young men who had started a ballgame in the field across the road. The players raced toward one goal, swerved round toward the other, scattered and converged, intent on their pursuit of the ball. Old men leaned on the fence and watched, smoking and laying bets.

Maud stood with Supaya. She was a small, shy girl, several years older than Supaya. As a schoolgirl she had admired Jacques and had dropped her large eyes to hide her pleasure whenever he had singled her out. Recently he had made his preference for her quite clear and she felt herself trembling on the edge of a great happiness, waiting for the day when Jacques would ask Jules to speak to her father.

"Your brother plays very well," said Maud.

"Mmm, yes," answered Supaya, her eye on Kineu, who could outrun all the others.

"I prefer the father," said Rhea, boldly.

Startled, Supaya turned to see who was so presumptuous as to openly refer to her father. Rhea was a girl Supaya knew only by sight. She was nineteen and had left school earlier than most of the other girls. Supaya had seen her at the store, flirting with Mr. Bonnet's son. Now she ignored Supaya, gazing past her at the players. The bland innocence of her sloe eyes and smooth, oval face, the little knowing smile curving her large sensuous mouth indicated an experience superior to that of the others.

"I hear he's been visiting the Widow Walker," said Rhea pertly. Embarrassed by Supaya's presence, none of the girls spoke up. Supaya looked stonily away, hiding her shock by pretending not to have heard.

"Oh well," said Rhea with a shrug, "she's too old. I bet he'd like someone younger." Some of the girls giggled, and Rhea tossed her head impudently. "You can have the boys. I want a man," she said and went inside.

"Do not listen to her, Suppy," said Maud softly so the others wouldn't hear. "She has a big mouth and will say anything."

Supaya nodded, but for her the celebration was ruined. She was sickened and humiliated to hear her father so spoken of. She wanted to go home, to draw her family close around her. She wanted what Rhea had said to be untrue. She left the group and went around to the back of the house, hoping to find Quayo. Quayo was in the lean-to, conferring with several other women over a piece of sewing one had brought. Through the door Supaya could see her father. He was standing with his back to the fireplace, smoking and talking to Mr. Jackson, the Indian agent, a stout, middle-aged man whose wide stance was partly for effect and partly for balance. He was explaining something with gestures and Jules was listening, looking down, a faint, thoughtful smile on his lips. Supaya started toward him. Then, as the people crowded around the tables shifted, she saw that his glance rested on Rhea, who sat in front of him, daintily eating a piece of pie and listening to his conversation, her coy eyes, shadowed by her long, loose hair, fixed on his.

Instantly, Supaya turned away and, seeking comfort, went to stand near her grandmother, but Quayo was absorbed in her own conversation. Feeling strangely dislocated and lonely, Supaya wandered outside and stood for a while watching a group of children down on their knees in a circle, playing with three moccasins and a shell, vying with each other, guessing in which mocasin the shell was hidden.

As the sun sank behind the trees, the evening grew chill. People drew closer to the fire. The ballgame came to a shouting finish, and the players came trooping back, thirsty and hungry. The old men argued over the plays and exchanged tobacco to pay off their wagers.

Rhea, seeing that Jules' conversation was going to continue, had risen and with a lingering glance at Jules, had gone outside. Jules was discussing with Jackson woodcutting privileges on the reserve when Cyrus joined them. Jackson nodded affably at his host. A single man, he enjoyed celebrations. And like a single man with no restrictions beyond those in the government handbook, was blunt and often unconsciously tactless. Over the years his manner, like his girth, had steadily broadened.

"My brother Wenonga is coming for a visit," said Cyrus. "He sent a message through my sister-in-law. He will come on tomorrow's boat."

"Wenonga!" said Jackson thoughtfully, as though this announcement were for his benefit. "He hasn't been here in a long time. Quite a troublemaker, that one. What's he want, Cyrus?"

"He is my brother. He comes for a visit," said Cyrus flatly, his face closed, his eyes resting coldly on Jackson's.

"All right, all right! Just so he don't stir up trouble. Mighty nice party, Cyrus." Jackson moved away toward the food.

Jules and Cyrus stood silent, as though they were alone in an empty space. For Jules, this blow came suddenly. He could not speak. He waited, hoping Cyrus would say, "He comes only for a visit with us. That is all." But as the silence between them lengthened, Jules knew the time he foolishly had thought would never come had, after all, arrived. He stared across the room, seeing nothing, his face set.

Cyrus shifted uneasily. Jackson was right in suspecting Wenonga's motives. Wenonga was a shaman. He never traveled without a purpose. That his purpose this time involved a friend, Jules, to whom Cyrus owed his son's life, was cause for sorrow. "He said he comes to see you, that he has business with you."

"Then," said Jules quietly, turning away, "I will expect him." He searched for his daughter. Quayo he saw in the lean-to, but not Supaya or Jacques. He found them outside with a large group gathered around the fire, popping corn. Jacques had said something amusing, and they all laughed. Supaya and Kineu were standing together, shoulders touching. Jules watched them, studying his daughter's face. Her wide brow and high cheekbones were softened by youth and spoke of a strength yet to be realized. But her eyes, large and slanted like his own, and her full, generous mouth spoke of a ready capacity for passion. That was clear enough to Jules, seeing the unconscious but ardent yearning in her face as she looked up at Kineu, with a look that matched Kineu's own. From the depth of his own worn years, Jules wondered bitterly what kept them apart.

Someone in front of Jules spoke. Supaya turned her head and saw her father, standing outside the circle, watching her. He met her eyes, not casually but keenly, as if he would tell her something, holding her eyes with his own, the corners of his mouth turned in a rueful smile that was unfamiliar and disturbing to Supaya. Standing there beyond the firelight in the dusk of evening, he seemed to recede from her, to become a stranger. A sudden fear struck her, and she almost called out to him above the others' voices, but then she saw that he was gone. She shivered with apprehension. That he intended a meaning she was certain. But what? Feeling lost and uneasy, she turned back to Kineu.

Before the half moon rose, everyone had gone. Jules had found Rhea waiting in the house. Unsmiling, he studied her, a glint of suppressed anger in his eye, which she, in her pleasure at his seeking her out, misunderstood. When he inclined his head and walked out the door, she rose and followed him.

Jacques walked home with Maud and her family. Quayo, not finding Jules, called Supaya. They gathered up Jules' gifts and walked home, Kineu accompanying them.

"Where is Father, Grandma?"

Quayo was evasive. "Talking, smoking." She was too weary to be bothered. Her old legs ached from standing. She thought only of her bed, downstairs to save her climbing the ladderlike stairs.

When they reached home, Quayo, mumbling to herself, went in at once, leaving Supaya and Kineu alone.

"Something is wrong," insisted Supaya.

"Why? What could be wrong?"

"Didn't you see him? The way he looked when we were standing by the fire?"

Kineu laughed softly. "I saw only you. Come," putting his arm around her waist. "Let's walk under the trees."

"He was telling me something, Kineu, I know it. Then he was gone. It was like a bad omen."

Kineu drew her into the shadow of the woods. Behind them, moonlight whitened the ridged, barren garden and shone frostily on the roof of the house, whose black shadow fell aslant the ground. On the whitened road lay the black, pointed shadows of pines.

"You see," whispered Kineu, drawing her round so she faced him, "it was a good omen. We are here, together."

"But Kineu, I think . . ."

He suddenly put both arms around her, pressing her so close that her breath came in a little gasp. "Think of me, Suppy!"

"Ah, but I do," Supaya whispered, forgetting her worry. "I think of you all the time." She relaxed against him, delighting in his tight embrace. She put her arms around his neck and he bent his head and kissed her gently, soft lip against lip. He kissed her cheeks and the curve of her neck.

"Suppy, Suppy," he whispered, holding her so tight she could scarcely breathe. She stroked his hair, passed her fingertips tenderly over his brow, traced the long, thin scar that he had gotten defending her. And as she had yearned to do, she caressed the line of his cheek and jaw and let her fingers linger on the curve of his mouth. They kissed again, and then, through the stifled beating of their hearts, they heard a sound.

Kineu raised his head. Listening, they heard not footsteps but a low, happy humming. "It's Jacques, coming home. Oh, Kineu, I must go in. Father might come! No, Kineu, please!" She braced her hands against his chest. "I must go."

They waited to be sure Jacques was in his room; then, after a last, lingering kiss and a slow parting of hands, Supaya ran to the door and let herself in.

Much, much later, when the moon had sunk below the still, black waters of the lake, and the road, like a tunnel, held only darkness, Jules came home. He hesitated briefly before opening the door, then moved soundlessly across the room. Supaya, blissfully asleep in the loft, never heard him, nor did Jacques. Quayo, muttering and twitching in the restless half-sleep of the old, mistook the figure that paused by her bed for the spirit of her father and dropped of to another dream of childhood.

The sun rose like a fiery, angry eye, then disappeared behind slate-black clouds that rolled slowly out of the west, bringing the first snow of winter.

Jacques lit the oil lamp, and Quayo set out cups of steaming tea, placing one before Jules, who seemed not to see it. Since rising, he had scarcely spoken, but sat facing the door, one arm resting on the table. Almost, thought Quayo, watching him uneasily, as though he were expecting someone. But she didn't question him, for there was that in his face that brought back the dreadful memory of the day her daughter Shooskonee, his wife, had died. Remembering, Quayo rested her hand lightly on his shoulder.

Supaya had just come downstairs when there was a knock on the door. Quayo and Jacques turned. Jules didn't move.

"I'll go," said Supaya. She opened the door and stepped back as a gust of cold air and a few whirling snowflakes blew in.

Wenonga stood on the doorstep.

CHAPTER FIVE

Standing in the blowing snow, Wenonga waited to be invited in. Snow clung to his shaggy hair and lay on his broad, blanketed shoulders. The wind buffeted against him, blew his hair across his face, but he stood massive and solid as a tree rooted in the earth. In the one startled moment between Supaya's opening the door and Quayo's coming to greet him, his large, bulging eyes took in everything—Supaya, the room beyond, Quayo and Jacques, both turned in surprise, Jules, not surprised, facing him across the table.

It was Quayo who came forward first to greet him. "*Ahnee*, Wenonga, *ahnee*! Please come in! Welcome to our home!"

He entered with a deliberate, stately step, following Quayo, who graciously offered him a chair by the fireplace. He flung off his blanket and settled himself, leaning slightly forward, his head resting between his thick, hunched shoulders.

Jules greeted him stiffly, then formally presented his son, Jacques, and his daughter, Supaya.

Wenonga looked back and forth at them all, moving only his eyes, looking from one to the other in the suspicious manner of a guest who knows that wherever he goes, he is more respected than liked, more feared than welcomed.

Supaya had never seen such eyes as his, large, red-veined, reddened even at the rims as if a fire burned inside him. They were powerful, compelling, and they lingered on her as though without raising a hand he would grasp her, hold her, penetrate her thoughts. She knew this was the shaman who had saved her mother's life when she gave birth to Jacques. Quayo had told them many times of the powerful shaman. Supaya had imagined him as an awesome but beneficent figure. Now she found him both repelling and fascinating, also frightening, and when Quayo sent her on the run to Neegonas for an extra pot and to the root cellar for vegetables, she went at once, glad to be out of his sight.

While Quayo and Supaya worked to prepare a meal of the best they had, Jules and Wenonga exchanged gifts of tobacco, and lit their pipes. They puffed in silence for a time. Then Wenonga spoke.

"I hear you healed my brother's son. That is well. They are grateful."

"I am happy that I was able to cure him."

"I lost my first son," said Wenonga, reminding Jules of what he already knew. "He was taken from me by a man jealous of my blessings. But I was revenged. He paid for his spite." Remembering, Wenonga frowned and glared at the fire, his eyes reflecting its red blaze. Jules and Jacques were cautiously silent. A shaman's retribution was fearful. Any discussion could bring it much too close.

Quayo brought the men hot tea, and as they drank, Jules turned the conversation to more general matters, inquiring about a cousin of his who the year before had transferred to the Two Bluffs Reserve where Wenonga lived, far away.

While the venison, onions, and potatoes simmered, filling the room with their aroma, Quayo and Supaya made berry pies and scone. Whenever Supaya turned or raised her head, she caught Wenonga's glance following her. She was disturbed, and would have spoken of it to Quayo, but Quayo, delighted to honor Wenonga, the man who had once saved her daughter's life, was oblivious to Supaya's uneasiness, intent only on serving every good thing she could, even the prized white cheese curds a friend had given her.

When the meal was ready, the men sat at the table, and Quayo and Supaya served them. Wenonga ate rapidly, gulping his food, glancing suspiciously at the others while he chewed. Jules scarcely touched his food, eating only enough to avoid being rude. Quayo, puzzled by Jules' lack of warmth, worked all the harder at making Wenonga welcome, urging him to eat more and more. Supaya hung back, staying behind Wenonga when she could, longing to be free to go and meet Kineu as she had promised the night before.

54

Finally Wenonga finished. He relit his pipe and tried to shape his deep, rough voice to friendly tones. "I see your younger daughter is a handsome young woman now. I see too that she wears a necklace of power." He smiled widely at Supaya, but to her it was as if a wild animal had bared its teeth, and she dropped her eyes, unable to respond. Addressing Jules, he said, "I have heard much about her from my relatives. I hear she is well-trained in our ways. Like her mother," he paused, emphasizing the word "mother," "she is a fine cook and a hard worker."

Quayo was pleased and began to praise Supaya's skills, but Jules interrupted coldly. "Quayo, bring more tea."

"Ah," said Wenonga, as Supaya placed the maple syrup near his cup. "Then she must have clever hands." He reached out suddenly with his broad, thick fingers to take her hand. But Supaya snatched her hand away and moved around to the other side of the table.

Wenonga said politely, "I have also heard good things about your son." But his eyes were on Supaya as he spoke.

"He is a dutiful son," said Jules shortly.

"As you know," said Wenonga, staring now at Jules, who sat with lowered eyes, "I have a second son. When his mother was taken from us, the agent sent him away to government boarding school for a long time. He learned many things there. Now he has returned home." He paused, drew on his pipe, then said, "It is time now for your payment."

Jules might not have heard, might have been struck by misfortune and sitting by himself, he was so pensive and silent. His voice seemed to have died within him. Quayo looked from one to the other, startled by Wenonga's unexpected claim of a payment and disturbed by Jules' silence. Jacques, sensitive to the growing tension, was puzzled and uneasy. He saw Wenonga's increasing impatience for an answer, his burning eyes fixed on his father, and he unconsciously braced himself for a spring. Supaya, wanting only to be gone, moved restlessly, and as she did so, her father spoke. His words were brittle as ice.

"I have not forgotten my debt. But I am not prepared to pay so soon."

Wenonga glared. The corners of his mouth turned down in fierce displeasure. "But I was prepared to cure your wife. And I have waited many years for payment. I will not be cheated." Scraping back his chair, he rose ponderously, His polite words thinly

55

masked the anger emanating from him. "It was good to smoke a pipe with you. I will go now." He wrapped himself in his blanket and strode to the door, where he paused, and ignoring everyone except Jules, said, "I will expect your promised payment before I return home."

As soon as the door closed behind Wenonga, Joe Crow swooped down from a rafter where he had been huddling in the shadows. He stepped nervously back and forth on his lame leg, squawking and ruffling his feathers. As the others watched, stunned and frightened by Wenonga's anger, Jules clicked his tongue, and the bird flew to his knee. Gently Jules stroked Joe Crow's feathers and murmured to him. Gradually the bird grew calm, then hopped onto his shoulder, nestled close, and blinked his eyes.

Unable to wait any longer, Supaya edged over to Quayo. "Grandma," she whispered, "I am going out now."

"Go," said Quayo. "Your father and I must talk."

Her coat buttoned up, her shawl wrapped snugly around her head and shoulders, Supaya took a path through the woods to West Creek. Overhead bare branches creaked in the wind. The earth was stone hard, and covered now with a layer of snow. West Creek was flowing fast, swirling over the stones, its water a cold, dull gray. Following the creek to where it emptied into the lake, Supaya saw Kineu near the water's edge, skipping stones out over the breaking waves. Thinking to surprise him, Supaya came up behind him and reached out her hands to cover his eyes. But as they encircled his head, he caught them and turned around.

She pouted. "How did you know!"

"How?" He laughed down at her, his dark eyes shining, his face ruddy from the sharp lake wind. "You made as much noise as a doe crashing through the bushes."

"Oh!" She tried to look indignant, failed, then clasped her arms about his neck and pressed her lips eagerly to his. Oblivious to the growing storm, they held each other tight, their cheeks burning cold, until a crashing wave flung its spume around them. Hands clasped, they ran up the narrow beach and into the shelter of the woods. In a grove of pines, they found a fallen log, and sitting close together, his arm tight around her, their faces touching, they made plans, their voices carried away by the wind that rocked the pine branches and scudded heavy clouds across the dark afternoon sky.

"Suppy, you know that meadow beyond the ridge behind your father's place? It wouldn't need much clearing. We could have

56

a house and garden. There's a good stand of trees for a windbreak. I think the Council would let me have it. I could start building now. Maybe Jacques would help me."

Supaya pictured it at once: the high, sheltered meadow, a small log house, maybe a few apple trees. Her eyes glowed. "I'll plant the garden and you can dig a root cellar and build a barn!"

"I already have my own boat and net, and I can buy my own traps." Gazing at her face so close to his, his voice trailed off. "Oh, Suppy," he whispered, "I want you now!" And for a time they forgot their plans, lost in their delight with each other. They might have met for the first time the night before, have come to truly know each other only now when every kiss, every caress seemed a revelation. The soft fullness of her breast, the curve of her body were realities beyond what he'd imagined. The touch of his hand on her flesh, the press of his body against hers made her forget everything but the desire she felt for him. Breathlessly, they kissed, as though their lips could scarcely bear to part, and Supaya whispered, "Soon, Kineu, soon!"

"I'll ask your father today, now, when we return. I don't want anyone else coming near you. I want everyone to know you are mine!"

"Kineu, there could never, never be anyone else." She held his head between both her hands and kissed him lingeringly, with all her soul, as a pledge, a seal, of her words.

After Supaya had left the house, Quayo, full of foreboding, pulled her shawl about her and, sitting down, faced Jules. "What," she asked, "did you promise Wenonga?"

Her question hung in the air. As if to shake off its weight, Jules rose, disturbing Joe Crow, who squawked a drowsy protest and flew up to a beam. Jules thrust a piece of wood into the fire and, leaning one hand against the mantel, stood looking down at the flurry of sparks. His back to Quayo and Jacques, he said, "I promised him Neegonas as wife for his son."

"But his son died," said Jacques, "as he told us."

"I knew his son died," answered Jules sharply. "That is why Neegonas could marry James. But his son's death did not wipe out my debt. As I had another daughter, so he had another son. As he told us," he added, in an angry, mimicking voice. Then he turned to face them and saw their sudden shock of understanding.

"You promised him Supaya!" exclaimed Quayo.

"I promised him Neegonas! *That* is what I said! I couldn't

know he would have another son!" They stared at each other for a long moment—he trapped and furious; she accusing. Then thrusting his face toward her, he spit out his words. "Damn you, old woman! It was *your* daughter's life I paid for!"

At that Quayo dropped her eyes and turned her head aside.

Jacques looked from one to the other incredulously. "You can't!" he burst out. "You can't give her away to that man's son! I am her brother, and I say . . ."

Jules took one step, grabbed him by his shirt front and shook him. "Never dare tell me what I can or cannot do! I made a promise! You understand? It means my life! The lives of your grandmother, your sisters, your cousins!" He paused, pulled Jacques closer, and added with biting emphasis, "Your life!" Then he flung Jacques from him and turned away.

Only the soft breathing of the fire and the wind sighing against the house filled the silence. Then, not looking at them, Jules spoke quietly. "I would have given anything I had for Shooskonee. Anything. Supaya did not exist. Even you were not yet born. Later I learned of this second son, but he was sent away. A long time passed and he did not return. I hoped . . . finally believed . . . he never would . . . that the debt would go unpaid."

With an effort, Quayo got to her feet and, going to Jules, laid her hand on his arm. "Son, come, sit down. Light your pipe. I will get us some tea."

Jules sat and lit his pipe, and Jacques came and sat on the floor beside him, head bowed. "Father," he said finally, hesitantly, "Supaya and Kineu . . . ."

Jules nodded. "I understand about Supaya and Kineu."

They were sitting together, drinking tea when Supaya and Kineu entered by the back door, throwing it wide and rushing in, laughing and breathless from running against the wind. Kineu latched the door and Supaya came forward smiling, drawing off her shawl and coat, her eyes sparkling.

On their way home, she had told Kineu of Wenonga's visit and his claim of a payment.

"Pay what?" Kineu had asked.

"I don't know. But I could see father was angry. Maybe you should wait and ask him about us another time."

"No. I must ask now. That has nothing to do with us. Your father will understand that."

Jules turned when they entered and watched them approach, their faces glowing from more than the cold, saw their quick, conspiratorial glances, their irrepressible smiles. In Supaya's radiant face he saw again Shooskonee and, stricken by this living memory, turned his gaze away, afraid his pain would reveal itself in his eyes. He knew Kineu would speak, and he waited.

"Uncle," said Kineu, standing at a respectful distance, "I have come to ask you for your daughter. We wish to marry." He paused, expecting Jules to smile, Jacques to leap up, Quayo to clap her hands, but all were still, their faces turned away from him. Thinking more was expected of him, he began again. "I have little, but there is land and wood for a house. I am able to hunt and . . . ."

Jules held up his hand. In that moment before her father spoke, Supaya suddenly perceived through the haze of her own happiness the tension that gripped her family. She saw Quayo turn away, and then Jacques. She recognized the forbidding lines of her father's face: the half-lowered lids, the stern set of his mouth. She was filled with dread before he spoke.

"Nephew, you have honored my daughter. But she cannot marry you. She is promised to another."

Supaya gasped. Kineu stepped back as if he'd been slapped.

"Father!" exclaimed Supaya, unbelieving, "Father, what do you mean? Promised! When was I promised? There isn't anyone else!"

"Tell her," said Quayo softly, "tell her!"

With great pain, Jules turned and met her eyes; but she saw only that his were cold and impersonal. "You will marry Wenonga's son. He came here to arrange for the marriage."

Supaya stared at him, speechless. Then, "Why?" she asked, her voice a whisper.

"I promised him a wife for his son as payment for healing your mother."

"Ayyyiii! But that was before I was born!" She rushed forward, flung herself down by his chair, and grasped his arm tightly with both hands. "Father, please, there must be some other way!" Her eyes filled with tears. "I love Kineu! I cannot leave him! I cannot leave my home and you and Grandma! I cannot marry a stranger!"

"Cannot!" repeated Jules, his eyes suddenly blazing, "cannot!" Finding relief in anger, he shook off her hands and raised his arm threateningly above her. "You will do as I say! You will remember your obligations! To me and your family! You are no longer a child! You will marry Wenonga's son!" He leaned toward

59

her, hoping his sternness would help strengthen her. "And you will not cry!"

Her eyes fixed on him, her fist pressed against her mouth, Supaya drew back. No one moved or spoke.

"Nephew," said Jules, "you are close to our heart. You will always be welcome in our home."

Kineu was too stunned to move or speak. In his blanched face, his scar stood out as a thin white welt. He stared at Supaya as if he saw her receding from him.

Jacques took Kineu by the arm. "Come," he said quietly. "You should go. I will go with you."

When the door closed behind them, Supaya, without a word, climbed the stairs to the loft. Later, when Quayo called her, she did not answer nor did she come down. By night the sky had cleared, but the wind blew with increased fury, churning the lake into heavy waves that arced high and crashed on the beach. Unable to sleep, Jules listened to the wind beating against the house, moaning in the chimney. He heard the restless mutterings of his son and a faint movement in the loft above him that told him his daughter also was awake.

Supaya knelt in the cold by the small window at the foot of her bed, looking out at the stars that glittered like ice. She cupped the stone bear against her cheek and whispered to it. "Grandfather Mukwah, help me! I cannot help myself. Soften my father's heart! Don't let him send me away from Kineu, from my home!" She had cried until there were no more tears. Lying with her head against the sill, she gazed out at the stars swinging across the sky until her eyelids closed of their own accord and she slept, the stone bear cradled in her hand beside her cheek.

The next day Hettie appeared at their back door. She came in rubbing her cold hands together, her cheeks pink, her large, humorous face almost comically mournful. She had come, she said, for a cup of tea and to report on Aunt Theresa, who was dying.

"She refuses to leave her house," said Hettie, warming her hands round her cup. "Cousin Minnie visits her and keeps her fire going."

Quayo nodded. "She wants to die in her own place."

Neither woman mentioned Jules, who had gone out early, saying he had to check his traps. Nor did Hettie speak of Kineu, who had come home with Jacques, then left by himself and had still not returned. Jacques had explained what had happened to his aunt, and now her moist eyes rested sadly on Supaya, who sat apart, saying nothing, her head bent over her work.

Supaya had come down only after Jules left. Eyes downcast, face full of grief, she moved as if in a trance, numb to those about her. Quayo and Jacques had watched her with concern. Now, Quayo and Hettie spoke aloud of daily matters, but their eyes said to each other: It is great cause for sadness. It is painful. We must give her time.

Supaya, weaving quills into the round lid of a birchbark box, clung to her work as the only stable thing in her shattered world. Automatically she made the regularly spaced holes with her awl, then poked the quill up through the lid, flattened it with her thumbnail, poked it down through another hole and pulled it taut. She scarcely saw the work she did, nor did she think of Kineu, or of leaving her home and going with Wenonga, but only of her father, stern and forbidding. She heard his words, over and over again until, feeling smothered, she abruptly thrust her work aside, and passing Quayo and Hettie without a glance, left the house.

The furious wind of the night before had stilled. Low clouds covered the sky like a soft, gray blanket. Occasional snowflakes drifted down. The air was cold but not bitter, and Supaya lifted her face and breathed in deeply. She walked aimlessly, through the woods and along the ridge toward the spring. Her father's words no longer sounded in her ears. Her mind was blessedly empty. She was conscious only of the woods, of its spare, winter beauty, with yesterday's snow drifted along the path and in the hollows. Following a barely discernible trail, she came to a large dead branch blown down by the wind. Lifting it aside, she saw pressed in the light powder of snow the print of a huge paw. Grandfather Mukwah! Startled, she looked about, but saw only leafless underbrush, rocks and trees, birch, cedar and fir, some split by the night's wind, their raw inner wood exposed. Cautiously, alert for any sound, Supaya walked on. Reaching the spring, she stopped to listen to its soft, steady murmur. A constant promise of life, it welled up from within the earth and rippled outward, crystal clear above the muddy bottom. On impulse, Supaya knelt down, thrust her cupped hand into the water, and lifted it to her mouth. Icy cold, it pained her hand and numbed her lips, but she drank eagerly, again and again, exhilarated by the chill that shocked her body, waking her senses and reviving her mind. Her vision cleared as if she had awakened from a nightmare and was grateful to find herself on solid ground. Curling her painfully throbbing hand inside her pocket, she started home. Her Grandfather had given her strength, had shown her the path she must follow. She would speak to her father again, this time quietly, calmly.

It was dusk when Jules returned and hung his catch from a tree for the night. Supaya was waiting for him, and when he stood by the fire warming himself, she came and stood beside him.

"Father, I must speak to you about my . . . my marriage." Jules inclined his head. "It is true? I must marry Wenonga's son? There is no other safe way?"

"No other way. If there were," and now he turned to look intently at her, "I would have taken it."

She kept her eyes steady and her mouth firm. "When must it be?"

"Tomorrow Wenonga comes and we will speak to the agent about your transferring to another band. Wenonga returns to his reserve on the next day's boat."

Calmly, Supaya said, "I cannot leave that soon. I will not be ready. I must gather my things."

Jules studied his daughter's profile, the high forehead and strong chin, the proud, haughty pose of her head, with gratification. He answered gravely, respecting her newly realized self-containment. "I will speak to Wenonga. We will arrange it for next spring."

"Thank you, Father," said Supaya and she turned away to help Quayo.

Watching her from a great and increasing distance, Jules pondered the possibility of their ever meeting again in loving trust as father and child. Suddenly, he felt unusually weary from his day's hunting. He lit his pipe and sat down before the fire, soberly contemplating the lonely ridge of his life.

CHAPTER SIX

It was Hettie who came with news of Aunt Theresa's death, her volatile nature changing from sadness over Supaya to breathless fright over the revelation of Aunt Theresa as a witch. She repeated Minnie's account, relayed through three others and embellished with her own sense of the dramatic. "She was lying still, breathing her last." Hettie demonstrated, holding her breath, shutting her eyes, and letting her mouth hang. "Suddenly," popping her eyes wide open and half rising from her chair, "she sat straight up and invited them in—the spirits! She called them by name!" adding, to forestall any questions, "Minnie would not repeat them. Then she insisted Minnie serve them tea!" She leaned forward, her voice hushed. "But Minnie sprinkled wild ginger on the fire when Theresa wasn't looking!"

"Maybe, but I don't believe it," said Quayo flatly.

"But it's true!" cried Hettie, wanting to believe. "She was trying to get up and come to the table with them when she died! Minnie had to stop her!"

Quayo shrugged.

"And when Minnie left the house, she saw a dog running off into the woods!"

"There are always dogs about," said Quayo.

Hettie's large mouth closed in a disappointed pout. She turned toward her brother Jules, hoping for his support, when there was a knock on the door.

Jules, who was shaping a leg for a new chair, put down his

work. Giving Supaya a warning glance, he went to the door and opened it wide.

Wenonga entered with a blast of cold air that made the fire swoop up the chimney. Hettie rose instantly. Tales of witches were one thing, Wenonga quite another. She murmured to Quayo and left hurriedly.

Wenonga sat again in Jules' chair, and though he acknowledged their greetings, his expression was thunderous, his eyes fiery, ready to blaze in anger. Jules, cool and self-possessed, offered him tobacco and fire for his pipe and said smoothly, "We will have tea before we go to see the agent," thus informing Wenonga of his intention to fulfill his obligation without quarrel.

Visibly surprised, Wenonga settled back. His tension relaxed but his suspicion increased. He stared at Jules, then at Supaya, searching their faces for trickery. Having readied herself, Supaya withstood his gaze coolly.

"We will arrange the transfer now," said Jules, "so the matter will be settled, but my daughter cannot leave her home with you tomorrow." He saw Wenonga's face tighten, his eyes flash, and he continued calmly. "It is too soon, too unexpected for her to be ready."

Supaya had been watching Wenonga and now, to their surprise as well as her own, since she had not anticipated speaking at all, she found herself saying haughtily, "I must prepare for such a journey. I have many things to gather." She spoke directly to Wenonga, flinging the words down like a challenge.

Wenonga turned and considered her, taking a long draw on his pipe to cover his surprise at this young woman who apparently was no longer afraid of him. He glanced back at Jules, whose impassive face hid the great pride he took in his daughter.

"She will be prepared to go with you when the lake opens in the spring," said Jules after an interval of silence.

Feeling obscurely at a disadvantage but unable to find an objection, Wenonga agreed. "That is well. I will come on the first boat in the spring." Then he added, not to be outdone in the matter of pride, "We, too, must prepare."

The wind was rising, whirling the snow falling from a distant, uniformly gray sky. Jules and Wenonga walked ahead, their footprints leaving faint outlines, Supaya following behind.

Jackson lived in the house built for the agent by the Indians. The largest, finest house on the reserve, it had two stories and a roofed verandah across the front and along both sides. One of the two spacious front rooms opening off the center hall served as office. Jackson's elderly housekeeper opened the door. She was gray-haired and always wore an apron as if her entire life were lived in the kitchen. In answer to Jules' request to see Mr. Jackson, she stepped back, opened the office door, and pointed. She never spoke to Indians, whom she saw as children—dangerous, unpredictable children. The silence she maintained was her only protective barrier. Jules and Supaya she knew by sight, but not Wenonga. Wrapped in his blanket, he filled the hallway like a huge, half-tame animal. The housekeeper stood aside as they filed into the office, then hurriedly shut the door.

Jackson, in vest and shirt sleeves, sat at his desk, his back to the bare windows, his balding head bent over a ledger. Except for several straight chairs lined against the wall and a framed print of the new king, Edward VII, the room was empty. A small iron stove in one corner radiated a slight warmth. Jackson seldom invited any Indian to sit down, believing it bad policy to allow them to feel too familiar, especially outspoken ones like Jules Cedar. He let them stand and wait while he finished a row of figures.

"Well, Jules," said Jackson, finally looking up at the two men. "I see you've come calling with a visitor. And . . ." he tilted his head to one side, ". . . your very pretty daughter."

"Mr. Jackson," said Jules, in the careful, distinct voice he used when dealing with a social inferior, "this is Wenonga Red Sky, from the Two Bluffs Reserve."

"Oh yes. I heard you were coming." His flat tone suggested Wenonga might better have stayed home. He leaned back in his chair. "Well, boys, what can I do for you?"

A flicker of amused contempt at this man's bad manners crossed Jules' face, an expression Jackson misread as simple friendliness. "My daughter, Supaya, is to marry Wenonga Red Sky's son in the spring. She needs a paper of transfer from this band roll to his."

"Well! Getting married, is she!" He looked again at Supaya. "Hmmn. How old is she?" he asked. "Fifteen? Eighteen?" Jules raised his eyebrows slightly, appeared not to understand. Jackson glanced again at Supaya. "Oh well," he said, half to himself, "I can look it up in the birth records. Probably none too soon anyway. Here, let me get the facts down. Sophia Cedar, daughter of Jules Cedar, will marry . . ." he glanced up at Wenonga, waiting for him to supply the name.

"She will marry Eli Red Sky," growled Wenonga.

"Eli Red Sky," repeated Jackson, writing. "Marriage to take place here or there?"

"There," said Jules.

"There. In the spring, you said?"

"Yes."

"All right," said Jackson. "I'll write you out a paper of transfer." He scribbled on a small sheet of paper. Silently they waited. When he finished, he held the paper up, uncertain which man should have it.

Again surprised at her own audacity, Supaya stepped forward. "I will take it." As startled as if a carved figure had spoken, Jackson hesitated and looked inquiringly at the men. "It is *my* transfer," insisted Supaya. "*I* will keep it." Imperiously she held out her hand.

Seeing neither Jules nor Wenonga so much as flick an eyelash, Jackson grudgingly handed her the paper.

"I can even read it," said Supaya tartly. She folded the paper and put it in her leather pouch. Then she turned toward the door, paused, and looked back impatiently at the two men as if to ask what they waited for.

Jules' eyes crinkled with amused understanding. Her anger, he saw, was deep and strong, unexpected even to herself. Such anger was good. It gave her strength.

"Thank you, Mr. Jackson," he said gravely, and they filed out of the office.

Later, when she was alone, Supaya took out the paper and read it, saying the words softly to herself.

Agent Gerald Toomis
Two Bluffs Reserve
Ontario, Canada

Sophia Cedar has contracted to marry Eli Red Sky. This marriage is to take place on your reserve and her name has to be removed from my band roll for Indians on this island. Please write Ottawa when this marriage has taken place and have them place her name on your band roll.

S. M. Jackson, Agent
Stone Island Reserve
Ontario, Canada

Refolding it, Supaya pondered the name—Eli Red Sky. She could form no impression from the name. She dreaded to think the son might resemble the father. But that name would become her name, and she would bear it with dignity. Meanwhile, she had until spring. She put the paper back into her pouch, wishing the winter might never end.

A wake was held for Aunt Theresa, the body laid out in Hettie's house since her husband, Arthur, was Theresa's nephew and her only living relative. Reverend Harris came to pray over the old lady whom he had once visited on her tiny island years before when he was newly arrived at Stone Island and wanted to introduce himself to all those parishioners living on several smaller islands included in the reserve. It was a visit he had never repeated. Theresa had been happy to see him, offered him tea and scone, and nodded encouragingly when he spoke, his voice straining uncomfortably to pierce through her deafness. At parting he had given her a small card with a verse from the Bible printed on it; whereupon, searching through a box, she had found a carved bone amulet which she had pressed upon him, smiling sweetly and instructing him that he should carry it always as protection against the water spirits. Now he murmured prayers above the shrunken old body while her nephew and friends solemnly watched.

After his departure everyone relaxed, and the wake took on a party air. Food and drink were served, and the older people present told humorous stories of Aunt Theresa's past, when her fierce independence combined with her deafness—which they exaggerated to a phenomenal degree—resulted in hilarious misunderstandings. Relishing such stories of the past, the watchers celebrated Aunt Theresa throughout the long night. With the coming of dawn, small items were brought forward and gently laid in the open coffin: her best needle, her favorite tea cup, and a new pair of moccasins to last her on her journey to the next world. Then the oldest man present, whose memories included a young, aggressively flirtatious Theresa, addressed her on behalf of them all. "Theresa, it is time for you to go. May these things we give help you on your journey. Our thoughts go with you. Soon we will follow in your path." Then the watchers dispersed, walking home in the pale dawn.

At midday Reverend Harris conducted the church service. The Cedars sat in the back row as they always did on those rare occasions when they attended church. Supaya could see Neegonas and James and their two small children sitting near the front, and two rows behind were Aunt Hettie and her family, Kineu at the end of the row. Supaya had not seen him since he had left the house with Jacques three days earlier.

Only three days, yet during that time her life had been severely wrenched. Her world was no longer secure, but uncertain and frightening. She saw now that one must do what was necessary, struggle to secure what blessings one could, and depend, finally, on them and oneself. Only one's guardian was forever constant and unchanging. This perception so abruptly forced upon her was revealing a strength of resolve and a capacity for action she hadn't realized she possessed. Even now she did not fully recognize her own capabilities, but reacted from moment to moment out of shock and anger at what seemed to her to have been a long deception. Gazing at the back of Kineu's head, she knew only that she wanted him, that she needed to take something, someone for her own. Sitting on the church bench, her face hooded by her shawl, she didn't hear the preacher's words or join in the singing. She was remembering the pressure of Kineu's mouth on hers, the touch of his hands, and her whole body ached for him.

She rose automatically with the others as the congregation filed out of the church and followed the coffin to the nearby cemetery. The Christian burial demanded by the church was carried out with difficulty; two men had worked for hours with pick and shovel to gouge a grave out of the frozen earth. Reverend Harris stood at the gravehead and the people gathered round as the coffin was lowered.

Across the backs of those lowering the coffin, Supaya saw Kineu, standing at the far edge of the group, looking directly at her. His face, always alight with energy and purpose, was drawn and sad, his eyes dull. Seeing him so was painful, yet she could not look away from him. The preacher spoke a prayer, then everyone joined in singing a hymn, their vigorous voices resounding in the cold air, reasserting life in the midst of the gray, cold cemetery with its white wooden crosses.

As the two diggers began shoveling back the raw earth, Supaya knew what she would do. Turning, she slipped through the crowd of singers. Once beyond them, she stopped, looked back at Kineu, then walked swiftly away.

Kineu allowed her a few minutes' start, then followed. When he saw she was heading toward the beach where Jacques had a small fishing shack and grounded his rowboat, Kineu turned aside and headed for his own boat.

The lake was frozen along the shoreline in grotesque, humped, and windblown shapes, forming in places conical ice volcanoes that spouted water. Beyond, ice floated in patches, lifting and falling with the rhythm of the greenish-gray water. Boats could still push their way through, their bows protected with metal plates, but soon the lake would be frozen across. Then it would be possible to walk to Aunt Theresa's little island, and men would begin fishing through holes in the ice.

Getting Jacques' boat to open water was difficult. Supaya dragged and pushed and pulled, slipping on the ice, wetting her feet and skirts. Finally she pushed it into the water. She rowed strongly, bending low and pulling the oars forward through floating ice. When she was more than halfway across, she saw coming from the far shoreline another boat, small and dark in the distance, with a solitary rower. She rowed past the point that sheltered the cove in front of Aunt Theresa's house. When she could go no further against the ice, she got out and hauled the boat across the rough, frozen ice up onto the beach. The snow that had been drifting down for several days was now falling heavily, a fine, swirling snow that was rapidly covering the ground, blending the lake with the shore.

Obscured by the snow and dwarfed by the dark woods looming behind it, the unpainted frame house looked even smaller than Supaya remembered. No light shone from its window, no smoke rose from the stack. Minnie's insistence that Aunt Theresa had been a witch had effectively frightened off any neighbor who might otherwise have been glad to move into an empty house. Supaya went around to the back door and found that Minnie had stockpiled a good supply of wood. She carried several armloads inside the lean-to before latching the door against the blowing snow.

Aunt Theresa's one-room home was, as her life had been, reduced to essentials: floor, walls, table, all were bare. No curtain hung at the one small window, no clothes from the wall pegs. Even the rope bed retained no impression of her frail body. Only the worn pad on the rocker seat and four untouched cups of cold tea gave any indication that she had lived there. Even so, and wet and chilled though she was, Supaya felt at home. She and Kineu had spent many afternoons with Aunt Theresa, had brought her supplies, climbed her apple trees, picked beans and squash for her, and played along the beach in front of her house. From Pine Point

Supaya had often gazed across the water at the hill where she had dreamed, and it was there that Kineu had found her stone bear. All these memories filled Aunt Theresa's bare house with warmth; only she herself, who had invested her home with a serenity of spirit, was missing.

Supaya shook the snow from her shawl and hung it on a peg. She got down an old oil lamp from the shelves in the lean-to, lit it, and placed it in the middle of the table, being careful not to disturb the tea cups. She was making up the fire in the stove when the front door opened and Kineu entered, covered with snow and panting from his run up the beach. He leaned against the door and stared at her a moment.

Then he said, "I could see the light from the shore. Even through the snow."

"I am glad," said Supaya. She approached him and put out her hand; then, suddenly shy before his questioning look, drew it back. "Your coat and feet are wet."

"So are yours."

She averted her eyes and turned toward the stove. "I have made up the fire. It should be warm soon."

"Suppy, what . . . why have we come here?"

A flash of impatience that he should have to ask made her answer petulant. "Because I wanted to! And I'm going to stay as long as I please!" In a softer tone, her face hidden by her hair hanging loose for Aunt Theresa's funeral, she added, "We can stay here if we want. No one will mind. I am free to do as I like until the lake boat returns in the spring. That is," she raised her head to look at him, "if you want to."

"Want to!" His face was suddenly alive. "Want to!" He gripped her shoulders, then caught her close in a tight hug and rubbed his cheek against hers. "I thought . . . I thought we'd never be together again!" They laughed together at this absurdity. He put his forehead against hers and gazed into her eyes with such an intensity of meaning that she caught her breath and pulled away.

"Let's see if there's any food left."

Reluctantly, he let her go and they began searching through tins and old birchbark boxes. They found half a can of tea, dried meat and fish, dried peas, dried apples, and two pieces of rock-hard scone. But before she could prepare food for themselves, Supaya had to make an offering.

She took some meat, apples, and bread to the stove and,

lifting off one lid, put the food into the flames. As it spit and crackled and the smoke curled upward, Supaya murmured, "We thank you, Aunt Theresa, for the use of your home and your possessions. Enjoy this food. May it give you strength for your journey. We will remember you always." Only after the food had burned and the smoke had faded away did Supaya put on a pot of soup for themselves and feel free to clear away the four cups of stale tea. Kineu climbed the ladder and rummaged about in the loft.

"What is up there? asked Supaya.

"Field mice," answered Kineu with a laugh. "And some old covers. Come and see."

Supaya climbed up until she could see over the edge of the loft. "Covers? We could use them."

"And there is an old trunk back in the corner. Shall I open it?"

"No. No, don't," said Supaya, descending the ladder. "We shouldn't disturb her things. Just bring the covers."

"The mice will be cold," said Kineu, carrying the quilts down.

"Let them climb in with us then," said Supaya airily, turning back to the stove. But Kineu's arms slid around her from behind; he nuzzled his face in the curve of her neck. "Suppy," he whispered, "you should take off your wet clothes."

"But the soup . . ." she protested weakly.

"I don't want any soup," he murmured, kissing the back of her neck where her hair fell apart. "I want you."

She turned in his arms, held his face between her hands. "All right," she whispered back, brushing his lips with her own. "Let me go then."

He watched as she smoothed Aunt Theresa's bed, spreading over it the covers from the loft. Then she turned down the oil lamp until it was only a soft dull glow in the dark shadowy room. She removed her wet moccasins and stepped out of her damp skirts, hanging them over a chair back and laying her blouse and undershirt across the seat. Shivering, she slid quickly under the old quilts. Kineu stripped rapidly, dropping his clothes on the floor. He stood for one brief, breathless moment, poised, looking down at Supaya, her hair spread around her shoulders, the stone of her necklace resting between her breasts, the two curved bear claws stark against her skin. He saw the gleam of her eyes before they closed and her arms reached out for him. They kissed as never before, mouths opening to each other. Their legs entwined, their bodies

71

straining to become one. Hungrily, he caressed and kissed her body until she arched, pushing up against him, her head falling back in an agony that found release only in his hard, muscular thrusting. Then her arms relaxed their grip and clasped him gently as he lay on her. Like survivors of a storm, they breathed deeply and peacefully. Heads tilted together, his arm flung across her, they drifted into sleep.

Hours later, Supaya awoke. The lamp still glowed, a soft, warm eye in the dark. She crossed the cold floor, put more wood in the stove and turned off the lamp. Sliding quickly back under the covers, she fitted herself as naturally against Kineu's sleeping form as if it had been a habit of years.

In the morning they woke simultaneously and smiled at each other. She reached up and stroked his head, caressed his shoulder, invited him with soft eyes; leaning over her, he smoothed back her hair and kissed the line of her throat and swelling breasts. This time their lovemaking was slower, more deeply satisfying, and afterwards they lay still, loathe to move, minds empty, bodies content.

Snow had fallen heavily all night and continued to fall all that day and the next. The wind had risen again, and when Kineu went out for more wood, he could scarcely see the backhouse through the snow that whipped about and blew up like a white veil in front of him. He reached elbow deep to find the wood and returned with snow thick on his clothes, his hair, coating even his eyelashes. Supaya laughed at him, circling round, retreating in pretended horror. They laughed a great deal that day. They were snowbound, cut off from the whole world, and their only concern, their only interest, was each other.

The third morning Supaya stood at the window and looked out at a white world. She had begun to feel restless, confined. She had no work to occupy her, and she imagined Quayo's and her father's concern for her, their possible need for her help. Outside, land, water, and sky had lost all boundary lines. Snow fell out of a white, luminous sky where the sun was only a pale, glowing disk, fell so thick it confined all distance to one great curve of white blending with a white earth.

"Kineu, we will have to dig out the boats." Kineu, sitting with his legs stretched out, chin on chest, didn't answer. "Kineu?"

"You want to go back, don't you," he said, stating it as fact.

Supaya turned. "We have to go back," she said gently.

72

"Our families will think we are lost. Besides, we can't stay here all winter."

"We could," he said sharply, accusingly. "You know we could."

At his words, knowing the hurt behind them, Supaya knelt beside him and sought to take his hand. "Kineu, we can come back! We can still be together sometimes. But I must go home, I have . . ."

Kineu withdrew his hand and coldly disregarded her words. "We could even leave here and go far away. They would never find us. But you don't want to."

Dismayed, Supaya dropped her eyes, realized she was on her knees, and stood up. She felt an anger she had never expected to feel toward Kineu, for his rebuff and his suggestion that she ignore her duty, endanger her family as well as themselves. Twice now she had knelt to plead with a man. She would remember never to kneel to a man again. She had tied up her moccasins around her ankles and was putting on her coat when Kineu touched her shoulder.

"What are you going to do?"

"I am going to dig out the boat and go back."

"Suppy!" His smile, his eyes begged her forgiveness. "I will come with you. We will go back together."

Kineu took two poles from the drying rack and together they went toward the beach. The snow blew into their faces, fanned up by a steady wind that bared the icy rocks in some places, formed long, deep drifts in others. The two overturned boats were covered with high domes of snow, easily knocked off. Their spirits revived by the bracing air, they found they could laugh again. Kineu showered Supaya with snow, and she chased him into a drift, where they fell and rolled over in mock struggle. He caught her and held tight, and she collapsed against him. Panting, their faces ruddy and eyes bright, they looked searchingly at each other, then suddenly kissed, a quick, vigorous kiss of mutual forgiveness.

They headed out across the frozen lake, each dragging a boat behind and thrusting a pole through the snow ahead to test the solidity of the ice. The sun, an intense spot of light in a white sky, alternately brightened and faded as strong wind gusts lifted the snow and whirled it around in a frosty, blinding curtain. As they neared Stone Island, the mass of trees along the shore gradually emerged. They hauled the boats well up on the beach near the trees and turned them over. Kineu led the way through the woods, breaking a path for Supaya. When they came in sight of her home, he turned off and she went on alone.

No comment was made when Supaya returned. No questions were asked. Jules had seen her leave Quayo's side in the cemetery and he had seen Kineu following her minutes later. When Jacques found his boat missing, they understood where she had gone. She quietly resumed her place in the family as if she had never been away.

The storm lasted for several more days, then tapered off and the sun shone blindingly bright, casting long, bluish shadows across the glittering snow. Eagerly people emerged from their homes, and soon a network of packed snow trails appeared, connecting houses, store, church, and school.

Hettie came to visit, rolling her eyes comically at Supaya while relaying the latest gossip to Quayo. Jules strapped on snowshoes and left to check his traps set out along the meadow streams and in the rabbit runs. Jacques went fishing on the lake with Kineu, where they set up a blanket windbreak for shelter, prepared to sit for hours hunched over the lines they let down through the ice. Supaya listened amused to Hettie's conversation while she carefully cut out some of the finest birchbark to be used as lining for her quill boxes. She had finished the quillwork on several—one small box, four inches across, and two larger ones to be used as collar boxes. She hoped to sell them to Mr. Bonnet in order to buy material for dresses she would need when she left in the spring. Quayo and Hettie discussed the New Year's feast, an annual communal dinner and dance held in the Council House. This event taxed the resources of every kitchen on the reserve. The two women were planning what dishes they would prepare when Neegonas stopped by with her two small children. Quayo poured another cup of tea and gave her grandchildren some fried bread.

As she drank her tea, Neegonas studied Supaya, only half listening to the older women. Finally she said, "I hear you will be leaving in the spring to get married." Supaya glanced up and nodded. "Of course, some girls will go with a man without being married. Or so I hear," she added in an insinuating tone.

There was a pause in both conversations. Supaya smiled at her sister. "And some girls," she said, "get married only because they get caught with a baby."

"Neegonas," said Quayo sharply, "what do you plan to bring for the feast?"

Neegonas shrugged. "Corn soup. Maybe a stew . . . bread." She wondered why she had bothered to come and soon left, giving her older son an unnecessary shove out the door.

"Miss Harris is teaching the children a song for the feast program," said Hettie. "Are you helping this year, Suppy?"

"No, Aunt Hettie, I'm too busy. You said you had an embroidery pattern you would give me. Could you show me now?"

Hettie did so and suggested that Alexandria, an old woman who lived on the far side of the reserve and whose eyesight was now too poor for her to do any embroidery, had several good patterns she might give in exchange for food.

Supaya, planning seriously for her new life, was eager for every pattern, every recipe, every medicine she could get. She was determined to be a good wife and not shame her family. She began visiting many of the older women on the reserve, exchanging beadwork, moccasins, or food for bits of their knowledge and skill. Often Kineu accompanied her and they would have an hour or two alone together.

When they visited Auntie Em to bring her food and keep up her fire, her old eyes sparkled at sight of Kineu.

"Ah, ah, you have come with your young man," she said to Supaya. "I know," nodding her head wisely, "you want to be alone. Up to the loft, go on! That's what we used to do. I remember well. But now I am tired. I will go to sleep." She promptly shut her eyes, pretending. After Supaya put the pot of stew on the stove and the pie Quayo had sent on the table beside her, she and Kineu climbed the stairs to the loft. Then Auntie Em's eyes opened and she rocked contentedly, smiling to herself, waiting to eat the pie until after they'd gone.

Mr. Bonnet did buy Supaya's boxes, and gladly, for her work was superior to others' and he could sell them for a better price. Supaya bought several lengths of cotton print and one of black wool to make a good skirt. Quayo offered to make her a special dress for her wedding, but Supaya declined her offer. Her marriage was a duty; she would dress in ordinary clothes.

At the turn of the year, Quayo and Supaya cooked for two days, preparing for the New Year's feast, for not one of the four hundred or so people on the reserve ate at home on that day. When all was ready, Jules and Jacques helped carry the dishes to the

Council Hall, then drove around the reserve with a wagon picking up the elderly who were unable to walk any distance.

The Council Hall was a large, two-story frame building with a large vestibule inside the front entrance. There were storage cupboards, rows of hooks for wraps, and, at one side a wide staircase to the second floor. The inner door opened onto one great room where tables would be set end to end in the shape of a large U, with chairs along only the outer sides of the U, leaving the inner space free for the serving of food.

When Quayo and Supaya arrived shortly after midday, many families were already there, and the vestibule was crowded with people hanging up coats and exchanging greetings. The women carried in dishes and placed them on the tables, now covered with white cloths. Large platters with a whole goose or a ham or venison or pork roast were placed at intervals around the table, with bowls of vegetables—potatoes, baked beans, turnips, cabbage, corn—bowls of cheese, bread, scone, and fruit pies.

All elderly people were seated and served first, being the ones most honored on this day. Quayo sat next to her cousin Em, and there was much laughter and recalling of previous feasts and the prodigious amounts of food eaten.

Upstairs, the program had already begun. The band chief spoke first, speaking from a platform that extended across the width of the room at the far end. In the slow, deep voice he thought appropriate to the occasion, he described the trip he had made to Ottawa with Mr. Jackson and one of his councillors to petition the government to restrain white fishermen from encroaching on Indian waters. Then he reminded the audience that next summer was election time and he hoped that they would reelect him as their leader for another term. His audience sat on benches and chairs and listened respectfully, the men smoking their pipes.

As the older people finished eating and went upstairs, their places at the table were taken by younger generations. Jules sat down with Cyrus Red Sky. When Supaya, who had been serving her family and relatives, went to serve him, she found Rhea ahead of her, filling his plate with the choicest food as though it were her right to do so. Resentful and embarrassed that this girl with the reputation of a flirt should pay such attention to her father, Supaya left the room and went upstairs.

A group of men singers had just finished singing a hymn and were beginning another. Reverend and Mrs. Harris were there, sitting at one side of the room. Feeling the distaste she always felt at the sight of Reverend Harris, Supaya crossed to the other side and joined Maud and friends her own age who were waiting to hear their younger brothers and sisters perform.

When the hymn singers stepped down, Miss Harris, some-what agitated at being·the focus of attention, shepherded her students on stage. The older children lined up behind the younger, trying to disassociate themselves from the little ones, who bumped shoulders, rolled their eyes and, catching smiles in the audience, burst into giggles. Miss Harris, seated at the piano sounded the note on her pitch pipe, but they made a false start because one little girl was waving at a friend and her companions were trying to pull her hand down. At a second, sterner sounding of the note, they began again and sang the song they'd practiced for three weeks, their voices and attention fading on the verses, gathering strength and volume on the refrain.

Miss Harris then announced that Elizabeth White Cloud would recite a poem. A short, round-faced little girl with bangs stepped forward. Having been told not to hang her head, she raised her chin and gazed wide-eyed down her snub nose at the audience. With sing-song precision she recited five verses expressing hope for the New Year. Then she closed her mouth with a satisfied air and stepped back into line, where friends leaned over to whisper compliments to her.

Miss Harris sounded the note for the closing selection. Now that their part was nearly over, they had come to feel at ease on stage and burst into song, finishing together on a discordant but clearly triumphant note. The audience clapped their approval, and the singers scattered, throwing themselves into the arms of their families to be petted and praised before going downstairs for more food.

After the children's performance, the Harris family left. Supaya and Maud went looking for Kineu and Jacques, whom they found leaning over the upper banister, exchanging banter with friends below. Most people were upstairs now, the elders seated along the walls. Young and old settled themselves to listen attentively to Keewahd'n, an old man with iron-gray braids, recount an experience of his youth.

He spoke with songlike cadence and great variation of tone, his voice as soft as a whisper or so deep and resonant it filled the room and vibrated against the walls. He was a famous speaker, one of several old men who took turns telling stories of their past. Raising his arm in a slow, sweeping gesture, his eyes looking into the past, he recreated for them all their former life of freedom, with no reserves, when the people were free to roam as they pleased and lived in harmony with their Mother Earth, enduring hardships with courage and strength.

He spoke of the Four Hills that all men must face: the first to be climbed in infancy, the second in youth, the third in middle age, the fourth in old age. He described the struggling young ones, the many who failed while climbing the first hill, who fell weak and gasping, never to rise. How sorrowful to see hope die, how saddened their brothers and sisters who could not pause but were driven to push on, scarcely stopping when their companions fell beside them. On they must go, climbing up the second hill and the third, despite the hazards of steep cliffs, narrow, rock-strewn paths, and paths that led nowhere. What pain they feel, looking back at their struggling loved ones! How hard to call out encouragement but be unable to touch their outstretched hands! The fourth hill was most frightening, the steepest of all, with the sharpest rocks. The words of those who reached this hill were most valuable, for they had climbed all four hills and had attained much wisdom. Those few who were fortunate enough to reach the top of the fourth hill disappeared into a mist. The audience listened entranced, seeing through Keewahd'n's eyes the never-ending cycle of birth, life, death, and renewal. When he finished speaking, three old men stepped forward, one of them carrying a drum. Together they sang a song thanking the Great Spirit for the gift of life, their powerful voices swelling, fading, and swelling again as they danced in a circle, lifting their feet to the beat of the drum, bending and swaying their bodies with the agility of young men. Arms raised, they gave one shout and the dance ended.

As though called into life, the audience rose and began shoving back chairs, clearing the floor. The fiddler sprang onto the stage and tuned up his fiddle. The caller came forward and gave directions for the formation of the first dance. Kineu, quick and graceful, was an especially fine dancer, and he and Supaya joined in at once, swinging round and about, weaving in and out, down the length of the room and back, following the pattern the caller sang out. The old people sat along the sides of the room and watched, tapping their feet and clapping their hands. Jacques and Maud joined in, and Hettie and Arthur, Neegonas and James, and Rhea and a young man, but Jules stood at the end of the room, smoking and talking with a group of older men.

When the fiddler and caller took their first break and the dancers sat down to catch their breaths, six men leaped on stage and acted out a skit they had made up. One took the part of the agent, who was shown as a buffoon and hilariously stupid. The audience, quick to recognize familiar characters, called out comments and clapped with enthusiasm. Bottles of rye whiskey were passed about, and when the dancing began again, the fiddler played a faster tempo and the caller chanted his pattern, moving his shoulders and swinging his arms. The dancers skipped and twirled, skirts ballooning, feet stamping and turning, their quickness and grace inspiring the caller to more and more intricate patterns.

Outside, the winter dark came early. The old people, except for a few who stayed to watch the dancing, and the children, sleepy after so much excitement and eating, were taken home. But in the hall, lamps were lit and the fiddler played on, encouraged by shouts and hand clapping from the whirling dancers, whose faces, warm from exertion and whiskey, gleamed in the lamplight. Couples dropped out, breathless, then, caught up by the music, joined in again. After midnight both the fiddler and caller went downstairs for food and drink. Some of the dancers followed: the rest stayed to watch some bawdy skits, laughing uproariously at the tipsy actors, whose mock-serious, droll expressions and drunken, uninhibited antics they found inexpressibly funny. When the fiddler and the caller, fed and rested, took the stage again, the dancing continued.

In a dim corner Rhea pressed herself against Jules. She had a half empty bottle and she held it up, offering him a drink. Angrily, he pushed the bottle away. "I am a doctor. You know I do not drink."

"Then take me home." She slid her hand inside his shirt and smiled up at him. "I want to go home now."

"Now I am going to take the old people home."

"Ah, well!" Rhea made a face. "I will wait for you here, but if you don't come back soon, someone else will be glad to take me home."

He watched her walk away, filled with disgust for her and loathing for himself for wanting her. Without calling Jacques, who was dancing with Maud, he got together the remaining old people and helped them into the wagon. By the time he returned, it was after three. He encountered Rhea in the vestibule. She had her coat on and was leaning against a man, one arm around his neck. Seeing Jules, she smiled, patted the man's shoulder, and walking unsteadily, came to slip her arm through Jules'.

Supaya and Kineu came downstairs in time to see them leave together, Rhea holding onto Jules' arm for support, her head against his shoulder. Supaya, ashamed for her father, pretended not to see him.

There was no moon, but the stars were bright and very close in an immense sky that imposed its own vast silence over the snow-covered earth. Supaya and Kineu walked toward her home, the cold pressing against their faces.

"Suppy, let me come in. Just for a while. Your father's not home."

"No." She knew her father was not home. That Kineu should refer to what they had seen touched her family pride, made her inclined to be irritable. Besides, it was her father's home, and she felt it unseemly for her and Kineu to be together there. "No," she said again.

But Kineu held her close and kissed her, brushing his lips enticingly over her face.

"I guess we could go in the barn," she whispered, "for a little while." Later, from her bed in the loft, she heard Jacques come home.

No one heard Jules. He walked silently and alone in the early dawn, past darkened houses and fields where only the fence posts showed above the snow. The stars had paled in the growing light. Only the morning star still glittered above the trees. Then clear on the still air came the long, sad, haunting cry of a wolf. Jules raised his head and listened as again, from beyond the hill, the wolf sang once more, its last falling note hanging on the cold, still air.

"Maheengun!" Jules whispered. "You are there and I would speak to you!" Suddenly he felt himself to be unclean, unworthy. Going to the pump, he held his hands in the icy water, leaned over and doused his face and head. Pushing back his wet hair, he lifted his face toward the east.

"Grandfather Maheengun, hear me! You who are fleet as
　　　thought, pure as flame! Touch me! For I am filled
　　　with shame! Purify my spirit!
"Oh Great Father, help me! You whose vision encircles
　　　the world! You who see all paths! Help me! For my

sight has failed! I am weak and can no longer find
my way! Touch me, that I may see again!
      "Oh Great Maheengun, lonely hunter! Singer of the
      Great Spirit! Teach me to bear my loneliness! For I
         am alone in the morning of the world! Speak to
         me!"
Face uplifted, Jules stood waiting, all his senses concentrated, straining to hear the most distant cry.
      Above the hills a delicate, rosy glow began to fan out across
the pale sky. But though he waited, listening, there came no answer.

CHAPTER SEVEN

The lake ice split with a sound like the crack of a rifle. Thick slabs of ice broke apart, moving ponderously, edge grinding against edge, up-thrusting in jagged peaks, the green-gray water swirling over half-submerged floes. In an agony of rebirth, the splitting and booming of the ice reverberated across the thawing land. Streams raced toward the lake, their swift currents carrying fallen branches and undermining overhanging banks of earth and softened snow. Roads became mires of mud and slush, and the meadows of dried, matted grass oozed water.

Home food supplies were running low for all on the island. Mr. Bonnet, who liked to keep his shelves well stocked, had emptied all his barrels and boxes; the empty shelf space grew larger week by hungry week.

Quayo still had vegetables and dried fruit, for they'd had a good garden crop the summer before, but their meat and fish were almost gone. Jules and Jacques worked hard to bring home meat, plodding miles through the woods in deep, wet snow too soggy to support their snowshoes, sinking in up to their knees in pursuit of game that was difficult to find. Fear of being caught in the freezing slush when night came limited their range. Often they returned weary and numb with cold, empty-handed or with a poor catch, thin from the hard winter and good only for soup.

Supaya, who had worked busily, even at times happily, during the bleak winter, saw with growing dread glistening drops on the ends of icicles hanging from the eaves and mud appearing in dark, soggy patches through the snow along the paths to the pump and the backhouse. But around her, others were delighted to see the melting snow and buds on bush and tree swelling to the bursting point as the sun moved north and the days lengthened. They emerged from their houses, smiling, eager to greet one another, excited and happy at having weathered possible disaster.

Supaya grew increasingly silent and moody, impatient even with Kineu. She had almost finished gathering her things together: two new dresses and a skirt lay folded in her tin trunk, along with a pair of new moccasins, a large supply of quills, carefully washed to remove the oil and then sorted and wrapped, packets of medicinal herbs and seeds from the garden. Aunt Hettie had given her a comb and a small, hanging mirror. These were in her trunk, along with a fine old buckskin blouse with quill embroidery on the neck and shoulders from Auntie Em.

"My mother made this for me," Auntie Em had said, touching the quills with trembling fingers. "I wore it when I married. You have been as a daughter to me. You take it. You wear it." Supaya had embraced her, pressing her face against the wrinkled old cheek. As she was leaving, Auntie Em called her back and put into her hand a small piece of dried, ridged root. "It will protect you on your journey." And Supaya had put it in the small pouch that hung from her belt.

From the steps of the general store, Supaya could look out over the lake. Small puffy clouds sailed high and fast above the distant moving line of free water, and nearer shore the water showing between ice floes grew wider day by day. Soon the steamer would begin its round of the lake ports, pushing aside the last, thin sheets of floating ice to bring mail and supplies to people cut off from both for nearly four difficult months. Supaya had been able to push away thought of leaving home so long as snow blanketed the island. But now the burgeoning spring gave her departure such immediacy that Supaya wished the steamer there that very moment, so she could face the disaster of parting now instead of anticipating it day after day. She felt herself already separated from her family, even from Kineu. Daily she saw them living as they would when she was gone. Their home was no longer hers. It had taken on the sadness of a dearly remembered place where once she had been happy. She lived in a vacuum, having no one and no home to take the place of those she was deprived of.

As she was on her way back from the store, Miss Harris called to her from the steps of the school building, holding the door with one hand and waving with the other to attract her attention.

"Sophia, do come in for a moment. I'm so glad to have seen you." Supaya followed her into the schoolroom, breathing the familiar odor of chalk, paste, and children's bodies.

"I've missed you these last years, Sophia. Now I hear you are moving away, going to the mainland to be married."

"Yes, Miss Harris. I have to go when the first steamer comes."

Miss Harris clasped her hands together on her desk and looked searchingly at Supaya's sober face. "That will mean a big change for you, won't it."

"Yes, ma'm," said Supaya, looking down.

Agatha stretched out a hand toward her, then drew it back. "Who is the young man you are to marry? Have I ever had him in class?"

"Oh no, Miss Harris. He has never lived on this reserve. I do not know him, but his name is Eli Red Sky."

Miss Harris stiffened. "You don't know him?"

Supaya shook her head. "No, Miss Harris." Agatha's shocked face made her feel as if she'd made an inexcusable mistake in simple arithmetic.

Agatha stood up, crossed the room and looked out the window, her back very straight. Trying to contain her disapproval and show only the sympathy she felt for this young girl of whom she was so fond, she turned and asked gently, "Is there anything I could do to help you, Sophia? Would you like me to speak to your father or grandmother? Or to my brother, Reverend Harris?"

Supaya, shocked by the alarming possibility of Reverend Harris' causing a terrible scene, exclaimed forcibly, "No, Miss Harris! It is all settled!"

Agatha was confused. "You mean you don't mind marrying a stranger?"

Supaya stood up and faced her proudly. Her words were courteous, but distinctly cool. "It is my duty. It has been well arranged."

Agatha, hearing the formal words and seeing the father in the daughter's haughty, impenetrable eyes, knew that she was to presume no further. "Well, Sophia, I am sorry you are leaving us." She turned to her desk. "I have something here I want to give you." Her tone softened. "You were my star pupil in reading, you know." She smiled shyly at this confession and held out two books. "I'd like you to have these."

Surprised, Supaya took them with both hands and smiled, too delighted to speak.

"Well," laughed Agatha, pleased by her response, "don't you want to look at them and see what they are?"

One was a leather-bound copy of the Holy Bible; the other a copy of Dickens' *Hard Times*, bound in dark green with a border of entwined flowers, and on its flyleaf Agatha had written: For Sophia, a fine student, with best wishes, Agatha Harris.

"Thank you, Miss Harris," said Supaya. Agatha's fond expression made Supaya suddenly aware how much she owed to this woman, what a bond there was between them. The late afternoon sun streamed into the quiet, dusty schoolroom, and for the first time in weeks, Supaya was on the verge of tears. She dropped her eyes and murmured, "I will keep them always, Miss Harris, and I will remember you always."

"Just be sure you read them," admonished Miss Harris briskly, walking her to the door. "You must keep up your reading."

"I will, Miss Harris," promised Supaya.

"We won't say good-bye, Sophia. When I visit the mainland, I will be sure to come and see you." Again she put out her hand, and this time permitted herself to pat Supaya lightly on the shoulder. "I hope you will be very happy in your new home, Sophia."

One day in late April when the snow lingered only in the woods and even there only along ridges and under banks, Supaya and Kineu went out to gather wild leeks, the first green vegetable to thrust its pointed shoots through the freshened earth. Given a firm tug, the leeks came out with damp soil clinging to their pale brown bulbs and hairlike roots. Supaya found a good-sized patch and, moving along, bent over, had half filled her basket when a sudden dizziness overcame her. She sank down on her knees, her head hanging forward.

"Suppy! What's wrong?" Kineu caught her round the waist and helped her up. "Come, sit on this rock."

"Nothing's wrong, Kineu. I'm tired, that is all." She had felt tired all week and faint once or twice before. She tilted her head back for the fresh breeze to dry her damp forehead.

All around them plants were budding or coming into leaf. Morels, their crinkled skin tan or velvety dark brown, had pushed up through the layers of dead leaves. Bright yellow trout lilies, dog-tooth violets, with sun-speckled leaves already bloomed along the slopes. Branches, with buds pink and swollen, stirred against a blue sky where crows sailed and tilted in the limpid air, settled in the swaying treetops, then lifted off again in answer to a distant cawing. Supaya sighed contentedly and smiled at Kineu, kneeling beside her. "I wish we could stay here like this forever." Then, matter-of-factly, "Oh well, Grandma is waiting for these." She began sorting through the leeks, brushing off the dirt. "There are a lot this year. We'll soon have enough."

Kineu took a package from his basket and held it out in a childlike gesture. "Suppy, this is for you." What he felt but was unable to express was: When you put this shawl around you, it will be my arms around you, warming you with my love. Instead, he said, "I wanted to be sure to give it to you before . . ." He stopped, then forced himself to finish, ". . . before you go."

Surprised, Supaya unwrapped the package and held up a dark blue woolen shawl. "Kineu! It is beautiful! I'll put it on now!" She shook it out and drew it about her shoulders. "There!" She looked up, expecting his admiration, but saw only pain in his eyes and knew that he was not seeing her but himself without her. "Oh, Kineu!" In a burst of anguish, she took his head between her hands. "Don't look like that! Please don't!" But the pain in his eyes remained, and she cradled his head against her breast, stroking his hair, murmuring his name, rocking slightly back and forth as if comforting a child. Leaning against her knees, he embraced her fiercely. His muffled voice shook with unshed tears.

"You are leaving me! You promised me! Yet you are going away to marry him! I should go and kill him! I want to kill him!"

"Kineu! Don't say that! You know why I must go, why I *must* marry him! There's nowhere we could go where we'd be safe! Not my family, nor yours, nor our . . . our children!"

"You'll forget me! You'll live with him and forget me!"

"Kineu! I will never forget you! Never! I couldn't!"

"But you're mine! Mine!" he insisted, holding her tight, his face still hidden.

"Yes, Kineu, yes." She leaned her cheek against the top of his head, forgetting her own sorrow and fear in her need to comfort him. "I will always be yours, always!"

Quayo stewed the leeks, and their pungent odor filled the house. She served them with fish Jacques had caught that afternoon. The men had just finished eating and were lighting their everyday, hawthorne wood pipes when Cyrus Red Sky came by to tell Jules that Wenonga had arrived on the steamer and would come for Supaya in the morning.

Shaken by the prospect of immediate departure, Supaya slept fitfully and rose early. She dressed in a full-skirted, long-sleeved cotton print dress with a high buttoned bodice, and the white woman's shoes she wore when she went to church. She was packing her few other clothes in the trunk when Quayo came up to the loft.

"Granddaughter, I want to give you this." She held out to Supaya a black velvet drawstring bag. "This was my father's, Negik, your great-grandfather. He was a wise man and a great healer. This was his medicine bag. He gave it to me. Now I give it to you. It has great power. I have put in it medicines for illness and medicines against evil. Look, I will show you." Quayo took out the medicine packets and laid them on Supaya's bed. "All these I have already taught you. But this one, *nimepin*, is to be used against witches, and this one against envious wishes and those who would harm you. Look, it glows. When you have it near, you will know you are not alone. You will be protected. Take great care of these. Use them wisely. You will be a stranger and may need to protect yourself." Then she took out a pair of moccasins beautifully decorated with glass beads. Brilliant red, yellow, blue, and white beads had been painstakingly sewed on the skin in a fanned-out, sunlike design, a blaze of color against the pale buckskin; the sides were bordered with a geometric design in deep greens and white. "These I made for you. May the path you walk in them be safe and happy."

"Grandma, they are the most beautiful you have ever made!"

"It is a design I used once for your mother, when she married your father. Now you may use it." Last, she took out a case made of birchbark bound with sweet grass and tied with leather thongs. "I made you this housewife. You will need your own now."

Supaya untied the thongs. Inside was a flannelette lining holding needles of various sizes, threads, and a special bone awl for her quill embroidery. This was a particularly fine one, smoothed and shaped, Supaya knew, by many hours of patient work, difficult for her grandmother's weak eyes and stiff fingers. She held it in her hand and looked at Quayo, her eyes glistening with tears. "Oh, Grandma," she whispered, hiding her face against Quayo's shoulder, overwhelmed with a sense of loss in parting from this old woman who had been both mother and teacher.

Quayo embraced her and smoothed her hair. "Ah, Grand-daughter, do not mourn. Part of me goes with you, and you will live in my thoughts always." Hearing Supaya cry, she said, "Do not be afraid. You will be a good wife. We will be proud of you. And remember, you have a great blessing in your Grandfather. You can always call on him for help."

Supaya sat up and drew a long, quavering breath. "Yes, Grandma, I will remember." She managed a smile and said, "I will come back and bother you often."

Downstairs a door opened, and the women heard voices.

"Come," said Quayo. "Wenonga is here." But before they went down, Supaya took off her blue stone necklace, for the first time since her father had placed it around her neck, and left it behind, lying on her bed.

Wenonga had come, wrapped in his blanket as before, but carrying gifts not only of tobacco, but of flour, sugar, and tea as well, all very welcome after a long winter. He was disposed to be friendly, his bulging, fiery eyes now more curious than suspicious. He sat at ease and smoked his wooden pipe with Jules and Jacques, whose polite, distant manner hid the pain they felt at Supaya's departure.

Supaya greeted Wenonga briefly and went calmly to the wash bench in the lean-to where she began carefully combing and braiding her hair, clearly taking what time she pleased.

Quayo served the men tea and scone, which they ate in dignified silence. Wenonga observed Supaya's preparations, and when she finally put on her coat, drew Kineu's shawl over her head, and picked up her carpetbag, he rose to go.

Then Jules addressed Wenonga in a stern, deliberate way that commanded everyone's attention. His voice was edged with a threat that none of them failed to hear.

"Wenonga, I have paid my debt. I have given you my daughter, Supaya, who is dear to us. We have cared for her, protected her. Now it is you who must act in our place. She is going among strangers, and it is you who must see that she is safe and well cared for so that when we next meet, we will rejoice in our daughter's well-being."

"My son and I will care for her," answered Wenonga. "Our home will be hers."

Jules turned away and stood by the fireplace, his back to them all. When he heard the door close behind them, he looked sharply at Quayo, who sat with her hands folded in her lap.

"Quayo, she was not wearing her necklace!"

"No," said Quayo. "I saw her take it off. For the first time since you gave it to her. She left it behind." Quayo saw his pain, then his fear, and said quickly, "Do not fear for her. She is protected. Her guardian is with her still." Jules bowed his head and said nothing. Quayo rose and laid her hand gently on his arm. "Your child is not lost to you. She is too young to know forgiveness. Keep her necklace for her, and one day she will want it back. You will see."

The steamer was late. Wenonga, Supaya, and Jacques, who had accompanied her and carried her trunk, waited by the wharf. A bright sun glittered on the choppy water that slapped against the pilings and the stony shore, wearing away the remaining rim of ice. The sun was warm, but the wind blowing off the water chilled their faces. Supaya held her shawl close under her chin and narrowed her eyes against the wind.

They heard the steamer's whistle blow as it rounded a point of land, signaling its arrival. It rode high in the water, having unloaded its freight on the outward trip. Returning, it would pick up mailbags and a few passengers. Wenonga preceded Supaya up the gangplank and entered the enclosed passenger section, expecting she would follow. But Supaya went instead to the stern and sat down on a narrow bench attached to the ship's side. Jacques put her tin trunk beside her, then left the steamer and stood on the pier.

Water frothed and boiled as the steamer, with one blast of its whistle, backed up and got underway. It veered out at an angle and to Supaya it seemed that the whole shoreline swung around and the general store and wharf rapidly receded. Jacques, a lone, diminishing figure, stood with his hand raised in farewell until he was lost to view as the entire scene shifted. Auntie Em's house appeared, surrounded by trees, and standing on a rock at the water's edge was another figure. Though she couldn't see his face, Supaya knew it was Kineu. He gave no signal, but Supaya, huddled on the bench, her back to the cold wind, kept her eyes on him until he and the shore sank into the lake and only the trees stood above the water.

Then it was that she saw, above and beyond the woods, the hill where she had dreamed. She had never before seen Stone Island from such a distance, and never had it looked more beautiful. In the bright morning sun it seemed to float on the sparkling water.

Rising out of the deep green of pines and firs, the hill stood out sharply against the clear blue sky. Gazing at it, Supaya was transported. She felt herself sitting once again in the little hollow, the boulders protectively above her, sunlight glancing off their sides, with only the boundless expanse of heaven above her. . . .

A shaft of light, glinting on the water, struck her in the eyes. She blinked, recalled from memory, and saw that Stone Island had sunk below the horizon. Only the vast lake stretched behind her, its choppy water foaming in the steamer's wake, curling outward in a constantly repeated pattern. Supaya leaned against the rail, her bag close beside her, her trunk at her feet. She faced backward, conscious only of the ship's pulsing, forward rhythm.

PART TWO
1901–1907

CHAPTER EIGHT

All day Wenonga watched Supaya through windows that in warm weather opened onto the back deck. Wrapped in his blanket, he sat as immovable as she, ignoring the other passengers, who glanced at him, then sat apart, conversing among themselves. He saw her raise her head when the steamer docked at stops along the way and knew she watched for his appearance on deck as a signal they had arrived. He saw one of the deckhands speak to her and when she lowered her head and pulled her shawl across her face, ignore her. He expected she would be driven inside by the bitter wind, but now, as the late afternoon sun slanted across the deck, he knew she would not. The steamer had rounded the lake and was headed northwest. They were almost at their destination.

Wenonga envied Jules his strong daughter. He envied his son, Eli, having her for a wife. She had dreamed. Unusual for a woman. And that dream had given her great power, which he respected. He wondered about the extent of her power. How long could she match herself against him? She would be too strong for Eli. Concentrating, he willed her to raise her head and look at him, but she remained still, her face hidden. It was good she had such strength, as well as beauty, for Eli would be too weak for her, and then he, Wenonga, would subdue and possess her. Watching Supaya, he thought how it would be to take her young, seductive body, and for a while his weak son, a sorrow for Wenonga, ceased to exist.

Indifferent to any scrutiny, Supaya withdrew into herself, enduring the chill, numbing wind and giving no thought to the food Quayo had packed for the journey. She simply sat, unfeeling, almost unseeing, while water and time flowed past. Whenever the steamer docked, she looked for Wenonga. Not seeing him, she scarcely noticed when they again put out from shore.

As the ship veered northward, the declining sun touched her cold face and shone in her eyes. Squinting ahead, she saw great reddish stone bluffs rising straight out of the lake, their tops green with trees to the very edges. Then the steamer swung about, throwing out a great curving backwash. The land opened out, revealing a long, narrow bay and a city whose buildings rose in tiers from the shore to the tops of the surrounding hills. Wellston, Ontario, was a small, grimy town, its largely frame buildings thrown up during a lumber boom, since declined. But it was such a town as Supaya had never seen or imagined. The steamer's steady pulse slowed to a heavy throb as it entered the narrow bay where gulls, dipping and soaring, filled the sky. Supaya was amazed to see not one but many piers lined with fishing boats; not one store and a house or two, but many buildings, two, even three stories high, leaning together, their steep, gabled roofs forming a jagged, irregular line. Only the width of a cobbled street, lined with buggies and wagons, separated the buildings from the seawall.

The steamer whistled and sidled in alongside a wharf where men ran forward with ropes. Passengers emerged from the cabin and clustered together, waiting for the gangplank to be lowered, Wenonga among them. Awed and fearful of being separated from him in this strange place, Supaya clutched her bag, braced the tin trunk on one hip, and came quickly to stand behind him. The gangplank down, Wenonga strode ahead, moving with proud, stately dignity among dockhands and stacks of freight. Cunningly, he did not look back, leaving Supaya to follow as best she could. Supaya tried desperately to stay close behind him, but her trunk, heavy and awkward, impeded her. She veered sideways to avoid bumping one man only to bump into another, who turned and spoke sharply to her. For a moment she lost sight of Wenonga and in her panic tripped on the rough planking, almost losing her grip on the trunk. She grabbed for a better hold, and an old man with a bristly gray chin and a stocking cap pulled down over his ears laughed at her. He was warming his hands over a fire in a tin drum.

"Fair loaded down, ain't ye?" he remarked, grinning at her through the tatters of smoke that blew up from the drum.

93

Supaya instantly averted her eyes and hurried on, dragging the trunk and hearing the old man's rasping chuckle behind her. Looking ahead for Wenonga, she saw that he had reached the street.

A dog, standing guard in a wagon, saw Wenonga and began barking. Infuriated, the animal leaped down and rushed forward, snarling, his lips curled back over his teeth. Front legs stiff and splayed in mixed anger and fear, he lunged at Wenonga, forward, then back, yapping hysterically, his eyes rolling wildly. Supaya shrank back, horrified. People turned and stared. But Wenonga, impervious to all that did not concern him, ignored the frantic dog and turned his head slowly, looking for his son.

Two men came from around the wagon. One reached out for the dog's collar.

"Hey, get back here! Back in the wagon!" He jerked the frenzied dog almost off his feet and swung him around. Half choked, the dog persisted in a half-strangled barking. "He never could stand them Indians, but he don't usually carry on so," the man said to his companion. He gave Wenonga a suspicious look and slapped the dog, who leaped, quivering, back up into the wagon.

Unconcerned with both man and dog, Wenonga saw Eli and started toward him. Following his glance, Supaya saw a young man coming directly toward them. He appeared tall and very slim in a dark suit and black felt hat that shaded his face. Overcome at his approach, Supaya lowered her head.

Eli had left the wagon at the end of the street. He had been there, sober and waiting, when the steamer arrived, and had watched with amusement his father's and Supaya's progress toward the street. Wenonga had told him Supaya's name and the many benefits he would gain by having as wife the daughter of a respected healer and one well-trained in the old ways. Eli had not objected. He liked women. This marriage pleased his father and his Aunt Nonen. He had nothing else to do; he might as well take a wife.

Eli met them just as a piercing blast of sound split the air. Supaya, nerves already tight, gasped and jerked up her head. Starting with fear, her eyes met Eli's. He was struck first by the loveliness of her face, then by her fear. He had seen blind panic in animals, had experienced it himself. He put out his hand sympathetically.

"Don't be afraid. It's only the train whistle." He saw she

didn't see him, didn't understand what he'd said. "Here, I'll take your trunk. The wagon is at the end of the street, Father."

Wenonga strode ahead. Supaya followed automatically, eyes down, scarcely breathing, hardly daring to look up. Walking beside her, Eli could see the tenseness of her hand as she clutched her shawl to her chest.

The wagon was small, pulled by a brown, shaggy horse who stood patiently, head drooping, one foot cocked. Eli lifted the trunk and carpetbag into the back and would have helped Supaya up, but she stepped quickly onto the wheel hub and over the side. Seeking at least a partial refuge in which to regain her composure, she huddled down on the wagon bed behind the driver's seat, her head bowed against her drawn-up knees, all but hidden by her shawl and long skirts. Her head was spinning. For a few moments, she was dimly conscious of the sounds of the street, people talking, drivers yelling and cracking whips, wagons jolting over cobbles, and above it all the raucous cries of the gulls. She heard Wenonga speaking to Eli, then felt the wagon swerve as it moved out into the street. As they rode along, the street sounds faded until she heard only the clop of the horse's hooves on the cobbles. She raised her head as they turned up a steep, graveled street with stone or brick houses on either side. Supaya looked with wonder at these houses, several stories high with long, narrow windows. She had never imagined a house would have so many windows or doors decorated with glass fans. Abruptly the gravel ended, and the wagon rolled along more quietly on a dirt road where the houses were of board and batten, small and drab and further apart.

As they rounded a curve at the top of a hill, Supaya had a sudden, brief view of the town, its streets in shadow, its chimneys and church spires still bright in the setting sun, with the lake beyond like a piece of rippled blue silk. Then the road veered north, into the countryside. They passed farms with larger barns than Supaya had ever seen and meadows where huge boulders shouldered up through the earth. Between groves of trees where darkness had already come, she glimpsed narrow bays cutting into the land, the distant water shining like silver far below the steep, rocky bluffs.

They traveled in silence except for the soft muffled sounds of the horse's steady jog, the chink and slap of harness, the creak of the wagon. Eli held the reins, and Wenonga sat beside him, his heavy head forward on his chest. Supaya, stiff and aching from the long, cold boat ride, felt every jarring stone and rut in what seemed an endless ride. With the coming of night, the air grew colder, but the sky remained clear and the evening star, a pale glimmer in the western sky, was familiar, though at home she would have seen it hanging far out across the lake. She thought of Quayo, her father, and Jacques, and of Kineu, but her sense of displacement was so great that they lacked reality. She felt she had parted from them a very long time ago.

It was quite dark when Eli pulled the horse to a stop in front of a store by the roadside. The storefront was in darkness, but inside oil lamps lit up shelves and counters and shone through the center door and two wide windows onto the long, shadowy porch.

Wenonga muttered a question, but Eli jumped down without answering and entered the store, banging the door open and shut, his figure dark against the light. Wenonga and Supaya waited in silence. The horse, eager to get home, blew softly through her nostrils.

Eli made a quick exchange across the counter and returned. He slapped the reins and they went on. Occasionally Supaya saw lighted windows and the dim shapes of houses set near the road; now and then a dog barked, noting their passing. Wenonga said something to Eli, whose answer displeased Wenonga, and he said in a louder, angry voice, "Now! It will be done now!" A few minutes later Eli stopped the wagon again, this time in front of a house. Wenonga turned. "You get down now," he said to Supaya.

Light from a single window slanted across a section of porch and a railing that split the light into bars as it fell into the darkness of a small, fenced-in yard. The fence palings were ghostly white. The gate, when Eli pushed it open, made only the faintest sound. Behind them, the tired horse, impatient for its stall and feed, stomped and whinnied, a sound apparently heard inside, for Wenonga had only raised his fist to knock when the door opened, giving the impression that he was about to strike the tall, thin man who appeared. Silhouetted against the light that shone into the hall from the side room, the man motioned them inside, saying, "Come in, come in. We were expecting you."

They followed him into the parlor, where a large oil lamp cast their lumpish shadows onto the flowered wallpaper. Light gleamed on the glossy black surface of a horsehair sofa and the polished backs of chairs. Lace curtains hung at the windows, and between the windows hung family portraits, in dark, ornate frames. On the floor beyond the edge of the rug, a row of dirt-filled flowerpots was lined up in front of the windows.

Supaya, standing back and to one side from Wenonga and Eli, was startled by the tall man's reaching out and grasping her hand with his bony fingers. "I am Reverend Crowell, my dear," he said, stretching his head forward on a neck too thin for its collar. "Welcome to Two Bluffs Reserve." His long thin face with eyes set close to a high-bridged nose expressed a solemn concern. "We have been expecting you, yes, we have, my wife and I. Mr. Red Sky told us you were coming. My wife will want to welcome you also." He raised his voice as if to summon her out of thin air.

"Mrs. Crowell! Mrs. Crowell! She's working in the back room with her plants, you know," he said to Supaya. Then to himself, "She does expend such energy! Well," bringing his attention back to his guests, "sit down, please sit down."

"We want the marriage now," said Wenonga aggressively. Eli, who had removed his hat and was about to sit down, straightened up again.

"Of course you do, of course. As soon as my wife . . . ." Reverend Crowell was about to call again when Mrs. Crowell entered. "Here you are! My dear, Mr. Red Sky has brought Eli and his bride-to-be from Stone Island. I knew you would want to welcome her."

Mrs. Crowell, who had stopped short just inside the room and looked to her husband for direction, came forward at once. "Oh yes, my dear, I *do* welcome you." A small, frail, fair-haired woman, she took Supaya's hand in both of hers and looked up at her anxiously. "You have come a long way, haven't you? I'm sure you must be tired."

Before Supaya, dazed and very tired, could form an answer, Reverend Crowell said quickly, "I think, my dear, the sooner we have the ceremony, the sooner they will reach home. The church is lit, so if you will get your coat, we'll just step next door to the vestry."

With Reverend Crowell leading the way, they walked through the gate, across to the church and down a path beside it to the rear entrance, passing in and out of the light shining from the high, narrow windows. In the vestry, a small room with a few chairs and a desk where each week Reverend Crowell struggled over the composition of his Sunday sermon, they all removed their coats except for Wenonga, who stood aloof in his blanket.

"Why don't you let me take your shawl, dear," said Mrs. Crowell. Without waiting for an answer, she drew it off and folded it over her arm. Then, touching Supaya's elbow, she guided her into the church and indicated where she and Eli should stand.

Supaya, who had not yet brought herself to look directly at Eli, was conscious of his shoulder and arm beside hers. She focused her eyes on the book in the preacher's hands and heard him intoning as Reverend Harris used to do, but was too fatigued to pay attention. She repeated automatically when asked twice or prompted gently by Mrs. Crowell. And when Eli stood ready with the ring, Mrs. Crowell had to whisper, "Hold out your hand, dear," which she did, like an obedient child, and saw, as though it were happening to someone else, Eli put a gold band on her finger.

Back in the vestry, Reverend Crowell filled out the certificate. He bent over the desk, the lamplight shining through the sparse brown hair that lay across his pinkish bony scalp, and wrote, murmuring the words to his pen.

"Now, if you will sign here, please." Eli and Supaya wrote their names where Reverend Crowell's finger pointed, then Mrs. Crowell, as witness, and Wenonga, who stepped forward, grasped the pen boldly and made his mark. Reverend Crowell held the paper up, pursed his lips, and blew on it.

"You must keep that," he said, handing it to Supaya, "and show it to Mr. Toomis, the agent, tomorrow."

Without looking at it, Supaya folded it away into her pouch. Wenonga turned immediately to the door. Mrs. Crowell had been watching Supaya as she might a plant with drooping leaves. Stretching up her arms, she draped the shawl around Supaya's head and shoulders, holding the ends together for a moment as she looked intently into her eyes.

"I hope you'll be very happy, my dear. Once you are settled, you must come and visit me. We'll have a cup of tea and I will show you my plants."

Through her weariness, Supaya saw the kindness in Mrs. Crowell's pale blue eyes. "Thank you," she said, wondering irrationally about all those dirt-filled pots. Later, the one clear image she had of her marriage was Amy Crowell's face, looking earnestly up at her.

The ride to Wenonga's house was short, and the horse, knowing the way, tossed its head and picked up speed. It swung briskly into a lane and would have taken them all to the barn had Eli not pulled up short beside a house where a dim light showed through one small window.

The door opened and a woman stood on the threshold, almost filling the doorway. "*Ahnee, ahnee*," she said, her voice deep and resonant. Eli, holding the trunk, stood to one side to allow Supaya to enter. "Come in, come in. Welcome to your new home. Eli, put her trunk in the bedroom." She turned to Supaya, who had stopped just inside the door. "I am Eli's *noshan*, his aunt." Like her brother, Nonen had a strong, broad stature, wide face, wide mouth. She was older than Wenonga. Her braided hair was gray, and her face had many fine lines. But she had a commanding, energetic presence and a sharp eye. She saw Supaya's sagging shoulders and heavy eyes.

"You have had a long journey. Take off your coat and sit down. We will have some tea."

Supaya hung her coat and shawl on a peg, then carried her bag to the table and took out two packages of dried berries, several strings of dried apples, some maple sugar, and a small jug of maple syrup. "My grandmother, Quayo, sent you these," she said. Speaking aloud the loved name and handling the familiar objects made her separation from her family all at once very real, the distance she had come very great. Her lip suddenly trembled, and she put her hand to her head.

Nonen set the teapot back on the stove and came instantly to put an arm about Supaya's shoulders. She drew her to her own rocking chair beside the stove.

"There, sit and rest." She spoke kindly to Supaya, who closed her eyes and rested her head against the chair back, but her eyes flashed angrily at Wenonga, sitting stolidly on the other side of the stove, and at Eli, just coming in from stabling the horse. "You have not taken good care of her! She is worn out." Her quick eye saw the gold band on Supaya's finger. "You should have brought her home first! Time enough for that tomorrow!"

Wenonga glanced at Eli, then back at his sister, but said nothing. Nor did Eli, who was looking at Supaya.

Nonen made a disgusted sound and reached for the teapot. She poured them each a cup of tea and took out of the oven a pan of warm bannock which she put on the table. Supaya started to rise, but Nonen said, "No, sit there," and brought the bread and tea to her.

The bread tasted unbelievably good to Supaya, who had not thought of eating all day, and as she finished one piece, Nonen brought her another and poured her more tea. As she ate, eyes downcast, she was conscious that the others, seated at the table, were talking, Nonen having asked Wenonga about their relatives on Stone Island. Their conversation became a quiet, almost comforting murmur. The initial shock of arrival was over, and warmed by the hot tea, Supaya gradually relaxed. Heat radiating from the large stove warmed her cheeks and caused her wind-burned eyes to droop uncontrollably, though she strove to keep them open. Her arms and legs grew heavy, then ceased to have any feeling at all. The room, the voices faded. Unable to rouse herself, she drifted into sleep. Her eyes closed and her head slowly tilted sideways against the chair.

At the table, conversation ceased. They all came and stood looking down at her. Gently, Nonen took the tea cup from Supaya's limp hand.

"Get her up," said Wenonga, reaching out to shake her.

"No!" said Nonen sharply, extending her arm protectively in front of Supaya. "Leave her alone! Go to bed and let her sleep!"

Wenonga's mouth drew down contemptuously. But after a moment he turned without a word, went into his bedroom, and pulled the curtain across the doorway.

Eli gazed thoughtfully at this sixteen-year-old girl who was now his wife. He had no wish to wake her. He understood the shock of displacement. Tomorrow she would feel better and they could talk.

Beside him, Nonen regarded Supaya with all the sympathy of her commanding nature. Thoughts of herself as a bride, and of her daughter, combined to focus all her maternal, protective impulses on this young girl asleep in her chair. She had finally acquired, in her old age, a second daughter. "You are lucky, Eli," she said softly. "She is very pretty."

"Yes," agreed Eli, "I am," realizing that for the first time in his life he had something of his own. She is mine, he found himself thinking in surprise, mine!

CHAPTER NINE

After a week of rain and blustery winds, the weather suddenly turned fine. Together Nonen and Supaya planted the garden. Working parallel rows, they sowed the seeds leisurely, enjoying the spring warmth, pausing to chat or notice who was passing by. But Supaya was really watching for Eli, who had gone in the wagon for supplies. As she worked the earth, her long hair fell forward, and she stopped to twist it around and tuck it out of the way, smiling to herself remembering how that morning Eli had caught her by her hair as she was getting out of bed and had pulled her back into his arms. He had laughed at her faint protest, drawing her hair to one side over her bare shoulder and breast, telling her she would never get away from him for he could always catch her by her hair. Now it seemed to Supaya he had been gone far too long, and she listened for the wagon.

Eager to return to Supaya, Eli came at a faster pace than usual. Nellie, enlivened by the spring air, needed little urging. Eli pulled her up near the lean-to, and she tossed her head as if to free herself of the reins, her rounded flanks gleaming red-brown in the bright sun. Jumping down, Eli carried the sacks inside, then came jauntily toward the women.

Supaya thought him very handsome. His hair parted naturally on one side, a strand habitually falling across his forehead. His eyes were large, like his father's, but clear, and his nose, broken in a childhood fight, had a slight bend, an irregularity that increased rather than lessened his attractiveness. He had the broad shoulders and developed muscular arms of a man of twenty-six. He crossed the rows they had planted, careless where he put his foot and grinning at their cries of protest. He halted in front of Supaya and threw out his arms.

"Who cares about planting on such a day! Come, let's walk to the bluff."

"But we're not finished! We have other rows to do."

"Do them tomorrow!"

Supaya looked at Nonen, who said, "Go. Go. I will finish." Nonen was happy to indulge them, happy to see Eli gay and smiling, instead of sitting about the house sullen and morose.

"Come! You have to do as I say," said Eli, laughing and throwing down Supaya's spade. He caught her hand and pulled her along past the barn, across the rocky meadow where Nellie usually grazed, and into the woods. Half-opened leaves were lacy against the blue sky, and sunlight, shining through, dappled the tender green undergrowth.

They walked close together, bodies touching. Eli found it hard not to touch his lovely, obedient young wife, and when they smiled at each other, the memory of their lovemaking was in their eyes. He was grateful, now, to Wenonga, for Supaya had given a focus to his empty pointless existence. As never before, his heart swelled with a vague, undefined hope for the future. With her, he felt sure his life would take shape.

Supaya was at home in these woods, which were very like the woods on Stone Island, more at home than in Wenonga's house. Although his was larger than her father's, had a bigger stove and two bedrooms downstairs instead of one, and a loft as well, she was not at ease in it. She missed the open fireplace, and Wenonga's presence pervaded the house. She felt his burning watchful eyes on them even in their own room with the curtain drawn across the door. She did not feel sufficiently comfortable to hang up her mirror and still kept her things in her trunk. But out in the garden or the woods, with Eli or Nonen, she was content.

The woods ended at the edge of the bluff. Though Eli had brought her there before, Supaya was always surprised by how high above the lake they were. A narrow bay cut deeply into the land and at its inner end the bluff sloped down to a rocky shore, but where they stood, facing outward, the water rippled far below sheer layers of striated, reddish rock.

Where a rocky outcropping formed a partial cave, they sat

down and looked out over the sunlit water where gulls lazily rose and fell in the clear air, their white wings flashing as they floated in long, banking curves down between the bluffs.

"The land at home is rocky too," said Supaya, "but we have no bluffs like these," nodding toward the opposite side of the bay. "The woods are the same. And we would be planting now too."

"Stop talking about what you did there! This is your home."

Supaya turned toward him. "Don't you want to hear about my home? My family?"

Eli met her eyes briefly; then his glance slid away, down over her rounded belly. "No. I don't. This is your home now," he insisted. "You forget all that. *I* am your family."

"But, Eli, I can't forget . . . ."

"Yes, you can. I'll make you!" He pulled her close, and holding her chin firmly, brushed his lips tantalizingly back and forth across hers as he whispered, "I will make you forget them all!"

And for a time she did forget, for Eli was a practiced lover. Supaya, knowing only Kineu's youthful outbursts of passion, reached eagerly for Eli's teasing kisses, responding spontaneously and ardently to his lovemaking. Eli, used to a calculated coyness, was enthralled by her innocently passionate response. For the first time he felt deep satisfaction and pride in his own masculinity and a new, exhilarating sense of power. He liked bringing her to the bluff, for here he'd discovered she was freer than in their room at home.

Afterwards, they lay stretched out, luxuriating in the sun. Supaya's head was on his chest, her mind at peace. The sun warmed her legs, bare below her rumpled skirts, and glowed red-orange through her eyelids. She raised one arm to shield her eyes. Then it was that she heard, or sensed, something or someone watching. In one swift movement she rose to her knees and looked sharply around at the tumbled boulders, the still trees. Only the tilting, mewing gulls circled endlessly above the bay. But her ears caught a faint, retreating sound.

"What is it?" asked Eli, squinting up at her.

"I don't know. Eli, let's go. There's work to do."

Eli rolled over and put his head in her lap. "Work! Who wants to work!"

Supaya smiled down at him. "I do," she said, stroking back his hair. "I want to help Nonen with the garden."

"You're supposed to help me, and I need a kiss."

Supaya laughed. "One," and bent down.

"More," he commanded, embracing her.

But Supaya, remembering the unseen presence, was uneasy and pulled away.

"Go then!" said Eli, pretending indifference. "You don't even know the way back."

Amused at such an idea, Supaya laughed and held out her hand. "Come. I'll show you the way."

Eli, pleased to humor her, got up and took her hand. But he led the way.

After the first day or two, Supaya had easily adjusted to her new home, even finding excitement and challenge in her new position as wife. Nonen treated her as her own daughter, welcomed her help, praised her work, and made easier whatever she could. Only Wenonga made her uneasy, his eyes constantly on her. But often he was gone all day. When he was home, Nonen and Eli were there too.

Eli had been adroit. At ease with her himself, he had put her at ease. The first day, after she was rested, he showed her the garden and the barn and made her laugh by introducing her formally to Nellie, whose flank shivered under her hand. They spent all day together, and he was amusing and companionable. There was little resemblance between him and his father, and for that Supaya was glad. She even thought him handsome. His broken nose was prominent, his chin angular, and his mouth, slightly unsymmetrical, gave his face a whimsical charm. And his admiration of her was apparent.

That night, when they were alone, he gave her a present, the one he had stopped at the store to buy for her on their way home, a hair comb of tortoiseshell set with cut steel in a lacy pattern. He approached her slowly, with soft eyes and a gentle hand. He caressed her long hair and told her she was to twist it up and wear the comb after the fashion of white women. In bed he stroked her as he stroked Nellie until, aroused and all constraint gone, she had embraced him with an unexpected ardor that flattered him and increased his desire for her. In the days following, they were constantly together, and though he made no public display of his affection, his eyes would linger on hers, possessive and enticing. Supaya, with no thought of the future and no questions for a present so full of love and warmth, rapidly settled down. The bitterness and sadness she had felt all winter were gone, replaced by a happiness she had never expected.

Her pregnancy, soon recognized, was accepted without comment. Nonen, delighted at the prospect of a child in the house, cautioned her about her diet. She mustn't eat the flesh of porcupine or the baby would be headstrong, with a prickly nature; or suckers, lest the baby have too large a head. Until the birth, Nonen flatly refused to serve potatoes, for they were white man's food and a contamination. She constantly asked Wenonga to bring home whitefish, trout, and venison. He grumbled but would return with the desired catch, flinging it down before Nonen as if answering a challenge, once bringing of his own accord a deer's head to ensure the baby's having good thick lashes and brows.

As her belly grew larger, Supaya looked forward eagerly to her child's birth, smiling to herself when she felt it move. At such moments she thought of Kineu and was filled with wonder, puzzled by her own happiness. She touched the shawl Kineu had given her, so long ago it seemed, remembering how much it had meant to her, how she had worn it proudly, as a kind of shield. And she was filled with pained confusion when she remembered holding him against her, comforting him with promises. She loved him still, she knew, but Eli was her husband, and he had made her love him also. Happening to look up, she encountered Eli's soft, dark eyes watching her, a slight, sensuous smile curving his lips, and she folded the blue shawl, carefully and sadly, and laid it away in the tin trunk.

One day Nonen thought it time to take Supaya to the store with her. Eli, having risen late as usual, was drinking his breakfast tea. Supaya, wearing Quayo's old shawl, stood before him.

"Eli, can I have some money, please? I need paper and pencils. I want to write home."

"Home?"

Abashed, Supaya said, "To my father and grandmother and brother, to tell them I am all right."

"I have no money," said Eli shortly, drinking his tea.

"I will buy them with the supplies," said Nonen, intervening. "Come, we'll go now." Eli said nothing more and did not look up as they left.

The silence between the two women was strained. Since the day she had come, Supaya had not known Eli to go hunting or fishing either by himself or with Wenonga. Nor had he gone to work on the reserve or at a lumbering camp. Except for occasional trips for supplies, he was always with her. The money Nonen spent was Wenonga's. Supaya glanced sideways at Nonen.

"Doesn't Eli work? Has he no money of his own?"

For the first time Nonen was evasive. "Sometimes he repairs harnesses. Sometimes he helps build a barn or house." She paused, then added, "He looked for work in Wellston, but there were no jobs for him." Seeing Supaya's expressionless face, she did not add that he often stayed several days in Wellston, returning in a surly, mean temper, his clothes dirty and ill-smelling. Or that when he did earn a little, he spent it on drink.

"Does he never hunt or fish?"

Nonen, hesitating to tell Supaya the truth, finally did so. "He is not a good hunter or fisherman. He was sent to government boarding school. He never learned how to hunt and fish. They taught him to read and write, to mend harness and nail boards together." She appealed to Supaya for understanding. "They took him when he was very little, when his mother died. They even beat him for speaking his own language. Now he has no skill."

Supaya knew Eli had been at boarding school, but had not realized she was married to a man who could not bring home meat or fish and who had no craft. How could he provide for their own home, which Supaya hoped to have, or for children? Wenonga was a good provider, as good as her father and Jacques. Why did Eli not go with him and learn so they would not always be dependent on Wenonga? These questions were like a weight on her mind. She said nothing further to Nonen, but she was determined to speak to Eli as soon as they were alone.

Down the road they passed the school, a building very like the one Supaya had attended, and beyond, the church where she had been married. In the front yard of the parsonage, Mrs. Crowell was down on her knees, taking weak, spindly plants from pots and putting them into the ground. Seeing the women, she sat back on her heels and said good morning, inviting them to stop; but Nonen, upset by their conversation about Eli, gave her a brief good morning and went on. All the eagerness drained out of Amy Crowell's face, though she tried to smile. Supaya, sorry to see her disappointment, promised to come another day, very soon, feeling sympathy for this little woman who seemed as unsuited to her location as her plants.

The general store was just outside the reserve boundary and was larger than Supaya had thought. Like Mr. Bonnet's, it was a gathering place for both Indians and whites. Men lounged along the edge of the porch, their hats tilted forward, shading their eyes. Others sat with their backs against the building, hands hanging limp over their drawn-up knees. As the women approached, conversation ceased and heads turned, following them as they came up the steps and crossed the porch.

Supaya, unused to such staring and ill at ease with her hair swept up, was grateful for Nonen's presence and passed them all with her chin lifted and eyes straight ahead. Inside, a white woman with blonde hair was helping three young Indian women. As Nonen and Supaya passed them, the girls turned, nudging each other and whispering. Nonen stopped at the side for grocery supplies. Supaya went past the yard goods and wearing apparel to the back of the store, where there were general farm and household supplies. She was scanning the shelves when a man spoke close beside her.

"Well, you're a long way from home, aren't you?"

Startled, Supaya turned. A tall white man with curly black hair smiled down at her. He wore no hat this time, or coat over his fancy vest and white shirt, but she remembered instantly his intense blue eyes laughing at her over a pot of soup. He was amused at her surprise, and his amusement deepened with pleasure when he saw she remembered. Out of her embarrassment, she said, "Yes," then, flustered, "No. I mean, I live here now."

"You transferred to this reserve?"

"I got married," said Supaya primly, looking away.

"Ah," he said and made a little bow. "Welcome to Two Bluffs, Mrs. . . .?"

"Red Sky," said Supaya, disconcerted by his bowing. At his slightly startled look she added, "Eli, Eli Red Sky."

"Oh yes," he said, his eyes flicking over the comb in her hair. "Well, Mrs. Red Sky, what can I help you with?"

"You know Mr. Fallon?" asked Nonen on their way home.

"I saw him once," answered Supaya. "He came to Stone Island, to our store." She said no more, pretending not to notice Nonen's curiosity, but she felt herself blushing unaccountably.

"That store is his," said Nonen, and added, without looking at Supaya, "That white woman with the yellow hair is his wife."

So he married too, thought Supaya, and immediately wondered at herself. Why shouldn't he marry. Anyway, what did it matter?

That evening she wrote a letter home. Eli sat across from her, watching suspiciously every word she wrote.

"What did you say?" he asked.

"Just that I am well and . . ." but before she could finish, he reached across and, to her astonishment, took the letter and read it.

"Who are these men you send greetings to— Jules, Jacques, James, Kineu?"

Supaya took a moment to control her anger, then answered,

each word flat and distinct. "They are my relatives, the ones you didn't want to hear about. Jules is my father. Jacques is my brother. Neegonas, whom you left out, is my sister. James is my sister's husband, Hettie is . . ."

Eli, hearing her anger, glanced up and, surprised to see her narrowed eyes and thin lips, said placatingly, "All right, all right!"

But she would not stop. ". . . my aunt, Kineu is my cousin, Maud is my friend and future sister-in-law. Why," she asked coldly, "don't you read it aloud? Then Nonen and Wenonga could hear it also? After all, they paid for it."

Embarrassed and intimidated before his father, Eli shrugged and tossed the letter back.

Wenonga, smoking his pipe by the stove, watched and listened, his reddened eyes alert and calculating, like a hunter sighting the first tracks of his prey.

Nonen stood up. "It is late. We should go to bed."

Supaya folded the letter and put it in an envelope, announcing as she did so that she was going to read for a while. Getting the Dickens book Miss Harris had given her, she opened it on the table and began to read silently.

Nonen went up to the loft, and Wenonga, the ghost of a smile on his lips, walked soundlessly to his room and pulled the curtain.

Eli sat still, waiting for Supaya to look at him, but she did not. She was too angry to give her full attention to reading, but after an interval she turned a page and continued. Eli rose, and going around the table, put his hands on her shoulders and rubbed the back of her neck with his thumbs. At his touch, Supaya's anger began to fade, but still she didn't move. Eli bent over, rubbed his cheek against hers.

"Come on, Suppy," he murmured, and reaching out turned the lamp very low. When she didn't protest, he turned it off altogether and slipping one arm around her waist, drew her up into his arms. At first she stood stiffly in his embrace, but as he kissed her, hard and long as if to draw out all her anger, her defenses melted, and he thought she repented of her fit of anger. But later, lying close against him, listening to his even breathing, she thought drowsily that he had not said he was sorry, and as she fell asleep, she resolved not to write another letter in his presence.

The next day Eli made a show of going with Wenonga to help repair a neighbor's barn. Eager to mail her letter, Supaya walked alone to the store. On the way back, she stopped at Mrs. Crowell's house, but not seeing her about, took a smaller, back road as a shortcut home. As she walked along, she heard voices behind her. She paid little attention until she realized they were speaking about her.

"Look at her! That's what they raise on Stone Island!"

"Girls so dumb they marry because they're told to! How can Eli stand her!"

Supaya glanced around and saw they were the same three girls who had been in the store the day before. She walked a bit faster, thinking they would fall behind and she would not have to listen. But they walked faster also and came even closer.

"She had to get married, that's why! Poor Eli didn't know he was getting a family!"

"Somebody ought to tell her he already has a family!"

"She thinks she can get away with it! But I'll show her! She can't steal my man!"

Shocked by their words, Supaya walked on as though she hadn't heard. Angered by her show of indifference and determined to provoke a reaction, they came closer still.

"Go on, Marie! Make her sorry! Show her no backwoods girl can come here and take our men!"

"Beat her up! That'll show her! Make her go back where she came from!"

There was a sudden hush as Marie, skipping forward, stuck out her foot and, catching Supaya's ankle from behind, tripped her. Supaya pitched forward, sprawling on the dirt road. Before she could roll over, Marie threw herself furiously on Supaya's back, landing with a force that took Supaya's breath and caused a sharp stab of pain in her belly. Marie snatched out Supaya's comb and threw it aside, where one girl stomped on it, smashing it to pieces. Marie fastened her hands in Supaya's hair and yanked back with all her strength. Supaya grunted with pain, drew her arms back under her, and thrust up and sideways, throwing Marie to one side.

"Hit her! Hit her!" shouted one.

Supaya and Marie rolled over and over, hitting with their fists, gouging, twisting, and kicking, their hair loose and flying, dust rising in a cloud about them while the other two circled round, urging Marie on. Striving to hurt Supaya's face, Marie raked her nails down her cheeks. Supaya, with more deadly intent, grabbed Marie by the throat and pressed both thumbs against her windpipe. Marie arched back, her mouth gasping for air.

"Grab her hands! Grab her hands! She'll kill her!" The two girls caught Supaya's arms and pulled back hard, breaking her hold on Marie's throat. As they twisted her arms painfully backward, Marie, wild with rage, pressed one arm across Supaya's face and began ripping away her clothes. Torn with pain, Supaya opened her mouth wide against Marie's arm and bit down hard on the soft under flesh. Marie screamed and threw herself off Supaya. Frightened by that, the others dropped Supaya's arms and backed off. Supaya drew her arms close against herself and sat panting for breath, her hair hanging about her face, the sickening taste of blood in her mouth.

Marie stared aghast at her bleeding arm. "She bit me! She bit me!"

"Kick her!" yelled one girl. "Kick her!"

Needing no urging, Marie kicked Supaya viciously in the belly. "I'll show you!" she hissed. "You go back where you came from or I'll kill you!" She kicked again, hitting Supaya full in the side. Supaya doubled over in a convulsion of pain, vainly trying to protect her belly. "You hear? I'll kill you!" Marie kicked, again and again, short, powerful kicks. The others moved in and kicked her side, her back. "Go home! No one wants you here!"

"What are you doing!!"

Startled, the girls turned. Unnoticed, a young woman had come up behind them, her expression one of horror and anger.

"Marie! Betty! You should all be ashamed of yourselves! Get away from her!" As they didn't move, she threatened them. "Go on! Get away! Just wait until your families hear what you have done!"

Sullenly, the girls backed off. "She's a man stealer! She deserves to be kicked!"

"And look!" Marie thrust out her arm, red and swelling. "Look! She bit me!"

"You've done something much worse! You should *all* be beaten for what you've done! Now get along off!"

"Come on Marie!"

Marie followed, then turned, taunting Supaya. "Just you remember! I'll get him back!"

The woman leaned over Supaya, who sat hunched forward, her arms across her belly. "Can you get up if I help you?"

Supaya raised her head. Her hair, covered with dirt, hung

across her smeared, bloody face. Her eyes glittered with anger and pain.

"I'm Susannah King. I live just over there. Let me help you home."

But Supaya suddenly turned away, crawled to the side of the road and retched, her whole body convulsed. When she finally stopped, she stayed on her hands and knees, head hanging, unable to move any further.

Susannah put her arms gently around her waist and lifted. "Come on," she said softly. "I'll help you home."

For a moment Supaya hung limp, then, bracing herself, she got shakily to her feet. Susannah kept one arm around her, and Supaya leaned heavily against her. "Red Sky," she said faintly.

"That's not far," said Susannah. "Let's try."

They moved slowly down the road, stopping at intervals when Supaya clutched Susannah's arm and doubled over in a spasm of pain. When they came within sight of the house, Nonen, working in the garden, caught sight of them and came running. She wasted no time on questions. Between them, the two women half carried Supaya into the house and eased her down in Nonen's rocker. Supaya, breathing in shallow panting breaths, rested her head back, her eyes half closed, her hands hanging limp. Susannah was telling Nonen what had happened when Wenonga and Eli returned.

"See!" burst out Nonen, rushing at Eli, "see what that trash of yours has done to her! Your father told you what she was!"

Stunned, Eli backed away, staring at Supaya but saying nothing.

Wenonga came to Supaya at once and studied her closely, his flaming eyes intent and professional. He laid his wide heavy hand gently on her forehead, examined the cuts and bruises on her face, then put his fingertips lightly on her belly, feeling for life within. After a moment's silent concentration, he growled deep in his throat and turned on Eli. "You have caused this!"

"Me! That's crazy! I had nothing to do with it!"

"Do not lie! That girl shames her family! Now she has harmed us, and it is you who have brought this harm upon us!"

Thoroughly frightened, Eli shrank before his father. "Everything is my fault! You brought her here, not me! It was you, this time! You!"

Enraged, Wenonga started toward Eli, but Nonen spoke up sharply. "Stop! You'll make everything worse. We must help her!"

Susannah, embarrassed at hearing private matters, spoke softly to Nonen, "I will go now. I'll come back later to see how she is," and left quietly by the back door.

Eli, unable to withstand his father's furious stare, turned and left the house.

Nonen washed Supaya and combed her hair. Wenonga bathed her cuts with an infusion made from the roots of the wild rose, elm, and bitter-root, then applied a plaster made from the crushed leaves of the boneset. Mixing the infusion with spring water, he gave it to her to drink.

Supaya's throat was parched, and she drank gratefully. But soon a restlessness seized her. Gritting her teeth with the effort, she managed to stand up. Nonen reached out to steady her, but Supaya motioned her away. Despite the persistent pain in her side, she began walking back and forth, pausing, breathless, to grip the edge of the table or a chair back when spasms doubled her over. Nonen and Wenonga, quiet and watchful as cats, let her pace.

Though Supaya, preoccupied with the stress of her body, seemed oblivious to her surroundings, her inner perception was painfully sharpened. In the glaring light of humiliation, she saw herself for the stranger she was in this house and among the people of this reserve. Nonen and Wenonga, the very furniture and walls of the house, all had a life of their own together. For her, an alien, they meant confinement, not security. She saw her husband helpless, her marriage, like a cracked bowl, coming apart in her hands. She saw that she was all but alone. Going into the bedroom, she pulled the curtain, shutting out the sight of their faces. She took out the stone bear and cupped it in both hands. Leaning her head against it, she addressed her guardian in an almost silent whisper.

"Grandfather! Help me! I am lost among strangers! My
soul is in anguish! Help me, who am weak and
without hope!

"Great Spirit! You whose courage is undying! Strengthen
my heart or I am lost forever!

"Great Bear! Your spirit is in all things, even one so weak
as I! Help me be worthy of my forefathers!"

By nightfall Supaya knew her child would be born soon—too soon.

Unable to rest, she still paced. Eli had not returned. Wenonga smoked his pipe and kept a watchful eye on Supaya while Nonen made preparations.

She spread a clean quilt on the floor of Supaya's room and placed on it two chairs, four hands apart, and laid a log across the seats.

The birth was slow and difficult. Kneeling between the chairs, Supaya grasped the log and pushed, breathing in short gasps. Her battered, discolored sides pained agonizingly with her straining. Beside her, Nonen, an experienced midwife, wiped her forehead and moistened her lips but would not let her drink. She spoke tersely, encouragingly, telling her when to bear down and when to relax. Finally, her chest braced against the log, Supaya made one tremendous effort, and the baby came. Nonen received it and laid it aside.

"Push!" she commanded, "once more."

Supaya gasped with pain as Nonen pressed down hard on her abdomen.

"There," said Nonen softly, "now you are finished."

Exhausted and dizzy from effort, Supaya clung to the log, resting her wet forehead against it. There was no cry of the newborn, and she knew before Nonen spoke.

"It is a son, stillborn."

At her words, Supaya began to whimper, then to wail, long, drawn-out, anguished cries. Wenonga, who had been excluded during the birth, came at once.

"Let her mourn," he said to Nonen, who was vainly trying to soothe her, "let her mourn!"

At that moment Eli banged open the front door. Hearing Supaya's cries, he staggered to the bedroom and leaned against the door frame, grinning drunkenly. "Cryin', eh? I have jus' what she needs! What we all need!" He held up a nearly empty bottle and lurched forward. "This'll do it!" He almost fell over Supaya, kneeling on the quilt, her forehead to the floor. Wenonga grasped him and dragged him back. Nonen, furious, twisted the bottle from his hand.

"What evil have you brought into this house! You bring shame upon us all with your ignorance! You have no right to enter where there is birth! You will be polluted by this blood! You will harm her and yourself! Never," she spat at him, still held by his

113

father's powerful hand, "never bring this," shaking the bottle at him, "into this house again! You hear me? Never!" Turning to the window, she emptied the remaining liquor outside.

Suddenly enraged, Eli wrenched himself free and slapped Nonen across the face, knocking her back against the wall. "Who do you think you are, old woman! Don' give me orders! Neither of you! Jus' a couple dumb Indians!" Wenonga reached for him, but Eli swung around, stumbled over Supaya, and grabbing one of the chairs, raised it up and slammed it into the wall. "An' you!" sneering at Supaya, "whyncha get up! Get up and go knock old Marie down! You make fuss over nothin'! Nothin'!" He tilted unsteadily toward her, his eyes glazed. "That's what I am! Nothin'! But if I'm nothin', what are you?" Peering at Supaya, he nearly fell, but Wenonga hauled him back onto his feet. Eli, pulling to get free, yelled at Supaya. "You aren't too good t'marry me and have 'nother man's kid, are you! Not you!" Struggling with Wenonga, he lost his footing and crashed down on the splintered chair. Awkwardly he got onto his knees, oblivious to a bleeding gash in his arm from the split wood. Dazed and weaving, he pointed at Supaya. "I know what you want! You're no diff'rent! You're ... le' go! Lemme go!" Wenonga, twisting his arm behind him, forced him to his feet, propelled him out of the bedroom and out of the house.

"Go sleep in the barn!" growled Wenonga, thrusting him away with such disgust and anger that Eli stumbled forward, arms flung out, and fell face down on the ground. Wenonga looked down at him. "That's where you belong!"

When Wenonga returned to the bedroom, Supaya was sitting on the bed and Nonen was wrapping the dead infant in a blanket.

"Give him to me," said Wenonga, holding out both hands. The infant's face was tiny and wrinkled, the thin skin over its closed eyes delicately veined, its mouth slightly puckered. "So," said Wenonga, his voice deadly quiet, "Marie Able did this. She will be sorry." He handed the baby back to Nonen. Looking at Supaya, distraught and exhausted, Wenonga remembered the charge her father had laid on him. "Do not fear," he said. "She will never attack you again." Then he turned and went to his own room.

Nonen brought Supaya hot tea and scone. "Eat this, then sleep," she urged. "I will be back soon."

There was a spring in the woods where Nonen and others went for water of special purity. And it was to the path leading to this spring that Nonen went, carrying a shovel and the dead infant and afterbirth wrapped up securely together. The sky was just beginning to lighten, and she moved swiftly, like a gray shadow. She did not wish to be seen, for the preacher would be displeased and demand a Christian burial. At the point where several paths merged into one and many women passed, she dug a grave and laid the bundle in it. Then she knelt and whispered.

"Great Father! Hear me! See this pure and helpless soul!
Forced into life too soon!
"Great Spirit! Giver of all life! Give this soul life again!
Help it to be reborn!"

Then she filled in the grave and tamped down the earth, treading over it and switching the dirt with a branch to hide all traces.

When she reached home, the lamp still burned, but Supaya had fallen asleep sitting sideways, her battered face sad in repose. Nonen saw with satisfaction that the cup and plate were empty. Gently she lifted Supaya's legs up onto the bed, covered her with a blanket, and turned off the lamp. Then she pulled her rocking chair squarely into the bedroom doorway so no one could enter. Tomorrow she would clean the room. She settled into the chair and rested her head back with a sigh. Her face ached where Eli had hit her, but far worse, her arms felt empty. She had hoped to rock a baby to sleep. She pulled her shawl close, down over her face. Now she must rest so she could care for Supaya, and then, perhaps . . . .

CHAPTER TEN

Marie's arm hurt; it was swollen and inflamed. But she got no sympathy from Eli. When she unwrapped it and showed it to him, expecting he would comfort her, he shrugged and offered her a drink. Resentfully, she rebandaged it and refused the drink, knowing it angered him when she refused.

"You didn't make her drink when you brought her here!"

Eli focused his bloodshot eyes on her. "So you spied on us!" His lip curled in contempt. "Sneak!" He had not been home in a week, not since Wenonga had thrown him out. Nor had he been sober. He had bottles hidden in the barn and one in the rockfall on the bluff. He sat slumped against the stone, glowering at Marie, seeing in her round, petulant face a threat to his happiness with Supaya.

Putting aside her resentment, Marie knelt beside him. "Eli," she said earnestly, "what do you want with her! You don't have to stay here! We could go away, together! We could take Jimmy with us. We could go to Wellston and you could get a job." She laid her hand on his arm. "Please!" she begged, "let's go now!"

"A job!" he said bitterly. He threw off her hand. "Don't talk stupid. Nobody will give me a job! Think I haven't tried?" His voice rose angrily and he waved the bottle at her. "What can I do? Tell me! You and your plans! Tell me what I'm fit to do!" He leaned toward her threateningly, raising his hand sideways as if to strike her. As she drew back, he said spitefully, "You, now. You have something you can sell. Why don't you go sell it and get off this stinking reserve!" Her eyes filled with tears, and he turned away, disgusted. "Ah, go 'way. If you're not going to drink, go 'way."

Knowing further talk was useless, she got to her feet. But as she was leaving he looked after her and said with a malicious smile. "You better be careful. My father knows it was you beat her up, and he's angry."

Walking back through the woods, Marie held her throbbing arm against her plump waist and thought about the rashness of her act—attacking the daughter-in-law of the shaman! What a fool she'd been! She should never have let Betty goad her into it! Wanting Eli back so bad, wanting to hurt his wife and drive her away, she had not thought until Eli's words reminded her that she'd brought on herself the wrath of Wenonga. The realization of what she had done, the danger she was in, wiped out all other worries. Eli wouldn't help. Nor could her own family. No one could help her. Though the day was warm, a tremor ran through her and a hard knot of fear felt like a weight just under her breastbone.

Hearing a sound behind her, she turned, hoping it was Eli, but there was no one, only the shine of sunlight on leaves. Alarmed, she walked on, faster. Again she heard something, a soft rustle in the underbrush. Nervously she turned, hoping to see someone, anyone, but again there was no one, only the sun-dappled leaves, unnaturally still. There had been a breeze. Now the woods were deadly still, hostile. She felt eyes were watching her. She went on, walking fast, almost running, certain that she heard a light, panting breath behind her. Panicked, she broke into a headlong run, snagging her clothes, stumbling over roots, running into branches that scratched her face and arms. Heart pounding, she suddenly emerged onto a road. She saw a man and a woman with a bundle, strangers, walking along. They walked straight on, not speaking or turning their heads. Not daring to look back or to pass them, she forced herself to a walk that kept her behind them until she reached the house where she lived with her father and stepmother. She would not go into the woods again. Not alone.

That night as she was falling asleep, she heard a dog barking in the distance. The barking came closer and grew louder, a deep-throated, powerful bark. As it came nearer, she listened with growing fear, her nerves tight. All at once the barking ceased. She waited, but all was quiet. She finally relaxed and was closing her eyes when suddenly, just outside her window, there was a long, low growl. Instantly, she was wide awake. Crouching on her bed, she

117

slowly raised her head, peered over the windowsill, and screamed in terror. There, as if waiting for her to appear, was a huge dog. His white fur glowed in the dark, luminous as the moon; his hackles rose thick and bristling along his back and neck. His eyes gleamed red with rage, and as she stared, hypnotized, his black lip curled back and he lunged at her, snarling, his sharp teeth snapping together. Marie tried to scream, but no sound came. Shaking with fear, expecting him to crash through the window, she dropped down and cowered under the bedclothes. There was another vicious snarl and a long growl. Then the barking began again, circling round and round the house. After what seemed a long time, the barking receded and finally faded away.

The next day, pale and shaken, Marie went outside and searched the ground. But there had been no recent rain, and the earth near the house was hard and dry.

Her father and stepmother were disturbed. They looked at her uneasily and wouldn't speak until she left the room. Then she heard them whispering. They knew, as everyone on the reserve now did, of her attack on Wenonga's daughter-in-law.

Later that day, Jimmy ran into the house, frightened and crying for his mother. A big dog had come after him, growling and snapping at him, a big white dog, and he held up his hand even with the top of his head. Aghast, Marie clutched him close and looked pleadingly at her father. His eyes like stones, he stared back at her, then left the room without a word.

That night there was a storm. Great jagged streaks of light split the black clouds, lighting the earth in lurid flashes. Thunder crashed and reverberated over the bluffs. Rain blew in gusts, drumming like hail against the windows, drowning out all other sounds. When the lightning receded to incandescent gleams far out over the lake and the thunder to a soft, distant rumble, the barking began again.

Angrier and more aggressive than before, the dog stalked round and round the house, a persistent, deadly hunter. He stopped by Marie's window, his bark deepening to a throaty snarl and then a long, implacable growl. Marie lay rigid in her bed, scarcely breathing, listening to scratching and snuffling alongside the house. Only thin boards separated her from those powerful jaws. Suddenly there was a jarring impact as the dog flung himself against the house. Paralyzed with horror, Marie felt the wall shudder and heard sounds of splitting wood as the huge animal attacked again and again. Then he moved off, still barking, as before, until his voice faded away.

A pall lay over the house. Her father and stepmother were speechless, their eyes bright with fear. Jimmy clung to her, refusing to let go his hold on her skirt. Outside they found impressed in the damp earth huge paw prints, larger than any they had ever seen. The wall outside Marie's room was damaged, the boards splintered where they had begun to split and bend inward.

Her father drew his wife aside, and they conferred privately. But Marie did not wait to be asked to leave. She packed a bag and asked her father to take her and Jimmy to Wellston in the wagon.

They rode in strained, chilly silence despite the bright sunlight that cast along the roadside a skimming shadow of horse and wagon. When they passed through areas where the woods grew close to the road, Marie watched fearfully. Once, smothering an impulse to cry out, she thought she glimpsed the sun gleaming on a white form slipping through the underbrush. She didn't see it again, but just before they turned out of the reserve onto the main road, they heard behind them, startling in its nearness, a deep, strong, aggressive barking.

The horse laid back its ears. Her father struck out with his whip. Marie held Jimmy tight and pressed her fist against her mouth as they moved faster down the road and the barking gradually faded.

CHAPTER ELEVEN

In old moccasins and a light cotton dress, Supaya walked along a gravel road on her way to meet Susannah. She and Soos were going out to pick sweet grass to dry for trimming boxes and making mats. The day was good for it. There'd been no rain for a week and the fields on either side shimmered under a hot, hazy July sun. Preoccupied with her thoughts, she didn't turn when she heard a wagon coming but kept to the side of the road. As the horse clopped past, trailing a cloud of dust behind it, a voice said, "Whoa, boy," and then, "Good morning, Mrs. Red Sky. Can I give you a lift?"

Supaya glanced up, her eyes flat. "I am going only a short way."

"A short lift, then," insisted Jess Fallon, smiling. He reached out to give her a hand up, but she ignored it. Rather than argue, she stepped up lightly and settled herself with her basket on her lap, her eyes straight ahead.

He snapped the reins and the horse stepped out. They rode in silence, he stealing glances at her as they went along. She had been in for supplies several times that summer when the cuts and bruises were still livid on her face, and he had felt concern for her. He had seen her pass the loafers outside disdainfully and turn with cold indifference from the curious eyes of women in the store. He couldn't know that she had accepted her position as a stranger in the community in addition to being the daughter-in-law of a feared shaman, and that now she imposed her own distance between herself and others. But he did observe that no one presumed to comment or question her. He saw that now her face was healed—Wenonga was a skilled doctor. And she was much thinner—too thin, he thought—though he admired the sharp, clean line of her cheek and jaw. But he missed her liveliness. Her spirit seemed to have fled, leaving only a shadow of her former self.

"Here," she said suddenly, with a nod of her head. She got down, said a brief thank you, and walked away.

Jess looked after her, noticing she wore no comb but had coiled her hair into a knot low on her neck. And despite her apparent lack of animation, her step was vigorous, her carriage as proud as when he had first seen her on Stone Island. Given a little more time, he thought, she would be all right. He shook the reins, feeling unaccountably happier.

When Supaya and Susannah had filled their baskets with sweet grass, they sat down near the stream to rest. Supaya lay back, her whole view the tops of wild meadow grasses and a vast blue sky with scattered puffs of clouds. The air was filled with the pungent, spicy aroma of weed and wildflower. Grasshoppers chirred and leaped, and a cloud of gnats hovered, moving mysteriously together in the radiant heat. The earth was solid and warm under her, and Supaya sighed, smiling faintly.

"It's nice here, Soos. Here I feel at home." When she had first set out to look for sweet grass and had found this meadow, she had been struck by its similarity to the one in her dream, and she had seemed to hear again the soft laughter of her mother. She felt at peace here, warmed alike by sun and memories.

Susannah would not presume to advise, but she and Supaya had become, during the past few weeks, good enough friends for her to ask, "Couldn't you have your own home, Suppy, you and Eli?"

"There is no empty house," said Supaya. In her rambles around the reserve, she had seen several abandoned houses, but their windows and doors were gone, their roofs caved in, and weeds grew up through the floors.

"Sarah," called Susannah, shading her eyes to look after her small daughter. "Come back."

Sarah came, her plump knees pushing through the grass, holding up a fistful of wild daisies. Delighted to find Supaya lying down, she plumped across her middle and offered her bouquet. "For you!"

"Sarah," chided Soos, "get off!"

"No, no," said Supaya, "I'm not sore any longer." She was fond of Sarah, and catching her under her arms, bounced and twisted her from side to side while the child giggled and went limp, amused at being flopped about.

"You could ask Mr. Toomis. He might know of one."

Supaya had met Mr. Toomis her first day on the reserve, when she had taken him her paper of transfer and shown him her marriage certificate. A younger man than Jackson, and much pleasanter, he had invited her to sit down while he recorded names and dates.

"If you wish, I'll go with you to speak to him," promised Soos.

For the first few days after the stillbirth, Nonen had insisted Supaya rest, and had brought her food, tempting her with fruit and soft, white cheese. For a week she had guarded the room every night should Eli return. She tried to comfort Supaya, whispering that she had buried her son where he might yet have a chance for life, if not with her, with someone else.

But Supaya, aching for the life she had felt within her, for the child that would have been hers and Kineu's, cried at night, eyes staring into the dark, while hot tears wet her cheeks and ran down into her hair. During the day when Nonen allowed her to get up, she sat in Nonen's rocking chair and thought of what she could do to make money. Most of all, she wanted her own house, to be independent and free of Wenonga's constant presence. For that, she needed some money. She could not depend on Eli, who had not returned, and could not bear being dependent on Wenonga. She had her quills from home, but she had no birchbark.

One day Nonen offered to get her a supply of bark. Shortly after Nonen left, Wenonga came home. He was surprised to find Supaya alone, and leaned over her ostensibly to examine the healing of her face. He brought his face so close to hers that she felt his breath warm on her cheek. His red-veined eyes gazed compellingly not at the healing skin, which he touched gently with his fingers, but into her eyes. Supaya stared back defiantly, her head pressed against the chair back, then, as he persisted, his face almost touching hers, she turned her head sharply away.

"Your cuts are healing," he said softly, and laid his hand on her belly, moving it caressingly back and forth.

Repelled and frightened, Supaya pushed his hand aside and sprang to her feet. "But your son," she exclaimed, "has not re-

turned! Where is my husband? Surely, it is your duty to find him."
Wenonga frowned. Seeing him hesitate, she said scathingly, "My
father would think it strange I should come this far to marry a man
who disappeared! If he is gone, I should return to my family!"

Wenonga, balked, knew she spoke the truth. "He is here . . .
in the woods, the barn. You have not been well."

"Now is when I need him most," said Supaya sharply. "I do
not believe he is in the barn. I think he is gone and I must return
home."

Wenonga glared, but she stood firm, masking her fear with
anger.

"I will get him," growled Wenonga and strode out of the
house.

Supaya went at once to her room, opened her trunk, and
from her great-grandfather's medicine bag took out a very small
birchbark box. She removed the lid and sniffed at the powdered
roots, bark, and fungus inside, smelling faintly of wild leeks. "You
will be among strangers," Quayo had said, "and might need to
protect yourself." Satisfied, Supaya covered it and put it inside the
trunk where she could reach it easily at night.

Nonen returned with strips of bark and a promise of more.
Supaya was busy cutting them into pieces when Wenonga returned.
Behind him came Eli, stepping as carefully as though the floor were
moving beneath his feet. He glanced quickly at Nonen, who was
ladling stew into bowls. The bruise from his blow was gone, but the
memory of it was in her eyes as she watched him slump into a chair.
He propped his elbows on the table and rested his head in his
hands.

No one spoke. They began eating the stew, and after a bit,
Eli, who still had not faced Supaya, began to eat also. Observing
him from across the table, Supaya saw he had difficulty keeping his
spoon steady. His face was gray, his shoulders sagged. She could
not forget his violence toward herself and Nonen, but he was her
husband, and seeing him thus stirred her sympathy. Somehow they
must make a life together; somehow she must help him.

"You need a bath," she said.

The unexpectedness of her remark made Nonen laugh. Even
Wenonga was wryly amused. Eli, who thought to hear only recrimi-
nations, looked up in bleary-eyed surprise.

Nonen began at once heating water for the tub. She was
grateful for Supaya's matter-of-fact acceptance of Eli's return, for it

seemed to her an assurance that after a bad time their lives would happily resume. Wenonga, smoking his pipe and watching Supaya making boxes, did not think so.

That night, Supaya took out the little medicine box, removed the lid, and placed the box on top of the trunk on her side of the bed.

Eli, still puzzled by her apparent unconcern over his behavior, asked what she had.

"It is a protection," she answered coolly, undoing her hair, "against anyone who would harm me. Get in bed. I will turn out the lamp." In bed he moved to embrace her, but she pushed him firmly away. "I am not ready," she said. "You need rest. Tomorrow we must talk." And she turned on her side so she could see in the dark the glow given off by Quayo's medicine.

At her invitation the next morning to come for a walk, Eli's assurance began to return. He thought she meant to go to the bluff, that she was ready to forget what had happened. But Supaya went only as far as the meadow, where they could speak without being overheard, and sat down, facing the house and barn so she could see if anyone approached.

"Eli," she said, "we should have a house of our own."

"A house of . . . ! Why?" he asked, mystified. "We don't need a house. We are fine where we are."

"We do need a house! We should not live off your father."

Eli stared. "How . . . I can't get a house! I have no money!" Immediately restless, he stood up, wanting to go.

"You have no job," corrected Supaya quietly. "You get a job. Then we will have money. Then we can get a house."

Desperately, Eli looked about at the rocks and grass as if searching for an answer. Seeing her waiting for a reply, he drew a deep breath, trying to control his nervousness, then spoke slowly and distinctly. "I cannot get a job. There is no steady work for me on the reserve. And in town the whites will not give me a job."

"But you went to school! You can read and write!"

He turned on her angrily. "They don't pay for knowing how to read and write! Hear what I say! I have tried!" He had said all this before, to himself, to his father and Nonen, to Marie, and now to her, his wife, whom he could not support. He knew he had been cheated, robbed of identity. He was at home nowhere, and years of humiliation and fruitless grappling with the problem had drained him of stamina. Mulling it over was painful. He wanted only to turn

124

his face away, to forget. "I need a drink," he said and started for the barn.

"No! Please, Eli! Wait! If you can't get a job, then we will hunt and fish. We could use Wenonga's boat and I will help you! We could make our own garden, and I can sell boxes. We could make enough that way, I know we could!"

Exasperated, he stared at her. "I'm no fisherman! Or hunter. Don't you understand! I'm nothing! Ask my father if you don't believe me. He is a great hunter. He even brought me home a wife I can't support—and a child!"

Out of his shame, he wanted to hurt her, but she was angered. Before his taunt had been that of a drunken man. Now he was sober. She regarded him with hostility. "*My* son," she said coldly, "is dead. *Yours* is alive."

Eli showed his teeth in a sharp grin. "Come on, we both need a drink."

"No."

"Come on, I said! What kind of wife are you? You do what I say!"

Giving him a scornful look, Supaya started for the house. She had tried and failed. If he would not help, she would work alone. As she passed him, Eli grabbed her arm. She spun around, eyes blazing with anger. "Go find Marie! She'll drink with you!"

"Marie?" Eli grinned again. "She's gone! Wenonga saw to that. He protects his own. You should be careful!"

That she must be careful of Wenonga Supaya already knew. Why couldn't Eli see that she needed him as he needed her! "Eli," she said urgently, "please do not drink! You pollute yourself! You waste what skill you have and become no better than the white man. I will not drink with you ever. And I will not be as a wife to you drunk."

But Eli only shrugged, and she left him standing in the meadow.

The need to make a living now occupied all Supaya's waking thoughts. Her days were filled with gardening, preserving food, making boxes, and weaving table mats of dried, pungent sweet grass to sell at the general store. When she lay down at night, her grief, buried during the day, came out unbidden, stealing over her heart, and with it worry over Eli and Wenonga.

Since their talk in the meadow, Eli had been sleeping in the barn, and one night, as Supaya undressed, she felt a prickling across her back. Turning swiftly she saw Wenonga's shaggy head at the window. His face was shadowed, but his eyes, reflecting the dim lamplight, gleamed as he stared in at her. Instantly she turned out the lamp, then stood trembling, ears straining for the faintest sound. She heard the front door softly open and close. She waited as if frozen, eyes fixed on the dark, curtained doorway. But the curtain didn't stir. After a long time, Supaya got silently into bed, lying so she could see the pale greenish glow from the birch box.

Early the next morning a man came for Wenonga. His child was ill. He begged that Wenonga cure him. At once Wenonga began preparations, ordering Nonen to make him a sweat lodge.

When Eli came in from the barn, Supaya was waiting for him. After her fright of the night before, she resolved to try once more. "Eli, today we can use your father's boat. We can go fishing, you and I."

His head ached, but he was sober. The morning air had a fine freshness and Supaya, her eyes pleading, took his hand. Grudgingly, Eli agreed. He knew locations where his father fished, but, he warned her, "I don't know the currents. We could get caught in a storm." The day was clear and dry; a storm seemed unlikely.

"Besides," said Supaya happily, "we won't go too far out."

Wenonga's boat was a good one, and Supaya, who had not been fishing in a year, was happy to be out on the lake again. She pretended not to notice Eli's awkwardness with the oars. That he had come at all she saw as encouraging. He would learn, she was certain. They paralleled the coast, rowing northward past a part of the reserve Supaya had never seen. When they reached a narrow bay, Supaya took over the oars and Eli let out the net.

By midday they moored the boat and walked along the narrow, rocky beach, a light lake breeze offsetting the strong sun on their backs. Being away from the house and working successfully together had driven off the anger and tension of past weeks and made them feel gay, almost shy of one another. They smiled at each other sideways as they had used to do, then laughed and clasped hands. They searched for a spot to sit down and eat the food Supaya had packed. Halfway up the cliff was an inviting grassy ledge. They climbed up the pebbly incline, holding onto bushes and exposed roots. Clowning, exaggerating their breathlessness, they flopped down on hands and knees and then onto their backs, side by side. They turned their heads and gazed at each other, their eyes bright, questioning. Seeing her face soften, her lips part, Eli pulled her close against him.

"This," he said, smiling, "is the kind of fishing I like." Supaya, wanting him and seeing him as he had been when they were first married, caressed him, kissed him hungrily, her body, craving the touch of his hands, giving itself completely, mindlessly, in its desire to once more come alive.

When the sun lowered behind the bluff, casting the beach below into shadow but still sparkling on the water offshore, they came down the slope. They were less giddy but happier: each content in himself and with the other. Supaya saw her lover returned, gentle and affectionate. He would learn to be a good fisherman and a skillful hunter. Together they would make their own home. And Eli saw the Supaya of months before but relieved of her burden and freer in her passion; a young wife who, having been upset, had a fit of temper and now was once again tractable and docile.

Supaya took the oars as Eli hauled in the net and extracted the fish, clumsily at first but with increasing skill despite his fumbling buffoonery. Their catch was a good one, and after putting some trout and whitefish aside to be split and dried, Eli sold the rest and came home with money in his pocket.

The next day Wenonga was performing his cure. Again they used his boat and brought home a sizable catch. This time Eli clowned less, but there was a satisfied gleam in his eye as he surveyed the drying rack hung with fish.

That evening Supaya settled down to do some quill embroidery. Laying the quills out in separate piles according to length and color, she began the painstaking work, using the fine awl Quayo had made for her.

Eli paced restlessly about the room, jingling the coins in his pocket. He stopped by the table, picked up one of the finished boxes, turned it about indifferently, and dropped it. "There's a party at Joe Martin's tonight," he said. "Why don't you stop that and come."

Supaya carefully inserted a quill and pulled it tight. "If I finish this box," she said, "I will have three to sell tomorrow. Then Soos is coming with me to see Mr. Toomis. He may know of a vacant house." She glanced at him. "Maybe you should come?"

Eli was annoyed. "No. Not me." He thought she had given

in, that she would forget about moving from his father's house, and he frowned irritably. Catching Nonen's suspicious eyes on him, he turned away and stood by the door.

"I'll need more quills soon," said Supaya. "Maybe tomorrow you could get me a porcupine."

"Don't nag me!" exclaimed Eli vehemently. Seeing the hurt in Supaya's face, he said sarcastically, "Oh sure. I'll go out and shoot one right out of a tree!" Supaya bent quickly over her work. After a brief, strained silence, Eli muttered, "I'm going to Joe's."

Nonen poured Supaya and herself a cup of tea and sat down opposite her. "You want to move?" she asked, her wide face solemn.

Supaya heard her disappointment and put aside her work. "Not because of you," she said earnestly. "You have been as a mother to me. But . . ." she hesitated, searching Nonen's face, reluctant in Wenonga's house to speak his name, ". . . he," emphasizing the word, "he spies on me. At night. And when you are not here he . . . comes too close to me."

Nonen understood at once. "It was that way when my daughter lived here, before she married and moved into my little hut." She pressed her wide lips together and shook her head. "Eli, he is not strong. . . ."

"When Eli is here, it is better. But I hoped . . . away from his father, in his own house . . . Eli would be . . . happier, more able . . ."

Nonen did not reply to that but drank her tea. After a bit, her face set and threatening, she said, "If he bothers you again, you call me. I am not afraid of him."

The next morning when Supaya spoke to Eli, he mumbled, rolled his head crossly, and refused to open his eyes. Realizing he had been drinking, Supaya pulled the curtain across the door, took her boxes, and walked to the store.

Mrs. Fallon, a trim, neat woman with a small waist, said she would have to call her husband. Her blonde hair, braided in two thick plaits, crossed the top of her head like a coronet. Her queenly manner, pale blue eyes, and almost invisible blonde lashes set her apart from everyone around her, as though she had just stepped out of the fairy-tale illustrations on the large Keen's mustard tins lining the shelves behind her. Like the princess seated on a bank of flowers, encircled by gold scrolls and twining lilies, her face was smooth, delicately tinted, her eyes touched with sweet condescension. She stood aside, then moved to another customer as Jess greeted Supaya and gave his attention to the boxes.

He examined each one, turned it about, removed and replaced the lids. Two were round with the quills arranged in a geometric pattern, the third, round with a leaf design on the lid. "You made these," he said, more statement than question. "I saw your work before, at Mr. Bonnet's." He saw the flicker of surprise in her eyes. "They're beautiful. Fine, distinctive workmanship. If they're for sale, I would like to buy them."

Jess counted the money into her hand. "I'll be happy to buy any others you might make," he added, and giving her a brisk smile, went on to another customer.

Supaya fingered some bolts of cotton print and looked wistfully at a pair of long lisle stockings. But more than she wanted them, she wanted to take all her money home, like a trophy, to prove to Eli what could be done. With the money from the fish, it was a beginning. He would see now how well they could work together.

Eli had just gotten up. "Did you have a good time at Joe's?" asked Supaya. Eli, splashing water over his face and head, mumbled as he rubbed himself with the towel. "Eli, look! I sold the boxes!" Eager for his reaction, she spread the money out on the table.

Nonen clasped her hands and exclaimed with pleasure. Eli raised his eyebrows in comic surprise. "That much for those boxes?"

"Yes, and he said he would buy any more I made! You see how we can manage?" she asked, striving to arouse his cooperation. "With this and the money from the fish, we already have a start." Eli nodded as he casually picked up the money and put it in his pocket. "I'll need more bark and more quills. You'll have to go hunting now."

"Sure," said Eli.

That afternoon Soos went with Supaya to see Mr. Toomis. Like Jackson's, his was a fine stone house with a wide verandah, and the office was in the large front corner room. Mrs. Toomis was not at home, but Gerald, a quiet, red-haired young man, took them hospitably into his office, which, like himself, had a comfortable, easy air. The windows were curtained and a small rug lay in front of the desk. He was sympathetic with Supaya's request for a house, but the only vacant ones were the derelicts she had already seen. If any were vacated, he promised to let her know.

Supaya began at once making more boxes, working in the evenings. Nonen was piecing together sections of old blankets as filling for a quilt. Wenonga, returned from the celebration of his cure, had a fine new blanket hanging from a wall peg and was filling his pipe from a fresh supply of tobacco.

"Abram was looking for you since morning," he said to Eli, who stood by the front door. "He wanted you to fix his harness."

Supaya, whose supply of quills was almost gone, looked up eagerly. "Were you hunting? Did you catch a porcupine?"

"No," said Eli irritably, "I was not hunting!" After a moment he muttered, "I'll go speak to Abram," and left the house.

Out of pride, Supaya went on working, concealing her disappointment. Eli was not responding as she had hoped. He'd been coming home late, and when she proposed fishing again, he'd refused, saying he was not a fisherman and would not go fishing every day.

Wenonga left early the next morning with a purpose of his own, saying nothing to either Nonen or Supaya, who were preparing to make soap. Nonen had already rendered the fat in a large kettle over the outdoor fire when she discovered she had very little lye left.

"Eli can bring us some from the store," said Supaya. Eli was just getting dressed, having slept late again.

"Sure," he said, "I'll get it. Give me some money."

Supaya stared. "Give you . . . what do you mean? You have money."

He brushed past her and went to the wash bench in the lean-to to comb his hair, stooping slightly before the mirror, his elbows angled out. Supaya touched his shoulder. "Eli?"

"I said, give me the money and I'll get the lye!" he exclaimed, exasperated.

"But you have money," insisted Supaya, suddenly alarmed, "all of it! The money for the fish and for the boxes!"

Eli swung round angrily. "I don't have any money! Why don't you ever listen to what I say! I don't have any money!"

Supaya was stunned. "What happened to it? What did you do with it?"

"A man needs money! I don't have to tell you what I did with it! It's gone, that's all!" His indignation giving him courage, Eli shouted at her. "You're my wife! You have no right to question me!" Then, unable to face her stricken expression, he said self-righteously, "I'm getting out of this house!" He turned to find Nonen blocking the door.

She regarded him scornfully, her eyes cold as Wenonga's. "You disgrace your family," she spat at him, then stepped aside contemptuously, inviting him to go.

Smothering her impulse to cry, Supaya went to Susannah's and borrowed some lye. Together she and Nonen made the soap, pouring the greasy, gray-white mixture into shallow tins which they set in the lean-to to harden. As they worked, Supaya said little, but by the time they finished, her wish to cry had changed to an angry determination to discover what Eli had done with the money.

She went straight to the barn. Nellie was out grazing in the meadow, and the barn, a small building with two stalls, was empty. Supaya began a rapid search, reaching into baskets hung from wall pegs, into the storage bin, into Nellie's manger. There, beneath the fodder, she found an unopened bottle. Behind two bales of hay stacked against the wall, she found another. Wedged between bin and wall, she found a third.

She carried them back to the house and without a word opened them. As Nonen watched, she poured the contents on the ground, and with grim humor, placed the empty bottles in a row by the back door. Then, eyes thoughtfully narrowed, she turned to Nonen, not really seeing her. She was thinking that none of the three bottles had been opened and Eli, when he left, had cut across the meadow toward the woods.

Nonen understood the depth of Supaya's anger and the direction of her thoughts. When Supaya struck off across the meadow, Nonen, seeing her straight back and angry stride, thought of fetching Susannah, but changed her mind. Wenonga would be home soon and she would speak to him.

Supaya headed straight for the bluff. She expected to find Eli there, with an empty bottle, but as she approached, she heard drunken voices, exclamations, and laughter. When she came around the end of the rockfall, she saw a girl, down on her hands and knees, her skirts tumbled forward over her shoulders and head, giggling as Eli, his arms clasped around her middle, his trousers down around his knees, was thrusting himself vigorously against her plump, naked buttocks.

131

For one moment Supaya stood horrified; then, seized by blind fury, she cried out, and looking for a weapon, saw an empty bottle. Her cry shocked Eli and the girl. Turning, they tumbled over in a heap. Eli rolled sideways, striving to sit up. The girl, struggling with her skirts, saw Supaya smash the bottle against a rock and screamed as Supaya came at them, grasping the jagged bottle like a knife.

Stupified, Eli shrank back against the ground, one arm raised to shield his face as Supaya, wild-eyed, stood above him, her arm on the point of a powerful, downward thrust. The girl was still screaming, waving her arms, frantically trying to ward Supaya off. She was, Supaya suddenly perceived, Marie's friend, Betty.

"You!" Supaya exclaimed, then saw, hanging loosely in the girl's tangled hair, a tortoiseshell comb. Smiling grimly, Supaya commanded, "Take that comb out of your hair!" But the girl continued to scream and flail her arms. Eli half rose, started to speak, but Supaya thrust the bottle at him. "Stay down! You! Take that comb out of your hair!"

This time the girl heard, and with shaking, fumbling fingers drew out the comb.

"Stand up! Stand! Now put that comb on the ground and stomp on it! Harder!"

Eyes rolling with fright, the girl obeyed, frantically stomping the comb into pieces.

"Now go! Fast!" Supaya advanced, jabbing the bottle at her as the girl, screaming at each thrust, retreated. "Don't ever come near him again or you will be sorry! Go! And," she added maliciously, "remember Marie!"

Sobbing, blubbering, the girl turned, fell over a rock, scrambled to her feet and ran.

Eli got up unsteadily, bracing himself against the boulder. His head hung forward, and he stared dully at Supaya from under his brows.

Her initial burst of rage having spent itself, Supaya looked down at the broken bottle and in sudden revulsion threw it from her, far out over the bluff. After a moment, they both heard the faintest shatter of sound.

Eli waited, uncertain what to expect, drained of all initiative. Supaya, in reaction to her violent anger, was overcome by a trembling weakness. Her breathing was hard as if she'd been running. She looked at Eli and saw that he was waiting for her to speak, that he had no strength left, that he was empty. Suddenly, in the bright sunlight, a chill struck her. Shivering, she crossed her arms tightly against herself. She sought to speak to him, and her lips moved, searching for words, but she could find none. Finally, hopelessly, she turned and walked away.

When she had gone, Eli raised his head and looked out over the expanse before him. In the still, limpid air, gulls veered and floated, rising and falling, their wings flashing white against the distant palisade, whose sheer rockface glowed reddish-purple in the strong sunlight. Below, the clear waters of the bay glistened with light, deepening to the rich blue of the lake. Far out was a toylike steamer trailing a tiny banner of smoke.

Overwhelmed by this vast world in which he had no place, bereft of all hope, Eli sank to his knees on the ground. He could not bear what he saw. He could not bear himself. Bending forward, he crossed his arms on the earth before him and rested his head against them, shutting out the light, withdrawing into the darkness of his despair.

Wenonga returned, and seeing the empty bottles standing by the door, needed no explanation from Nonen. Together, they were waiting when Supaya, heartsick and disoriented, came across the meadow. Full of sympathy, Nonen stepped forward to meet her. But Wenonga, with a wide, complacent smile, held out to her two large, plump porcupines.

Supaya stared, then put out her hand and waved them away. She tried to speak, but her throat constricted and tears filled her eyes. She turned her back so they should not see her weakness, but they had seen.

Wenonga laid the porcupines on the ground beside her and went inside. Nonen, her hand on Supaya's shoulder, said softly, "Take them, Suppy, take them."

Sobbing, Supaya shook her head.

But Nonen urged her again. "Take them. They are for you. Pull the quills, and when you finish, I will make us all a fine stew." Then she went inside.

Through tear-blurred eyes, Supaya looked down at the porcupines' limp, spiny bodies. She too was limp, drained of emotion, of anger and of what she now knew was a vain, unreasonable hope. She was done with hoping. Relying solely on her guardian, she would do whatever she had to do, matter-of-factly, and the two porcupines were facts. Sitting down cross-legged, her back against the lean-to, Supaya began pulling out quills. She worked calmly, steadily. Her hands were soon scratched and bleeding, but beside her the pile of quills grew.

CHAPTER TWELVE

Supaya sat on a log at the edge of the woods, her old shawl pulled close against the chill of a late fall afternoon. Beneath the trees, the earth was layered with leaves, weathered to shiny brown by the autumn rains. She was returning from Soos', where they had slaughtered a pig, and had stopped, as she often did, to sit down and view her fine stone house, Nonen's "little hut." Supaya smiled at Nonen's calling it so because the house was larger than most, with one bedroom downstairs and two up. Besides the usual black iron stove, it had a fireplace like the one in her father's house, and Supaya, from the moment she entered its empty rooms, had felt at home within its stout walls. She and Eli had lived in it for two years now, ever since Nonen's daughter, Mary, and her husband, John, had transferred back to his reserve in the north.

Mary had come one day to Wenonga's house. Stiff with resentment, she made her announcement. She barely touched the tea Nonen poured for her. Her jealousy of Supaya was such that she spoke bluntly to her mother, who seemed to prefer this stranger to herself. "We are leaving the reserve, transferring back to John's reserve."

Nonen was shocked. "Why? You have a home! John is doing well here."

"His mother needs him. She is not well and *she* doesn't want strangers to do for her."

"But my grandchildren!" exclaimed Nonen, dismayed.

135

"When will I ever see them?" She waited, hoping Mary would invite her to come with them.

But Mary said coolly, "It cannot be helped."

Supaya had excused herself and left the room, not wanting to witness Nonen's pain and embarrassment.

Several days later Mary and John had departed, their bed frames, bedding, and a few chairs piled in their wagon. Their small daughter, perched on the bedding, steadied a crate of chickens. Their son dangled his legs over the back and held a rope tied around their cow's neck. As the horse stepped out, the cow bawled in protest and tossed its head at being pulled along at the horse's pace. Nonen stood at the roadside, her hand raised, the children calling, "Good-bye, Grandma!" She watched them until they were out of sight, but her daughter never turned her head.

The next day Nonen had gone to the agent and transferred ownership of her house to Supaya, to be hers now and after Nonen's death.

Before moving in, Supaya and Eli had given the plastered walls and ceiling a fresh coat of whitewash, and he, with an unusual show of vigor and interest, had repaired the broken table legs and built a new bed frame. The shelves had been left on the wall, and with some boards Gerald Toomis gave Supaya, Eli constructed several more and attached them.

Supaya was now thinking that next spring she would enlarge the garden, putting in more potatoes and pumpkins since she got a good price for them at the store. Suddenly it occurred to her that if Eli were to build a small shack with a pen for chickens on one side and a pigpen on the other, she might buy a few chicks and even a shoat in the spring, as Soos had done, to fatten and slaughter in the fall. Since Eli neither hunted nor fished, their meat supply had been scant during the past two winters. Nonen, when she could do so without rousing Wenonga's resentment, had brought them meat and dried fish. But Supaya, knowing how jealously Wenonga guarded his own stores, always tried to give something in return. This year the garden had done well and Supaya was satisfied with what she had laid away in her own root cellar.

A wisp of smoke curled up from the stack. Eli must be home. He had gone with Wenonga to cut wood for their winter fires. She would speak to Eli about building a small barn and pigpen. When he was occupied, he didn't drink so much and seemed more at peace. She had almost reached the house when she heard her name called and saw Nonen running up the lane, her heavy body unwieldly in its blanket but moving fast. Her distress was apparent, and Supaya hurried to meet her.

"You must come!" gasped Nonen. "Sarah fell into the kettle!"

Aghast, Supaya rushed into the house, snatched the velvet medicine bag from her trunk, explained quickly to Eli, and rushed out again, not waiting for Nonen, who followed more slowly.

Before Supaya reached Soos' house, she could hear wailing and screaming. The neighbor's children, who had been racing about, playing with Sarah, had spread news of the accident. Several old women had already arrived and were stooped over Sarah, who was screaming and thrashing about on the ground. Arguing excitedly over what should be done, they were trying awkwardly to remove her clothing. Soos knelt beside her, sobbing hysterically. Behind them steam rose from the huge black kettle set over a pit fire, the scalding water bubbling around the body of the slaughtered pig. Sarah's father, George, and two other men stood helplessly by, somber and tense, watching the women.

"Soos," said Supaya urgently, shaking her shoulder, "bring scissors and a pan of water." Soos, her eyes unfocused, seemed not to comprehend. "Quickly!" Supaya shook her again, and Soos got to her feet, rushed inside, and returned in a moment with scissors and a basin. The old women stood back, weeping and wailing, as Supaya deftly cut away Sarah's clothes. Using roots and leaves from her medicine bag, Supaya combined some root of the swamp tea plant, *kinnikinnick* leaves, white poplar root, and balm-of-Gilead poplar root, pounded to a pulp, and added enough water to make a strong infusion. Speaking calmly to Sarah, Supaya gently rolled her over and bathed her neck and back with the solution. As she did so, a large section of hair and scalp came off in her hand, exposing the raw, red back of Sarah's head. Soos gasped and fell forward, hiding her face against her knees; the wailing of the women increased in volume. Working rapidly, Supaya ordered Soos to make a bed of cedar boughs in the house and cover it with a clean quilt. More women had arrived and stood about crying and wringing their hands. Others silently watched or helped Supaya by holding Sarah's head and arms as she bathed the burns. Sarah had tripped and fallen backwards into the kettle. Luckily, the pig's body had kept her head from going under, and one of the men, hearing her screams, had grabbed her legs in time to keep the lower part of her body from falling into the scalding water.

When the pallet was ready, Supaya and an old woman carried Sarah inside and laid her face down, her head turned to one side. All the old women filed inside after them and lined up around the walls of the room, their lamentation rising like a chorus. One sank down on her knees and rocked back and forth, her shawl shading her face, keening in a low, sorrowful voice.

Supaya cut short Sarah's remaining hair and gave it to Soos, who put it in a bag with the rest for George to bury. Then Supaya mixed dried lady slipper root in a cup and coaxed Sarah to swallow it, pouring a little at a time into her mouth and massaging her throat to induce her to swallow. "Now cover her just to her waist. I will be back soon."

In a nearby field Supaya gathered plantain leaves. With these she made a warm, wet poultice and spread it over the burned areas. Soos sat on the floor beside the bed, her eyes red, her face strained with fear.

"She will sleep now," said Supaya. She laid her hand comfortingly on Soos' arm. "She will be all right. I'll come back soon and stay with her."

When Supaya returned in the early evening, she brought a jug containing a solution made from the soft inner bark of the basswood tree. Sarah had wakened and was whimpering. Speaking softly to her, Supaya bathed the burns, applied a fresh poultice, and again gave her a sleeping potion.

The old women were still there, now silent spectators. Some had gone and returned with food for Susannah and George. The woman who had been keening, Sarah's grandmother, sat against the wall, her face shadowed by her shawl, but her eyes gleamed in the lamplight, alert to all that Supaya did. Soos, five months pregnant, gripped her hands nervously together, and George stood close beside, his face grim.

Using her sleeping powder, Supaya made them both a hot drink. "You must get some sleep," she told Soos. "This will help you. Now go, both of you. I'll stay with Sarah." As at a signal, all the old women silently filed out of the house. Supaya turned the lamp low and pulled Soos' rocking chair close to Sarah's pallet. Now and then Supaya dozed, but several times during the night, without waking the child, she bathed the burns and renewed the poultice.

The next day the old women returned, taking a deep interest in Sarah's condition and Supaya's treatment. With Susannah and George, still anxious but composed, they watched as Supaya bathed the burns, now turning a dark reddish purple, and put on a fresh poultice. They could see that her curing was good and complimented Supaya indirectly by making quiet, reassuring comments to the parents.

That night also Supaya stayed and then came to treat Sarah each day until the healing had progressed well enough for Soos to care for her.

News of Sarah's curing spread rapidly. At church, women who had ignored Supaya as an outsider and kept their distance because she was Wenonga's daughter-in-law now spoke to her politely, indicating their willingness to accept her. Supaya returned their greetings with equal politeness, but sat, proud and dignified, where she always sat, in the back row with Soos, and made no effort to cultivate their friendship.

Supaya had begun attending church partly to please Susannah, who wanted her company, and partly to please Mrs. Crowell. Shortly after Supaya had moved into Nonen's "little hut," Amy Crowell had appeared at Supaya's door, looking as surprised to find herself there as if she had arrived accidentally. She held a potted plant against her chest and stood half turned from the door, ready to hurry off at the first alarm. When Supaya opened the door, she smiled and stepped back as though her presence were an embarrassment to them both.

Supaya, truly pleased to see her, put out both hands and drew her inside. "Welcome! Welcome! Please come in. I am happy you have come." She indicated one of the two straight chairs Nonen had loaned them. "Please sit down. We will have a cup of tea."

Amy Crowell sat. She had not been inside an Indian home since coming to the reserve, and she gazed about with childlike curiosity at the bumpy, whitewashed walls and dark ceiling beams, at the clothes hanging on pegs and the bare, wooden floor. There were no curtains at the small windows and few dishes on the shelves. But there were large, colorful tins of cornstarch, tea, and baking powder, decorated with scenes from Aesop's Fables and portraits of Queen Victoria, all in soft, muted shades of blue, brown, red, and gold. And on a shelf near the fireplace were books, several that had belonged to Supaya's mother as well as her own, including a composition book in which she recorded sales of baskets, mats, and vegetables.

"Why," said Amy, "we have cottages like this at home in England!" She settled back in her chair, then remembered she was still holding the pot. "Here, my dear, I wanted to bring you this. Reverend Crowell is making calls this morning, you see, and dropped me off here. He thinks I don't get out enough. He always wants me to go calling with him, but I . . .," she paused, looking flustered, ". . . you understand what it is to be a stranger, and . . . but I wanted to come to see you! He doesn't know that," she added, her pale eyes suddenly sly, as if she had played a trick on her unsuspecting husband. "I wanted you to have this. I raised it from seeds from my home in England. It's fine for borders. Of course . . ." she hesitated, perplexed, "no one plants borders here. But you could . . . could . . .," she broke off helplessly, at a loss to say what Supaya could do.

Supaya turned the pot about admiringly. "I will start a border. I'll plant it beside the front door." Gently she touched the drooping leaves and fragile blossoms. "It's very pretty, and it's kind of you to give me a flower from your home. It will always be special to me."

Reassured, Amy happily drank her tea.

A few days later Amy came again. This time she carried several rolls of wallpaper. Eli was home, putting an ash splint seat in a chair he had made. Unused to his presence, Amy stood back shyly while Supaya unrolled the paper, a few leftover pieces from Amy's living room, patterned with red roses and twining green leaves.

"Eli, look!" Supaya exclaimed. "It's so pretty!"

Embarrassed by their gratitude, Amy tried to explain her gift. "You admired it, so I wanted you to have it. I thought . . . you could use it . . . that is, it's not enough to . . ." Suddenly realizing that what she had brought was insufficient to cover even one wall of the room, her eyes darted about in dismay. "Maybe . . ." she appealed to Supaya, ". . . maybe you could . . ."

"I will line the backs of the shelves with it," said Supaya confidently, and Amy, rescued, smiled with relief.

She was curious about what Eli was doing, and he kindly explained, showing her as he would a child how he wove the splints. He believed, as did all the Indians, that Amy was not like other people. In a world where evil was always mixed with good, she had been blessed with total innocence. Her fragile spirit was naturally confused. Because she could never be at ease, she must be treated tenderly. Reverend Crowell, absorbed in his work and unaware of the special light in which his wife was viewed, would have been surprised to know to what extent the faithful attendance and cooperation of his flock was due to their care for his wife.

Lizzie Toomis had also come to call when Supaya moved into her own house, announcing herself by a loud, forceful knock. Energetic and at home wherever she went, Lizzie took a frank, lively interest in Supaya's house, and recognized immediately Amy's wallpaper. "How clever of you to use it that way," she remarked, accepting a cup of tea. "But you need curtains, don't you? I'll look in my trunk when I get home and see if I have anything suitable." She brought Supaya a china teapot, white, with sprays of pale pink flowers. "I thought you'd like a teapot," she said firmly, having never doubted it.

Supaya responded to this forthright young woman and expressed her delight with the teapot, admiring the gold-edged spout and twisted gold handle on the lid. It was her first piece of china, and she placed it prominently in the middle of a shelf.

Lizzie did look in her trunk and found two pairs of curtains, which Supaya hung at the living room windows. Remembering how Wenonga had watched her through the window, Supaya now slept upstairs in the front bedroom.

Wenonga had not come to her house, and Supaya saw him less often now. Occasionally Soos, lowering her voice as if Wenonga could hear her no matter where she was, whispered gossip about him, how he had left one man's wife and pursued another's, who had been compelled to give in to him for fear of what he might do to her family.

Supaya was never quite sure when she first saw the white dog. She often took a shortcut through the woods to Soos' and several times had caught a fleeting glimpse of a white shape slipping through the brush, or the sun glancing off the white back of a dog disappearing through the trees. She thought little of it.

But one morning on her way to the store, she rounded a bend and there he was, standing by a tree, his eyes fixed expectantly on her as if he'd known she was coming. Supaya stopped dead. He was huge, and his size, the richness of his fur that fanned out in a thick ruff about his ears and neck, the extraordinary expression in his eyes, as if he could speak if he chose, the sense of power that emanated from him, all made clear that he was to be feared.

Now Supaya understood her mistake in thinking past glimpses of him had been mere chance. She felt his strength projected powerfully against her, willing her, compelling her to falter, to retreat. Almost imperceptibly he extended his neck and lowered his head, never taking his eyes from hers. Bracing herself, Supaya faced him unwaveringly, trying to mask the deep fear she felt of so deadly an antagonist. But she knew she must do more than just withstand him. She must move first. Remembering the stone bear in her pouch, she addressed it silently, "Grandfather, help me! Give me courage!" And forcing herself to move, she took a bold, challenging step forward. Watching her with shining eyes and one paw slightly lifted, the great dog hesitated briefly. Then, tossing his head in a playful motion, he leaped aside and bounded away into the woods. Supaya did not look after him, making herself walk on, as though unconcerned. But she drew a deep, shuddering breath and her shoulders were limp with relief.

At the store, Jess Fallon came to greet her as he always did, smiling and pleased to see her. "Good morning, Mrs. Red Sky. How are you today?" He laid his hands flat on the counter and leaned slightly forward.

"I am well, thank you." Her voice sounded stiff and unnatural in her own ears, but Supaya was always confused by Jess Fallon. The sparkle in his blue eyes made her unaccountably blush, as the look of no other man ever did. Feeling her face grow warm, she would hold her head all the higher, trying to be dignified. But then she suspected him of being amused, and because she was never certain of whether he was teasing her or not, her voice, to her chagrin, would almost die away.

She had brought more boxes to sell. He examined them, commenting so anyone could hear. Supaya, pleased by his praise but also embarrassed, sensing the notice taken of her by others in the store, made a slight, impatient gesture.

Perceiving her embarrassment, Jess put the boxes aside and paid her, one dollar per box, "You know," he said, "you could make more money and with less work and time." Surprised, Supaya looked directly at him, her eyes wide and questioning. "You could make splint baskets. See, like these." He pointed to a low shelf behind the counter where ash splint baskets of various sizes were stacked. "They sell very well. I could pay fifty cents for the apple and lunch baskets, seventy-five for the clothes hamper, maybe more for a good sewing basket."

Immediately Supaya saw the possibilities and began wondering how she could get some splints. Maybe Eli could . . .

Watching her, Jess saw her eagerness and speculation. "Just a minute." He went into a small storage room and returned with a bundle of splints. "Old Joe traded me these the other day. Why don't you start with them." Supaya drew back, unwilling to accept any favors. "Go on. Take them. I'll deduct the price from the baskets when you bring them in." Still she hesitated, looking at him doubtfully. "I mean it. See, I'll make a note of the amount." He scribbled some words and figures on a pad by the cash drawer and then smiled, as if inviting her to share in a joke.

Uncertain whether she was being teased or not, Supaya, her cheeks a dusky pink, took the bundle of splints and said primly, "Thank you. I will remember."

On the way home she kept to the main road and was alert for any movement or rustle in the underbrush, and was particularly watchful at the bend in the road, but the white dog didn't appear.

She put away her money in a box that also held Quayo's glowing powder. She had kept it there ever since the day she had surprised Eli with money in his hand and the can she had hidden it in empty on the table. She had told him to put it back.

Eli, startled, then angry and defensive, had yelled, "I am the man in this house! I take what I want! It is mine by right!"

"It is not yours to waste on drink! Or," seeing his slight sneer, "to buy fancy combs for your women! That is not a man's way! A real man would not soil himself or his family!"

He grinned at her and kept the money in his fist. "I was man enough for you! But you have given me no family! Others have. Maybe it is you who are no good as a woman!"

Cold with anger but, like her father, deceptively quiet, she said only, "Put it back, Eli."

"No," he answered rashly, thinking that settled the matter, and turned to go.

With catlike swiftness, Supaya snatched up the hatchet from beside the stove and came at him, holding the gleaming, knife-sharp edge at an angle before her. "Put it back," she repeated, her lips scarcely moving, her eyes narrowed with purpose. Her hand gripping the haft, she moved the blade slightly back and forth.

Stunned, Eli stared at the blade, then, as she moved deliberately closer, he saw the deadly intent in her face. After the briefest hesitation, he laid the money down.

143

Still holding the hatchet, Supaya got Quayo's little box of powder. As she opened it, Eli shrank back. "Now," said Supaya coldly, "I will no longer hide the money. It will be here, with this box, and you, the man of the house," with scornful emphasis, "will always know where it is."

Sullenly, Eli backed still further off; then, intimidated and unable to bear her contempt, he fled from the house.

All during the fall and into winter Supaya worked on splint baskets. When Soos and George saw what she was doing, George, feeling deeply obligated for Sarah's healing, offered to cut the ash when spring came and pound it into splints, thus keeping her well supplied.

Soos had her baby, another girl, and to relieve her, Supaya often took Sarah for the day. There was strong affection between them. As Supaya worked, Sarah learned by imitation to make her own little baskets from scraps and pieces. Her burns were now healed, and her hair had grown back, thick but still short, giving her a pert and saucy look. Supaya promised to help her make her own lunch basket for school and her own sewing basket.

One chill, gray afternoon when snow clouds rolled in low and threatening, Supaya and Sarah sat at the table working. Supaya was finishing a long, narrow bread basket designed to hold eight loaves in a row for the lady shoppers in Wellston. Sarah was painstakingly weaving natural and brown splints into a basket as a present for her mother. The teakettle simmered on the stove, and bannock, a treat for Sarah, filled the room with its aroma. Supaya glanced up in time to catch sight through the window of a wagon pulling up before the house. When she opened the door, Jess Fallon stood on her doorstep, holding his black, wide-brimmed hat in his hand and smiling.

"Afternoon, Mrs. Red Sky. I'm pleased to find you home."

Supaya, finding her voice, said. "Welcome to my home. Please come in."

Sarah, abandoning her work at sight of him, smiled broadly, her head coyly to one side, waiting for him to notice her.

"Why, there's Miss Sarah," he exclaimed, and catching her under her arms, swung her up and down again. Sarah kicked her feet and laughed with pleasure. She liked this big man who slipped her cookies when she came to his store with her mother.

"Please sit down," said Supaya, grateful for Sarah's presence. "We will have some tea."

"Thank you. I'd appreciate that. It's a chilly day." He sat down, very much at ease, filling the room with his presence and looking not at all chilled. "But it's very cozy in here, isn't it, Sarah." He reached in his coat pocket and drew out an envelope. "A letter came for you, Mrs. Red Sky. As I was passing, I thought I'd drop it off."

Supaya turned instantly. The envelope was small and thin. The writing she recognized as Jacques'. Restraining her eagerness to read it, she poured tea and brought the bannock to the table.

"Go ahead, read it. Sarah and I won't mind, will we?" Sarah, totally engrossed by Jess, leaned against his knee and gazed at him with big, shining eyes. Her mouth full of bread, she shook her head in agreement as if mesmerized.

The letter was brief. Jacques and Maud were married and living in Auntie Em's house. She had died last spring and had left her house to Quayo, who had given it to them. Neegonas was going to have another baby. Joe Crow had died. They had found him one morning lying by the fireplace.

Reading the letter, like hearing unexpectedly the voice of a loved one, made Supaya suddenly long for home. She could not bear to know that Auntie Em had died or Joe Crow, or that anything had changed at all since she left. Silently she folded the letter and put it away.

Though she kept her head bent, Jess saw that her lip trembled. Suppressing an impulse to take her hands and comfort her, he tried to divert her. "This is fine bread, isn't it, Sarah. I think you need another piece. And if that pot has a bit more tea in it . . ." He held out his cup, and Supaya, recalled by the demands of hospitality, hastened to refill it. He examined the baskets Supaya and Sarah had been working on. He praised Sarah's and, to her delight, asked that she make him one just like it. Taking up the bread basket, he admired Supaya's geometric variation on the usual checkerboard pattern.

Her attention finally caught, Supaya looked critically at the long basket. "Do you have any dyes?" she asked, "white man's dyes, red or green? Maybe yellow?"

He pondered. "I may have." He saw that in discussing the baskets and dyes, she had spoken to him more naturally, as to a friend, and he added quietly so as not to break her mood, "If not, I can get some next time I go to Wellston."

"Red or green would be prettier, brighter than brown. Or,"

145

putting her head to one side, "I could combine them. And I wondered about lining the sewing baskets with cotton print. What do you think? Would that make them sell better?" She turned to him suddenly and caught in his eyes a dreamy, gentle warmth as they rested on her, a look so preoccupied he seemed not to have heard a word she'd said. But as she paused in surprise, his expression altered so swiftly she thought what she'd seen a mere trick of the fading winter light. He answered at once, in a businesslike tone.

Sarah, fascinated by his gold watch chain, extended one stubby finger toward it, and he had just taken out his pocket watch and held it to her ear when Eli entered through the back door.

Seeing the three of them, he stopped short and stood stiffly by the stove. He nodded his head once in response to Jess' greeting and refused the tea and bread Supaya offered him. He had been gone several days. His clothes were dirty, his hair uncombed. Heavy-eyed, he stared antagonistically at the elegant white man sitting at his table.

"Well," said Jess, "I must go. Thank you for the tea, Mrs. Red Sky. I'll see if I can get those dyes." Sarah followed him to the door and waved as he turned the wagon smartly and held up his hat in salute.

"What was he doing here?" asked Eli sullenly. "Come to see my wife?"

Angry that she had to feel ashamed of her husband, Supaya said coldly, "He stopped to bring me a letter from home. My brother is married, and my Auntie Em died."

Eli, immediately losing interest, went into his own bedroom and pulled the curtain.

Snow had come early that year, and the winter was long and bitter. Many had severe colds or developed pneumonia. Having witnessed Supaya's skill in healing, women began coming to her for cures. They had known her father was a shaman, but now, impressed by her own ability as an herbalist, they appealed readily to her for help. Otherwise they kept a respectful distance. Though she lived apart in her own house, she was still Wenonga's daughter-in-law, and aside from Soos and George, her friends were white. Increasingly, Supaya spent more time preparing medicines and walking from house to house, visiting patients all over the reserve. Sometimes, if she were to be late, Eli accompanied her until he developed a cough, which he seemed unable to get rid of and impatiently refused to let her treat.

Always she watched for the white dog, whose huge paw prints she occasionally found outside the house in the early morning. One moonlit night, looking out from her upstairs window across the pale, glittering snow, she saw him, luminous white against white, standing on his own oblique black shadow. Slowly he raised his head and stared upward. Though she stood in the dark, she felt that his eyes, struck by the moonlight, looked straight at her. Suddenly he turned and ran off, his shadow gliding smoothly beside him over the snow.

In return for her healing, she was paid by gifts of food, and so she and Eli fared better that winter than in previous winters. She made and sold many baskets. Jess stocked the dyes she asked for, and once he brought back from Wellston a large bundle of cotton print remnants.

"For lining the baskets," he said, showing them to her.

Supaya wanted to buy them; some pieces were even large enough for a blouse or a summer dress for Sarah. "But not today," said Supaya, thinking of the flour and tea she had to buy, as well as the dyes.

"Take them," said Jess. "They're free."

"Free!" Supaya exclaimed, looking at him in disbelief.

"I got them for nothing. Only had to carry them back." Innocently, he raised his eyebrows at her. "The warehouse was throwing them away." Seeing her disbelief, he added guilelessly, "They're a wasteful people."

Supaya smiled slightly. "Then I will pay you for your trouble."

He appeared to calculate, then said, solemnly, "I figure it at fifteen cents."

Equally solemn, but suddenly shy and pink-cheeked, Supaya carefully counted out the money.

In early January the chief held his annual feast in the Council Hall for all members of the band. For three days all the women of his family busied themselves preparing food. Supaya was up unusually early because she had promised Soos, the chief's third daughter, to help set tables and serve food. She stepped outside to a pearly gray morning. But to the east, above the trees, a red glow was spreading across the sky, casting a rosy light on the snow. Wrapped in a blanket, Supaya walked along the road between drifts

147

as high as the fence posts. Her breath hung like smoke in the dry, still air. Far off, she heard the cawing of a crow, its voice clear and resonant. Gradually it came nearer, and she saw it, black against the sky, a lone crow soaring and circling. When she entered Soos' back door, the warm air making her face tingle, she could still hear its call.

The feast was attended by everyone living on the reserve. Grandly the chief received them all, making them welcome and inviting them to sit and eat. Supaya ran back and forth all day, helping Soos, her mother, sisters, aunts, and cousins serve the guests and keep the platters and bowls full for each successive group. When all had been fed and were listening to speeches and singing songs, Supaya, feeling weary, whispered to Soos that she was leaving early.

There had been no wind all day. The light was fading as quietly as it had come. The snow, packed down by wagon wheels, squeaked faintly underfoot. She was nearly home when suddenly, with a clap of wings, a crow swooped past her, skimming low. He veered from side to side across the road ahead, then landed and folded back his wings. Cocking his eye at Supaya, he strutted ahead of her, thrusting his head forward to utter short, rasping squawks. Astonished, Supaya saw that he pitched to one side. Like Joe Crow, he had one injured leg. Drawn to him, she moved closer. With a heavy flap of his wings, he rose in the evening air and soared ahead, landing on the ridge of her roof. Loath to lose sight of him, Supaya ran after him and stood with arm outstretched, clucking at him, hoping to coax him down. But he only cocked his head and stepped restlessly back and forth, turning in little circles. When only a narrow ribbon of deep red showed on the western horizon below the darkened sky, he took off again, with a heavy beat of his wings, into the last light.

With a pang as if a heartstring had snapped, Supaya looked after him until he was only a black speck against the dying day and then vanished altogether.

That night she slept fitfully, starting awake from confused and frightening dreams. Toward morning she fell into a deep sleep, awakening later than usual, with only one clear memory: her father, his face shadowed, speaking her name.

She dressed and made up the fire. When Eli came home, yawning, she was standing by the window gazing out at the snow-drifts, wishing with a deep sense of urgency that winter would soon be over. She resolved that when the lake ice split in the spring, she would go home.

CHAPTER THIRTEEN

No one knew she was coming, for there was no way a letter could arrive before she did. Nor had she spoken of her intention—not even to Nonen or Soos. Her request, put to George, to be taken into Wellston had surprised them all. Only Jess Fallon had known, since she'd depended on him to tell her the first sailing date.

Six years had passed since her arrival in Wellston. Supaya was no longer an inexperienced girl of sixteen to be frightened by a town that was smaller and dirtier than she'd remembered, or by strange people, Indian or white. Calm and composed, she boarded the steamer, choosing, this trip, to sit inside the cabin. Other passengers, carrying odd assortments of bags and bundles, entered, letting in cold gusts of air. Proximity and the exhilaration of beginning a journey together made them convivial, and they struck up small conversations. But Supaya sat apart, her face turned to the window.

She watched as the steamer plowed its way through the dark, cold water, ice floes swirling aside from its prow. At each stop along the way, freight was loaded and unloaded, mailbags exchanged for other mailbags, and passengers, clutching their belongings, hurried down the gangway past others who were hurrying up. Supaya took little notice. Only once, later in the afternoon, when the stopover seemed unusually long, did she rise impatiently and walk about the now nearly empty cabin. The sky, overcast when they left Wellston, was clearing. Long rifts appeared in the ragged, cottony clouds, revealing a bright blue above, and through those rifts sunlight shone down in hazy columns that glittered on the distant ice. Becoming aware of her own reflection in the glass, Supaya wondered uneasily now that the time was almost come—Stone Island was the next stop—how her father would greet her. Concern for him, a deep conviction that something was wrong and her help was needed, had made her determined to come. But the reality of their meeting had not struck her until this moment, as she faced her own dim, transparent image.

She had parted from him without a word, leaving behind, like a slap in his face, the most treasured gift he had to give her. She longed to see her home again, and her grandmother and brother, but most of all her father, to restore the harmony between them. Like a repentant child she wanted him to know that time had brought her some understanding, that she had long since seen he'd had no choice. Of Kineu, she dared not think.

Raising her shawl over her head, Supaya went out on deck. The wind blew hard. It whipped her skirts and caught her breath. But she held her shawl across her mouth, braced herself against the rail and stared intently ahead, over the choppy water.

Gradually Stone Island appeared, rising out of the lake. To the west the lowering sun glanced across the surface of the water, setting off millions of shifting, sparkling lights and illuminating the island in a soft, warm glow. A dream island, it floated above the water, its bare, rocky peak clear against the fragile evening sky. Supaya's memory, like a soaring bird, looked down from a height upon the summit, at the hollow hidden among the rocks, where she had lifted her arms to the Great Spirit and been blessed with a vision.

Startled by the steamer's whistle, its vibrations carried away by the wind, she saw they were passing Auntie Em's house, where she and Kineu had made love in the loft as Auntie Em had rocked in her chair, smiling and eating Quayo's berry pie. Now Auntie Em was dead, and the boy and girl that Supaya and Kineu had been no longer existed. Now Jacques and Maud lived there and the shadows of others had faded away even as the smoke from Maud's fire thinned and faded into the air.

The steamer rounded a point of land and the end of the wharf came forward to meet them, chunks of ice nudging its weathered piers. On the rocky beach lay a few small boats, hulls up. Beyond the wharf and an open stretch of ground was the general store, all just as before except that everything had shrunk. The wharf was flimsy and narrow. The ground beyond was not the wide space she remembered. The store, bleached as a dead tree, looked absurdly small, and its porch roof sagged in the middle. Responding to the ship's repeated whistle, several figures detached themselves from the porch and moved toward the wharf. Behind them a man in shirt sleeves hurried down the steps, braving the chill wind that whipped his apron. He waved his arms and called out, striving comically to make himself heard. Supaya smiled to herself: Mr. Bonnet, ordering people about. That, at least, was the same. Carrying her bag and basket, she stepped down the gangplank and walked toward him, thinking with amusement how different he'd find it if he tried to bargain with her now. As she passed, he paused in his shouting long enough to nod politely at an attractive stranger. A second later, arms still raised, he turned in surprise, to stare after her.

Supaya walked on, having no time to waste on Mr. Bonnet. She did not hurry in her white woman's shoes, stepping carefully to avoid muddy, water-filled ruts. The time of year was the same as when she had left—trees just coming into leaf, gray-brown fields sodden with melted snow. But only the time was the same. The circumstances were entirely different. She had come only because she herself had resolved to come. She had paid for her passage and the gifts she brought with money she herself had earned. She had come when she chose and she would leave when she chose. Only planting time limited her freedom. No longer did anyone—certainly not Eli—presume to order her about, and she smiled to think how proud her father and grandmother would be of her independence.

She passed the agent's house, stone, like hers, but its porch columns badly in need of paint after a hard winter, and further on, the schoolhouse, its windows glassily reflecting the fading sunset. Near the crossroads stood the preacher's house, already shadowed by the growing dusk under the fir trees. Beyond was the stone church, light still touching its narrow bell tower, and the cemetery, where her mother had long been buried and where in a cold November they had buried Aunt Theresa and this past winter, Auntie Em.

Turning off onto a smaller road, Supaya saw a man walking toward her. She caught her breath in sudden panic. Could it be Kineu? The twilight was deceptive, and his straight-brimmed black hat shaded his face. She had not expected to meet him like this, in the middle of a road! She tried to maintain her composure, but her feet, carrying her forward of their own accord, stumbled, and like a fool she soaked her shoes and splashed her skirt with mud. The man came steadily on. Feeling quite faint, she forced herself to look at him as they passed each other, then closed her eyes for an instant, limp with relief. He was not Kineu! He was no one she knew. But eager now to have the moment of meeting over, she hurried on and reached her father's doorstep as twilight was deepening into night.

She knocked and at once a cry came from within as if she had struck the living bones of the house. She waited, wanting to smile, fighting an impulse to cry. She heard voices arguing; then the door jerked open and Rhea, her hair disheveled, confronted her belligerently. The lamplight fell on Supaya, and from within the room a tremulous voice cried:

"Come! Supaya, come!"

Astonished, Rhea stepped back as Supaya rushed past her and embraced her grandmother, sitting in her rocker by the fireplace.

"Ah! Ah! I knew you were coming! I knew!" Quayo, her face alight, leaned her gray head against Supaya's and clasped her with arms still strong and wiry. "Let me look at you." She held Supaya's shoulders and studied her. It was then that Supaya saw that Quayo's eyes, once shiny-black as a bird's, were cloudy gray. "Ah," said Quayo, touching Supaya's face, "you have learned much. You have climbed a long way."

Supaya, choking back her tears, whispered, "It is good to see you, Grandmother! It is good to be home!"

Smiling, Quayo leaned back in her chair and said, "Rhea, some tea. My granddaughter has come home."

Supaya rose, and turning, saw her father standing in his bedroom doorway. The sight of him struck her heart like a blow. He, who always stood so proudly erect, whose jaunty, swaggering step caught every woman's eye, now stood bent over, shoulders hunched, his head thrust forward at an angle. His hair hung about his face, straggly and uncombed.

"Father!" Supaya could not hide her dismay. She reached for his hand, but his fingers were stiff and curled like a dead bird's claw, and she could only cradle it in her own.

With a wry smile that hid the shame he felt at her seeing him so, Jules said, "Welcome home, Daughter. Our hearts rejoice to see

152

you. Come, we will sit down and speak together. You must have much to tell us."

That night Supaya was glad to climb the steps to her old bed in the loft. She needed rest and time alone with her thoughts. She knew now she'd been foolish for doubting her father would welcome her, and was ashamed for having so misjudged him. And she had been right to come. Another year would have been too late. Jacques and Maud came to help them, but otherwise they were left to themselves, except, as her father contemptuously remarked, for Reverend Harris, who came too often, demanding that Jules marry Rhea in the church. Supaya understood why they were shunned. The three of them, like the house, were dirty and unkempt. The air stank of unwashed bodies, dirty clothes, and pots. How it must grieve Quayo, always proud of her appearance and her home, and Jules, proud of his skill as a healer and prowess as a hunter, now crippled so he could no longer heal, or hunt, or fish. Visitors would not be comfortable with such a distressing host or in such an oppressive, caustic atmosphere. Whose secret envy or resentment could have brought this evil on them? Whoever it was, whatever the cause, she would need all her blessings to cure it.

As they had drunk their tea, Jules, obviously in pain, had listened attentively as she'd told them of her new life, hearing what she said and what she did not say. Rhea sat apart, like an outsider, nursing her resentments. Supaya was conscious of her envious eyes studying her hair, her clothes and shoes.

Supaya said nothing of her stillbirth, but spoke warmly of Nonen and the fine stone house she'd given her. She told them of Soos and her white friends, Amy and Lizzie, and of her rapidly increasing work as a healer. Jules saw then that his daughter was respected but set apart by her own people. And Supaya told about the kinds of baskets she made and the white man who helped supply her with materials and who bought her vegetables and baskets. Jules' sharp ears heard the subtle change in her voice when she spoke of this white man whose name she avoided pronouncing.

"And your husband?" asked Jules. "Does he bring home much meat, fish?"

"Eli," said Supaya, her chin lifting, "does not hunt or fish. He grew up at a government school. They taught him to be a carpenter." Jules and Quayo were silent, waiting to hear more. But

153

Supaya would not say: He is a drunk, a woman-chaser, a lost man with no vision and no purpose.

"Is he a good husband?" persisted Jules, his voice strained.

"He is *my* husband," answered Supaya proudly, with a flash of her old anger.

Then they understood, and Rhea, in the shadows, smiled spitefully. Jules turned away, as if his pain had suddenly increased. They had not talked long after that.

Drifting into sleep, Supaya planned what she would do, if only she would be granted the strength. . . .

By half-light Supaya was dressed and downstairs. She felt a sharp hunger, since she'd eaten nothing on the boat and Rhea had offered no food, but she would not eat and had determined that no one else should until the house was clean. She made up the fire in the stove and instead of getting food to cook, brought in water from the pump and set it to heat. When Rhea appeared, yawning and ready for tea, Supaya turned on her.

"No one eats until this house is clean. It smells worse than a barn. Look at it! Dirt everywhere! Fireplace filled with ashes! I wonder you could live here! And it's clear you've not given Quayo a bath or washed her hair in many days! The water is heating. While I help Quayo bathe, you sweep out the fireplace and clean this house!"

Rhea stared. "Why should I?" she asked, shrugging a shoulder.

Supaya regarded her scornfully and said coldly, "You *are* the woman in this house, though you do not look it. Your hair, your clothes are filthy. One might think you a beggar. But you *do* live here. You *do* eat my father's food. You *are* my father's wife, though you do not act like a wife!"

Stung, Rhea gasped for words. "You! You always resented me! Now you come back with your hair like a white woman's and . . . and fancy clothes! You think you can . . ." Her voice trembled and her face puckered up like a child's. "I don't have to do anything you say! Maybe I'll go and not come back!"

Supaya, carrying hot water to the tub in the lean-to, answered shortly, "Then go."

Cornered, knowing her family would not have her back, Rhea cried out, "Your father may . . ."

"My father," interrupted Supaya, suddenly furious, "is a sick man. You have done nothing to help him. Now you will help or get out!"

So Rhea, sullenly, making a great show of slamming things about, went to work as Supaya helped Quayo into the tub and washed her hair. When, much later, the house was scrubbed, a fire burned in the fireplace, and scone and fried fish were ready to be eaten, Jules had to be urged to the table. Supaya chided him gently.

"Please, Father, come and eat. You are too thin and weak. You must eat for strength."

To please her, he got out of bed, pain like fire in all his joints. He was ashamed to have his daughter see him in the light of midday. But he was gladdened by Quayo's neat appearance and the clean house, and grateful for the warmth of the fire. To show his appreciation, he tried to eat all that Supaya placed before him. He refused to be helped and managed to feed himself by holding his food between his stiffened hands as between two sticks.

"You had good luck in hunting this winter, Father." Supaya, checking their stock of dried fish and meat, wondered how he had been able to hunt and fish.

Jules understood her remark. "My hands were not like this," he said, "until late winter. For two seasons past they have been sore and my back caused me pain. Still, I could go out to hunt and fish. And," he added proudly, "I was able to heal the pain of others. Even this winter, when my fingers began to twist, I was still blessed. The aim of my gun was true. My traps were cunningly placed. Fish leaped into my nets. This," he said grimly, looking at his hands, "this curse did not come upon me until the snows began to melt, at the time Joe Crow died."

"If you had come home," said Rhea angrily, "it would not have happened!" She turned to Supaya, wanting to impress her with the outrageousness of what Jules had done. "He stayed out in the woods all night! Night after night he left us here alone!"

Jules looked at her coldly. "If you had made a home here, I would have come back to it, but you are a slut!" He hit the table with the side of his hand, ignoring the pain it caused him. "You are lazy! Useless! Content to live in dirt!"

Shamed before Supaya, Rhea began to cry. She covered her face with her hands, watching slyly between her fingers for a sign of Jules' relenting. Jules growled in disgust and turned his head away.

"Rhea," said Supaya quietly, "I need my brother's help. Please go to his house. Tell him I am here and ask him to come."

Rhea, sniffling and pouting, made no objection but got up at once as if eager to go. Supaya was surprised at her readiness and wondered at her leaving by the back door when the front was more direct. Then, seeing a contemptuous, knowing look cross Quayo's face, Supaya understood. She reached the back door in time to see Rhea entering the barn. Too many times she had seen Eli go to the barn in just such a self-pitying mood. Sickened by the familiar pattern, she went to the barn and pulled the door open as Rhea was lifting a bottle to her lips.

"Give me that!" Angrily Supaya snatched the bottle. Fending off Rhea's frantic attempts to stop her, she poured out the contents onto the ground.

"Look what you've done!" wailed Rhea. "And it's so hard for me to get!"

"Where are the others? Give me the others!"

"What others?"

Supaya grasped Rhea's shoulders and shook her. "Don't lie to me! Get them!"

"Stop! Let me go! There's only one!"

"Then get it!"

Reluctantly, Rhea got it from behind baskets piled in a corner and watched, whimpering, as Supaya poured it out.

"No wonder you drove him from the house!" exclaimed Supaya, throwing down the empty bottle. "Not only do you not act like a wife but you pollute yourself and you would pollute him also! You are worse than useless!"

"Useless am I!" Rhea thrust her face forward. "I'm not useless in bed! And that's where he wants me! He's not so pure! You think because he's a healer he won't drink! Well, he was drunk! For a whole week! You didn't know that, did you!"

"He is a shaman—a doctor!" said Supaya furiously. "He would never do that!"

"He did! He did!" shrilled Rhea hysterically. "Ask your brother! Last fall! For a whole week! And he kept me in bed all that time! He's worse than the young. . . .!" Her voice broke off in a cry as Supaya struck her face. Screaming, Rhea tried to run, but Supaya grabbed her, thrust her violently against the barn wall and struck her hard again. Blood ran from Rhea's nose and from a split

156

at the corner of her eye. Welts showed red on the side of her face. She cowered against the barn, one arm raised to shield herself as Supaya, eyes blazing, stood over her, hand ready to strike again.

"Never speak of him like that again! Never! You are trash! You are nothing! It is an honor that he allows you in his house! You speak of him with respect or you will be sorry!"

Tears mixed with blood ran down Rhea's mouth and chin. Sobbing, she slid down onto her knees. "But he won't marry me!" she wailed. "Not in church or in the old way! He is ashamed of me!"

"Why should he marry you! You drink! You sleep with anybody! You think he doesn't know? He's always known. Everybody knows! Look at you! Your own people wouldn't want you back! Soon you'll be ugly! Then no one will have you!"

Rhea cringed, pressing her hands to her bruised, blood-smeared face, shaking her head in horror at Supaya's words.

"Oh get up!" said Supaya with disgust. "Get up!"

Fearing another blow, Rhea slid up cautiously, her shoulders pressed against the wall, the back of her hand across her mouth. From under her tangled hair she stared at Supaya, not knowing what to expect.

Supaya examined her coldly. "You were always a man-chaser, but you never looked like this. Dirty! Stinking dirty, that's what you are! No man would want to come near you. Today you wash yourself, and from now on you will keep yourself clean! You will comb your hair as you did when my father first saw you. And you will dress yourself with pride fitting the wife of a doctor!"

"But I have no other clothes!" cried Rhea, filled with wonder at this interest in herself.

"Then we will make you some. And you will keep your home clean and comfortable so you need not be ashamed of it! You will help Quayo bathe and brush her hair for her! You will cook the food your husband brings home and care for him as a wife! And," Rhea shrank back as Supaya leaned forward threateningly, "you will keep your self-respect! You will walk with pride and not invite other men or keep bottles hidden in the barn! You understand? If you do, I will know of it, and you will be sorry!"

In the silence that followed, Rhea stared into Supaya's hard, uncompromising eyes and saw that, with her, crying would be useless. She also saw the possibility of assistance from where she had least expected it, and lowered her eyes submissively.

"I will help you," said Supaya, understanding her need for help, "but first we must cure my father. Wipe your face. Then go and bring my brother here."

When Supaya returned to the house, Jules and Quayo were sitting by the fire. Neither inquired about the cries they'd heard, and Supaya offered no explanation.

Jules' treatment began with sweat baths. Jacques built a lodge of saplings, covered it with blankets, lined it with cedar branches and heated large stones. Every day Jules sat for hours in the hot steam, splashing water on the sizzling stones and rubbing himself with cedar. He shut his eyes against the burning and breathed deep the almost choking steam that beaded on his skin and penetrated his body, easing his painful joints.

Supaya and Rhea moved Jules' bed frame into the living room. They covered it with freshly cut cedar boughs and newly washed blankets and placed it close to the fireplace, where a fire was kept burning all day and night. When Jules came in from the sweat lodge Supaya had him lie down and covered him with warmed blankets.

After several days of sweat baths, when Jules could endure manipulation of his joints, Supaya heated blankets in the oven and bags which Jacques had filled with sand. As Jules lay face down on his bed, Supaya laid the heated blankets across his back and on top of the blankets the heavy, hot sandbags. Once their heat penetrated his body, she removed them, and she and Rhea took turns massaging his back, neck, and arms with herbal water. Then the reheated blankets and sandbags were laid on again, and he was again massaged.

So occupied was Supaya with curing her father, cooking, laundering, and sewing, that even with Rhea's now willing help, she had little time to think of Kineu or to visit her Aunt Hettie.

One gray afternoon when a soft spring rain was falling, Hettie came, bringing a pot of stew. Rhea was putting the blankets back into the oven and Supaya was bending over Jules, massaging his back, putting her full strength into the downward push. Without breaking her rhythm, she greeted her aunt, who sat down and commented at once on Quayo's new blouse.

"It is a gift from my granddaughter," said Quayo proudly, her milky eyes resting on Hettie.

Politely, Hettie inquired about Jules and made solicitous remarks, but she was busy noticing everything—the clean house, Jules' neatly cut hair, Rhea's new dress and facial bruises. Hettie's long droll face was openly curious. Sensing a deeper change behind these obvious ones and eager for details, Hettie said, "I see you have been busy since you returned, Supaya. That is why you have not come to see us."

Quayo smiled but said nothing.

Supaya, knowing her aunt's gossipy tongue, said only, "We *all* have been busy curing my father." As she spoke, she glanced sideways at her aunt and then noticed a man, standing in the doorway of the lean-to, watching them. With a shock, she realized it was Kineu, and for the space of a breath, everything stopped: her hands kneading Jules' back, Hettie's loud voice, the creak of Quayo's chair. Then Rhea banged the oven door, brought Supaya a hot blanket, and set everything into motion again.

The next few minutes were blurred in Supaya's memory. But someone—herself? Quayo?—asked Rhea to put on the teakettle, and it wasn't until she had helped Jules on with his shirt and wrapped the heated blanket around his shoulders that she dared turn, trembling, to face Kineu and saw that the space where he had stood was empty.

He had come and gone without a word.

Somehow she helped Rhea serve tea and put food on the table. Somehow she answered Hettie's questions about her life at Two Bluffs. She waited for Hettie to speak of Kineu, but, perversely, she did not, and Supaya could not bring herself to say his name aloud. When Hettie left, she insisted Supaya visit them soon.

Having promised, Supaya went several afternoons later. Walking along the old, familiar paths, she wondered if Kineu would be there. Surely he would—he must be! But when she arrived, only her aunt, uncle, and their young children greeted her. Unwilling to believe he was avoiding her, she looked expectantly at the door each time it opened. She waited for Hettie to offer an explanation of his absence. Then, as she held her tea cup and responded absentmindedly to their questions, a shattering thought occurred to her: he had found someone else! He no longer loved her! That must be why no one mentioned him to her! Suddenly faint, Supaya put down her cup. She tried to pay attention to their conversation but couldn't for the pounding in her head. Their faces ringed her about, pressed on her, smiling, wanting answers. With a mounting inner hysteria, she abruptly rose and made excuses, conscious of their polite amazement but unable to stop herself. She was half running along the path toward home when she heard her name.

"Suppy!"

She stopped. Then, with a flash of hope, whirled around. There he stood, taller and broader-shouldered than the boy she'd left, his face familiar yet changed, his dark eyes regarding her gravely.

"Kineu!" Her voice was scarcely a whisper. She waited, uncertain, confused by this mature, stern-faced Kineu.

After an endless moment, he held out his arms. Unthinking, Supaya rushed forward and threw her arms about his neck, calling his name over and over. Feeling his arms tight around her, his face against hers, his mouth on hers, she began to cry, violent sobs, long withheld, that shook her body, tears that burned her eyes, for the boy she had left and for their child that, like their dreams, had died without ever having lived.

Kineu, his world whole once more, held her close and let her weep. His head bent against hers, they stood as one, her tears speaking for them both. After a time, Supaya lifted her head and gazed at him, marveling that they were together. She shut her eyes as he kissed her, tenderly and long. With that kiss all the years of separation vanished.

Slowly they walked through the spring woods. She told him of her fear that he no longer loved her, and they laughed softly to discover he had felt the same fear. She had waited for him to come to her. He, not wanting to meet her in the presence of others, had waited long hours at their old meeting places, in the woods, by the creek, along the shore.

"Come, I know a house where we can be together." He caught her hand and struck off on another path.

Supaya pulled back, surprised at his words. "Kineu, I can't."

"Can't?" His voice was knife-sharp.

"Kineu, I'm married!"

He dropped her hand and faced her in sudden anger. "It made no difference before, though you knew you were promised! I have waited long for you!"

"But then I wasn't married! I didn't even know . . . him. And . . ." her voice was faint, near tears again, " . . . I loved you."

"Now you don't."

"Kineu!" She reached out to touch him but he backed stiffly

160

away, his eyes hurt and angry. "Kineu, you know I love you! But before, my father . . . he was sorry for us . . . he let us have the winter together. It is different now. I cannot shame my family!"

Kineu began walking again, his face closed and withdrawn. Supaya walked beside him, watching him anxiously. When he spoke, he looked straight ahead, and his voice was hard.

"You love that drunk you're married to?" Supaya was too surprised to answer at once. He turned to her, his face and eyes fierce. "Well? Do you?"

"How . . . how did you know?"

"What difference how! I met a man from Two Bluffs when I was working in a logging camp. He told me plenty. Well?"

She was glad he knew, and though her pride was stung, she answered frankly. "It is true. He is what you say. But it was not like that at first! At first I thought I could help him . . . I even thought I . . . loved him!" Kineu's eyes narrowed, his whole face tightened. Angry at his failure to understand, Supaya cried out, "What choice did I have? He was my husband! And you were not there!" After a moment she went on more quietly. "But I failed. I was not able to help him. After that I came to feel only anger and disgust for him. But, Kineu," imploring him to understand, "he was not as blessed as we were. He was sent to government school. He has nothing! He belongs nowhere!"

Kineu only answered contemptuously, "Now you want me to feel sorry for *him*!"

Seeing Kineu's set face, Supaya wondered how she could ever explain it all: Eli's drinking and womanizing, her struggle to make a living for them both, her dread of Wenonga, who pursued her constantly. How could she make him understand! How could she ever wipe out his reproach!

Her appeal to him, her longing for him to understand made her vulnerable. With an angry, bitter smile, Kineu pulled her close to him, his fingers painfully tight. "You speak words," he said, "but not the truth. The truth is that you are mine!" Roughly, he grasped her hair, and pulling her head back, kissed the curve of her throat and the hollow at the base of her neck. Holding her firm as though it were his right, he undid her blouse, stroked her shoulder and breast, caressed her with his lips. Supaya, unable to speak, leaned against him and he whispered in her ear, "Come, we will go now, together."

She allowed herself to be drawn along, her will having deserted her, until through her desire came a shaming thought. "Ah!" she exclaimed.

Kineu, firmly grasping her arm, looked down questioningly.

Her voice tight with pain, she said, "I want to go with you! I do! But afterward, I will be no different than he! I will despise myself!" Covering her face with her hands, she sank down on the ground and cried.

Around them a soft spring breeze stirred the trees, just coming into leaf. Large patches of sunlight fell through branches that soon would shade the path. A blue jay flittered nearby, raucously protesting their presence.

Kineu took her elbows and pulled her up. Gravely he studied her tear-stained face. There was nothing boyish in this man facing her. He had grown in her absence, changed, as she had, in ways she could not know.

"I think," he said slowly, "I understand you. You do not love him. You pity him. I would scorn to be so pitied. But one day I will go to Two Bluffs. I would see this man who thinks he has nothing! Now come. You must go home. Your family is waiting for you."

During the next few weeks, Kineu came several times to the house. He brought water from the spring for the herbal solution Supaya rubbed on Jules' back. He spoke politely with Quayo and Rhea and joked with Jacques. He brought ash splints and birchbark for Jules to work with to loosen his fingers. But he never touched Supaya or spoke with her alone again.

One day Reverend Harris, plump and sleek as a pigeon, came to their door. Rhea hid in the bedroom, but Supaya calmly invited him in and offered him a chair. Quayo, pretending to see less than she could, looked straight ahead.

Ill at ease, but determined, the preacher sat down across the table from Jules. He was thankful, he said, clearing his throat, to see Jules in improved health, but he wished to speak about Jules' spiritual health, indeed, the spiritual health of the entire reserve.

Jules, a blanket draped round his shoulders, could now sit erect. His hands, fingers almost straight, rested on the table before him. He widened his eyes slightly and hoped, politely, that the reserve was not in danger.

"Don't," said Reverend Harris sharply, "pretend not to know what I mean! After my last visit, I expected you would bring that girl you keep here to the church so I could marry you in the sight of God and man."

Jules turned his hands, palms upward. "Surely, God, who sees all, has seen that I do not *keep* her here, but that her home is here with me. We live together."

"But she should not live here!" exclaimed Reverend Harris. "Not until you have been married in the church! I've told you . . ."

"He didn't marry my daughter in your church," said Quayo, suddenly interrupting. "Your church," she said scornfully, turning her milky eyes on him, "means nothing to us."

"Have a cup of tea," said Supaya, placing a steaming cup before him. "And some scone."

Reverend Harris, on the point of jumping up, settled back in his chair as Supaya leaned in front of him. Nervously, he smoothed his lapels. "Oh yes. Thank you." He took a moment to collect his thoughts, aware they were watching him. "Jules," he began, finding it unfitting to address an Indian as mister, "Jules, you cannot continue to live in sin with this girl. Besides setting a bad example, you degrade yourself and you degrade her. You will ruin her life! I am sure you would not want to do that," he added, thinking to cajole him.

Jules sipped his tea. "You are right," he said thoughtfully, "I would not. But," he asked, with a smile, "how do I ruin her life? I give her a home, food, clothes, a family." His smile deepened as he invited understanding, "A man to sleep with."

A flush spread over Reverend Harris' face. He looked fixedly at Jules to avoid the embarrassment of meeting Supaya's glance. "You . . ." He drew a deep breath and strove to control his temper. "You are deliberately . . . you must understand that until you are properly married in the church, you give her nothing! You are mocking the word of God!"

"Ah!" said Jules, as if finally convinced. "I understand you. Being married in your church is important to you."

"Then you will come! Tomorrow afternoon would be . . ."

But Jules held up his hand. "I," said Jules, his tone gently rebuking, "have understood you. Now you must understand me. What is important to you is not important to me. My father and mother were not married in your church, yet they were man and wife. I was not married in your church, yet I considered myself married. I do not belong to your church. I will not be married in your church. Your church means very little to me."

Reverend Harris flinched as if struck. Temporarily speechless, he clenched his hands, then leaned across the table toward Jules.

"You are a bad influence! A bad influence in this community! You cannot," he exclaimed, thumping the table, "you cannot be permitted . . ."

Jules, eyes innocently wide, raised his hand again. "Please, you are a man of peace! Let us speak together in peace. You choose to live here among us, and we do what we can to keep you happy. We come to your church on Sundays. We listen when you preach. But we cannot do everything you ask! We go part of the way with you, but you can't expect us to go *all* the way! That would not be reasonable."

In the silence that followed, Supaya could hear the preacher's ragged breathing. His head lifted in a series of little jerks as though his collar were too tight. Suddenly, lifted by an explosion of anger, he rose, knocking his chair aside; and pointed a trembling finger at Jules. "I've known all along! Calling yourself a doctor! Meddling with the work of the devil with your charms and chants, that's what you've been doing! The devil has a strong hold on you! You mislead these simple people! Now you're corrupting this girl! Keep me happy indeed! Doing my duty to my God is my happiness! And my duty is to save souls from such as you!"

He strode to the door, turned, and was further infuriated to see them all politely attentive and perfectly calm. His hands opening and closing, he paused, struggling for words. "I'll speak to the agent about you! I'll have him charge you under the law! Let me tell you, you'll be sorry for flouting the church!" Then he rushed out, leaving the door ajar.

Quietly Supaya shut it behind him. Rhea came out of the bedroom. They all had a fresh, hot cup of tea, and no one spoke of the Reverend Harris.

The days steadily grew longer and warmer, and each day Jules improved. He still took a sweat bath every day, but he could stand erect and exercise his joints and muscles himself, enjoying thrusting back his shoulders and swinging his arms. He continued to work with the ash splints and bark Kineu brought and began hunting again. Rhea, without prompting, took his catch and prepared it for cooking and drying.

One day Jules got out his hawthorne pipe and filled it with tobacco Supaya had brought him—a special tobacco, Jess Fallon had told her, the finest he carried. Rhea and Supaya watched, smiling, as Jules tamped it down and lit it himself.

164

"Very fine tobacco, Daughter," he commented after a few puffs. "If you will fasten the hat band you brought me on my hat, I will take a walk. I might meet Mr. Jackson."

The band Supaya had made herself, a background of white beads for a geometric design of her own in brilliant green, red, and blue with a touch here and there of yellow, all sewn onto soft leather. It gave striking color to Jules' black hat, which he wore at an angle.

"Oh, oh!" said Quayo, raising her hands. "There he goes! All the women should stay indoors! No one will be able to resist him!"

"Old woman, it is good you cannot see! Or even you would run after me!"

They all laughed, but Jules looked to Rhea. She made no move toward him before Quayo and Supaya, but her sensuous glance and appreciative, coquettish smile made him laugh again.

He walked off down the road with the proud, jaunty walk Supaya remembered.

"You have healed him," said Rhea, her face expressive of the gratitude she felt.

"We healed him together," said Supaya, and their eyes met for the first time in real understanding. "Come, we must finish your sewing."

On his way home from the store, Jules was hailed by Sam Jackson, the agent, coming out of the Council Hall.

"See you're on your feet again, Jules!"

Jules smiled slightly and inclined his head.

"Also heard your daughter's home. Will she be staying?"

"She came for a visit. She returns soon."

Jackson squinted thoughtfully. "You be shorthanded without her?"

"No," said Jules, coolly. "My mother-in-law, my . . ." a faint, deliberate emphasis, " . . . wife and I need no help."

"Mmn." Jackson ruminated, his mouth slightly ajar. "You mean that girl . . . Rhea . . . she still living with you?"

Jules stood very still. Under his hat brim, his eyes were hard, intimidating, and he spoke with a terse finality. "She is my wife. My home is her home. You can enter that in the register."

And for Jackson, that settled the matter.

The lake ice was now entirely gone. The roads were dry, the fields turning green. It was time to plant the garden, and Supaya knew she must leave. She had not seen Kineu for several days and hoped she would not, for it was then easier for her to go. Only one thing remained which she must do.

Very early, when the sky had just begun to lighten, and trees and fields were emerging into a soft, gray dawn, Supaya quietly left the house. Quayo, hearing her go, knew where she went.

Supaya walked swiftly through the damp, cool woods. Moisture trembled on every branch and hung like tiny jewels on spider webs spun on firs and cedars. The hill was high and steep, but she was taller and stronger than before. She climbed upward vigorously, grasping the cold rocks, steady and sure of her direction. As she climbed, her sense of excitement grew. She could have found the hollow with her eyes shut, so straight she went to it. With an elation both new and remembered, she stood within its shelter once more and leaned against the massive rock. She found her vision marvelously sharp. Gazing down in the growing light, she could see the hillside with its tumbled, jagged rocks, then the woods, like a great green wave, misty with fog caught in the treetops, and beyond, like another sky, the blue, faintly wrinkled surface of the lake. To the east, the glow from the not yet risen sun glorified a long rack of cloud. Exalted, Supaya held up her arms and faced in turn the four directions of the world.

"Grandfather! Hear me! I speak with grateful heart!

"Great Spirit! You have healed my father! Out of your
great heart you have renewed his strength! Give him
of your wisdom that he may now live content!

"Great Father of all things! I am nothing, yet you have
guided me! My heart is full!"

CHAPTER FOURTEEN

The house was dark and empty when Supaya reached home. George insisted on coming in with her and lighting the lamp. Happy to be in her own house again, Supaya was too tired to wonder about Eli, who often stayed away, or George's obvious reluctance to leave her alone.

The next morning she had just made up the fire when Nonen came to her door, bringing some bread to welcome her home. She embraced Supaya, then glanced about uneasily.

Supaya thought she understood. "Where is he?" she asked.

"Who?" Nonen's wide face was innocently blank.

"Eli! Where is he?" That morning she had seen he'd begun building the shed and was pleased. Part of the frame was up and pieces of lumber lay about. In the lean-to tools were lying on the floor beside a keg of nails. "He wasn't here when I came last night."

Nonen didn't know where he was. "He came to see us a few days ago." She hesitated, her large eyes troubled. "He had been drinking. Wenonga was angry . . ." Her voice died in midsentence.

Supaya knew Nonen worried about her, living alone with Eli when he was drinking; now she seemed unusually disturbed. Supaya asked, "Yes, Nonen? What is it?"

"You had a good visit? How was your family? Nonen's face was solemn, her change of subject abrupt. Supaya was puzzled, but she told about her grandmother's fading sight and her father's recovery. Nonen listened, but so absentmindedly that Supaya questioned her.

"What is it? What is wrong?"

"Nothing. Just that Eli . . . I think he did not want you to go. He may . . . Suppy, come back with me until . . ."

"Nonen, you are kind! But you must not worry. Eli will come back, as always. I will be all right. Here, my grandmother sent you some maple sugar and some dried berries. She knows how good you have been to me."

Later Supaya walked to Soos' house, taking her a gift of maple sugar and squash seeds and for Sarah a new cotton dress. It was from Sarah that she first heard about the bear.

Sarah, playing outside, saw her coming and ran to meet her. She flung her arms about Supaya's waist and squeezed. "Oh, Aunt Suppy! I missed you! You stayed too long!" Excitedly she pulled Supaya along. "Come see Mama! She'll tell you about the bear!"

"What bear, Sarah?"

"A big bear! In the woods! He's been stealing food! He killed a white man's cow!"

Soos and George were worried about the bear. He had been seen several times near houses on the reserve, and some white farmers whose land skirted the reserve had come across with guns, hunting for him.

"He comes in close at night," said George. "The dogs go wild."

"We can't get a shoat to fatten until he's caught," said Soos.

Nor can I, thought Supaya, although she would urge Eli to finish the pen, for the bear surely would be caught soon.

After they had spoken of the bear and Soos had thanked her for the gifts, there was a strained silence. Several times Soos seemed about to speak, then changed her mind. Finally she inquired politely about Supaya's journey and the health of her family. Sarah tried on her new dress, and over the child's head, Supaya caught Soos looking at her, her brows puckered in a worried frown.

Walking home, Supaya puzzled over Nonen and Soos' strange behavior. Why wouldn't they speak? They all knew something she did not, and that made her uneasy.

Eli still had not returned. Resolutely she put worry aside. George was coming to plow the garden; she must sort out the seeds. Some she planned to give to Amy Crowell. She was on her knees in the lean-to putting them aside, when she heard the front door bang open.

Eli! She looked up, ready to greet him. She would make him something to eat, give him the shirt she'd brought him, thank him for building the shed. But when he appeared, filling the doorway, all such thoughts instantly fled. He braced his hands against the doorframe as if to block her escape and glared down at her. Only once, at the time of her stillbirth, had she seen his eyes so wild. His lips lifted back from his teeth and his chest swelled with such anger that for the first time she was frightened of him. Slowly, not taking her eyes off him, she got to her feet.

"So! You came back! Couldn't wait to get back to me, could you!" His voice was raw as if he'd been shouting.

"Eli! I . . . I did think you'd need me. And the garden . . ."

"To hell with the garden! And to hell with you!" He suddenly lunged forward, grabbed her arm, and twisted it. "My wife! My good wife!"

"Eli, please!" She bent over, trying to ease his hold on her arm. "You hurt!"

"Think you can shame me, don't you! Treat me like I was nothing!" He twisted her arm viciously. Agonized, she swung around.

"Eli!" her voice tight with pain, "what is it! What have I done!"

"Done!" In a burst of fury he let go her arm and smashed his fist into her face. Her head snapped back. She screamed, spun sideways, and collapsed on the floor. Blood welled out of the split over her cheekbone and ran down her face. "You slept with him! That's what you did! You went home and slept with him!" Straddling her, he bent close, his face furious, fists ready to hit her again.

She tried to look up, to speak, but the room rocked about her, and a stunning pain filled her head. Her sight blurred, but she was conscious of his leaning over her. Somewhere in the recesses of her brain his words echoed, and she gasped out, "No! I didn't! I didn't!"

"Lie!" he roared. "Lie!" and socked his fist into the side of her face.

Pain seared her head. There was a roaring in her ears and the sickening taste of blood in her mouth. Convulsed, she doubled up and rolled onto her side, knocking him off balance. He stumbled backward, and Supaya, desperate to get away from him, crawled on hands and knees, blindly reaching out for something to defend herself with, knowing he would kill her. Her outstretched fingers touched the nail keg, the tools, the axe! Her fingers closed round the haft, and pulling herself onto her knees, she turned to face him.

Eli, crouching forward, arms raised, grabbed for her, but Supaya held up the axe, slanted, ready to strike.

"No closer!" she warned in a whisper, her words coming strangely through numbed lips.

"You would kill me, you bitch! Then he could move in!"

Supaya, uncomprehending, shook her battered, throbbing head, tried painfully to form a question.

Eli watched, hands ready, waiting for a chance to grab the axe. "You know! He even came to see the house! Damn him! He thinks well of himself, that . . . that cousin of yours!"

Supaya gasped. Her arm wavered, and Eli snatched, his fingers missing the axe as she quickly swung it up again. "What . . . what happened?" Holding onto a shelf, she got dizzily to her feet, holding on as the room turned about her.

Eli narrowed his eyes, but said nothing.

"Tell me!" she suddenly screamed, and swung the axe.

Eli ducked away, his arm raised defensively.

"Tell me!" Her head rocketing with pain, she drew the words out in an agonized, unrecognizable voice and swung the axe again.

"Put that down!"

"Tell . . . me!" Supaya swung again, tearing his shirt and the flesh of his arm.

Backed against the wall, he snarled at her. "You want to hear it? What you already know! What you planned! Your . . . cousin . . . Kineu Bruley . . . is here, living with his uncle! Everybody knows he's here! Everybody knows why!" His face crumpled in drunken grief, then changed to a sly vengefulness. "But you don't look so good now! He may wish he'd stayed home! My father knows! You'd better be careful! Remember Marie?" His voice shook, weak tears filled his eyes. "You'd better remember! And you'd better tell that . . . cousin . . . about Marie!"

The room throbbed around her as if everything were breathing in and out in great shuddering gasps. In a small, remote part of her consciousness, she thought, Kineu! Here! Why hadn't one of them told her, why! She felt she was weaving, and tried to steady herself, to focus on Eli, who stared at her through strangely swimming eyes. She tried to speak. "I didn't know . . . I didn't . . .," but the rest was lost in choking sobs.

Eli, holding his bleeding arm, watched her dully. The axe hung at her side, but his anger and energy were spent. He stumbled into his bedroom, fell across the bed, and rolled over, mouth slack, his cut arm lying awkwardly across his chest.

Seeing Eli turn away, Supaya lost all feeling, all consciousness. The axe fell from her nerveless fingers, and she slumped to the floor.

With returning consciousness, Supaya became aware of her own pulse. She listened to it with a vague, detached interest as she floated in a dull, semi-awareness. Gradually her vision cleared. She saw the floor boards, the walls and shelves, of the lean-to. She lifted her head and instantly a terrible throbbing pain seized it. She saw blood smeared on her blouse and skirt. Shakily, she got to her feet, the effort making her skin moist and clammy. Leaning on the wash bench for support, she bathed her face, which was strangely numb and puffy. Looking in the mirror, she was stunned to see the whole left side of her face discolored, her left eye swollen shut. Her mouth and cheek were distended to twice their size, like a grotesque mask. Blood had caked on an ugly gash over her cheekbone and still seeped from a split in the tight-stretched skin of her lips.

Eli slept the rest of that day and until noon of the next. The house was empty when he woke. Stepping outside, he saw Supaya working in the freshly plowed garden.

Coming up behind her, he spoke apologetically. "Suppy, please stop. Come in and . . ." but as she straightened up and faced him, his words died in his throat.

"And what?" she asked. Her head still throbbed with pain, her lips still bled when she spoke or tried to eat. She saw, with indifference, the horror in his face.

Eli swallowed and looked away, his face pinched as if in pain or in an effort not to cry. "Nothing. I . . . I thought we might talk."

"It hurts to talk." She had to speak very carefully. She only wanted him to go away. "Why don't you finish the shed."

Unable to face her again, Eli nodded dumbly and went.

Nonen came by to see if Eli had returned. She gasped when she saw Supaya and put out her hands to her, but Supaya ignored her and continued spading the earth. Since Nonen had chosen not to warn her, she chose, proudly, not to recognize Nonen's concern. Or, when they came to see her, Soos' and George's. They brought her food, which she formally accepted, but they dared offer no other help. Supaya's cool eye did not permit it.

But when Supaya appeared at Amy Crowell's door, Amy clapped her hands over her mouth, horror-struck. When she could speak, she cried, "Sophia! What happened to you!" She drew Supaya inside, made her sit on the horsehair sofa, and insisted she put her feet on a stool. She clasped and unclasped her hands agitatedly and went to call her husband.

"No, please, Mrs. Crowell," said Supaya, trying not to smile lest she split the cuts open again. "Please, sit down." She patted the sofa, "I am all right. Sit down beside me, please."

Afraid the least jostle would cause Supaya pain, Amy finally brought herself to sit gingerly on the edge of the sofa.

"Here, I brought you something from my home."

Amy's small, pale eyes opened in amazement. She was not accustomed to gifts. Her husband said that food and drink were gifts from the Lord and the only gifts one needed. She marveled at Jules' box which Supaya had decorated with quills in a floral pattern, and became excited over Quayo's squash seeds.

"I'll plant them right away!" she exclaimed, jumping up. Then, catching herself, sat down again, embarrassed. "Oh, I'm sorry! I'll plant them later, of course. Now I'll make us a cup of tea." Suddenly worried again, she asked, "Can you drink a cup of tea?"

Supaya smiled a half smile. "No, thank you, Mrs. Crowell. I must go. You *should* plant those seeds now."

"I should?"

"My grandmother," said Supaya, going to the door, "said you were to plant them as soon as you unwrapped them."

"Sophia!" Mrs. Crowell came very close and put her fingers lightly on Supaya's arm. "Sophia, . . . could you . . . call me Amy?"

"Yes, I could if you wish it. Good-bye now, Amy."

Amy smiled with pleasure and quickly shut the door.

As Supaya turned out onto the road, she caught sight of a man coming in her direction. He raised his arm, but she went ahead, pretending not to have seen him. She heard him call, "Suppy!" and stopped, but did not turn. It was Kineu. She had hoped to avoid him at least for some weeks. But when he spoke her name again, softly, just behind her, anger flamed in her. She lifted her chin and turned.

He started as if she had slapped him. His lips parted, but finding no words, he stared unbelieving at her swollen eye, the black bruise spread over the side of her face, her gashed cheek and lips.

172

She saw his eyes narrow, his face harden with murderous anger, but she said nothing. Proudly, with cold eyes and the shadow of an ironic smile, she waited.

Kineu's brows drew together in a frown as he strove, eyes intent, to grasp her meaning. Suddenly, pierced with understanding, his head rolled back as if he found it difficult to breathe. He turned his stricken gaze to the sky, the trees, the fields, anywhere but on her.

Certain, now, that he would keep his distance, Supaya turned without a word and walked away.

Amy watched from behind the lace curtain. Clutching the box and packet of seeds against her chest, she murmured to herself, "Terrible! Terrible! I should have called Reverend Crowell! I should have!"

"But he could have killed you!" exclaimed Lizzie, striding about her kitchen, too indignant to sit still, scarcely able to thank Supaya for her gift of seeds and maple syrup. "If only you had come here first! I didn't know you had returned, or I would have warned you! We knew he had come, of course. He came to register. He asked about the location of your house. I should have spoken to him then!"

Supaya reassured her. "No, Lizzie, no. It is over. I am all right. Besides, it would have made no difference."

Only Jess Fallon greeted her as she would have wished. She felt his shock when his smile abruptly faded and his face grew taut. But he allowed her her pride, looking directly into her eyes and ignoring her face, as if they shared an understanding.

That evening Wenonga knocked at her house for the first time. He said nothing to Eli who opened the door, but went to Supaya. Without preamble, he lifted her chin and scrutinized her face. She held quite still, and when he had seen enough, he opened his medicine bag and took out several ingredients of his own mixture, including the leaves of the boneset plant. Making a paste, he applied it gently to Supaya's face. He left her an additional supply and instructed her. "Make a paste of this and put it on every night until you are healed," he said, his face angry and stern. Supaya offered him tea and bread, but he thanked her gruffly and left as abruptly as he had come.

Over the next few days, Eli made good progress with the shed, now finished except for hanging the door. He had only to put up the fence for the pigpen on one side and build the chicken roost on the other, and it would be done.

Supaya, busy planting the garden, put off buying a shoat and chickens because of the bear, who continued to raid white farms and was occasionally seen in the reserve woods. Stories circulated of his carrying off farm animals and mauling dogs, of his frightening appearances in the woods, looming up suddenly where an instant before there'd been only trees.

A meeting was called at the Council Hall to consider this common problem. Stories of the bear's size and prowess were repeated. Pipes were smoked and old men told stories from the past of great hunts and hunters. Various stratagems were proposed for trapping and killing the bear.

Eli and his friends, standing at the back of the hall, listened, glanced at each other, and laughed to cover their embarrassment at not being able to join in the storytelling, at their failure to emulate, much less rival, the deeds of their fathers and grandfathers. They passed a bottle and began clowning, drawing stern, disapproving looks from their elders.

Eli saw Kineu, sitting with his uncle, John Bruley, who offered one of the plans for killing the bear, a plan suggested, he said modestly, by his nephew, a fine hunter recently come from Stone Island.

As the drinkers grew more boisterous, the Chief stood up and asked them to be quiet or leave. His request set off a burst of hilarity, and they left, after declaring they had the best plan. They would get the bear drunk, lead him to the Council Hall, and he would die of boredom, listening to old men tell tales.

Eli did not come home until noon of the next day. Supaya, hearing him enter, went to stir a pot of stew on the stove, where she could easily reach the axe should she need to do so.

But this time Eli kept the table between them as he rambled on, waving his arms, telling her about the meeting.

"You should have been there! The room was full of hunters! All great hunters!" He spoke sarcastically, rocking back on his heels. "Your . . . cousin was there. Mr. Bruley! He's a great hunter too!" Eli swung his arms wide. "The great hunter from Stone Island! Ha!" He leaned forward, bracing his hands on the table, and narrowed his eyes. "What's so great about shooting a gun! Eh? My father showed me how to shoot a gun! Yes, he did! Any fool can shoot a gun! Even I!" He grinned at her. "I bet I can shoot better than those old men! Maybe even better than Mr. Bruley! What would you think then, eh?!" With surprising quickness, he circled the table, stumbled into the lean-to, and before Supaya realized what he was doing, he had the shotgun in his hands.

"Eli!" she cried, rushing toward him. "Put it back! Please!"

Eli swung the gun at her like a club. "Keep back! Keep away! You want your head broken again? I can do that too!"

Supaya stopped, but seeing him load the gun with fumbling, awkward fingers, she begged, "Please, Eli, don't go! I'm afraid!" She started toward him again, but he swung up the loaded gun and aimed it at her.

"Afraid! My wife! Afraid I won't come back or afraid I will!" He grinned. "But I'm not afraid! Mr. Bruley's not afraid! Not us great hunters! You'll see!" He rushed out the door and headed toward the woods.

Supaya watched to see his direction, then took the axe and followed him.

The day was sunny, but a fresh, strong wind blew from the west. Large masses of white clouds moved swiftly in rapidly changing shapes across a vivid blue sky. Birds soared up from the fields, wheeled in flocks, and streamed away, riding down the air currents. Trees bent like whips in the wind, and in the woods all the branches were in motion, leaves forming and reforming patterns of bright sunlight and shade, misleading and tricking the eye. Supaya paused, listening, searching for an indication of the path Eli had taken. The wind pressed hard against her, and she was filled, suddenly, with a deep foreboding. The whole earth was astir; everything moved with a power that coursed like invisible lightning through the air. She began to run, hurried by the wind at her back. Thinking she glimpsed Eli, she called out, but her voice was carried away. The light shifted, and Eli was not there. Then, right before her, she saw the tree, its bark ripped and torn by long claw marks. Below the clawing, tufts of black hair were snagged in the rough bark where a bear had rubbed its back! And on the ground were paw prints!

Whirling around, Supaya ran, ran against the wind as fast as she could toward Wenonga's house. Whipped by the wind, her hair came loose and streamed back from her face; her lungs ached for breath.

Nonen, working in the garden, dropped her hoe and hurried forward when she saw Supaya racing toward her.

"Wenonga!" gasped Supaya, "where's Wenonga?"

"There, in the barn. Supaya, what's wrong?"

As Supaya ran toward the barn, Wenonga appeared, leading Nellie by her halter. "Wenonga! Come quickly! Eli took the gun and went after the bear! And he's there! I saw his claw marks! Wenonga! He's big! I have such dread!"

Wenonga thrust the halter at Nonen. "Which way did he go?"

"Toward the bluff!"

"You stay here!" he yelled, running to the house for his gun.

"Supaya! Come back!" cried Nonen, but Supaya was already running back toward the woods.

Now the wind pushed her forward and blew her hair maddeningly across her face. She ran until she had to stop for breath, then ran again. If only Wenonga would hurry! Nearing the bluff, she heard deep, angry bellows resounding hollowly through the woods. Her heart constricted with fear, she came out onto the bluff near the rockfall and saw them both: Eli, standing on the edge, the blue of lake and sky behind him, paralyzed with fright, not aiming the gun but holding it like a stick before him, and the bear, standing upright, snarling and bellowing, dropping onto all fours and weaving, then rising upright again, pawing the air.

"Shoot, Eli! Shoot!" cried Supaya.

Roaring, the bear suddenly rushed forward, slashing out with his paws. Eli jerked backward, stumbled, lost his footing and fell over the edge, arms flung out, the gun like a standard in his hand. His scream carried on the rushing air and echoed against the far bluff.

"Eli!" shrieked Supaya, running forward.

At her cry the bear turned, snarling, his black lip wrinkled back from his great teeth, and Supaya stopped, aghast, utterly still, the bear's frightening, musky odor heavy in her nostrils.

Startled by another antagonist and seeing Wenonga racing forward, the bear hesitated, the heavy ruff on his neck and shoulders riffled by the wind, his long, blue-black claws gleaming. Backing away, he pawed and snorted, then dropped to his feet and swiftly, with one long, powerful stride, leaped onto the rockfall just as Wenonga shot, leaped again from the rocks and vanished in the sunlit, windblown woods.

Supaya rushed to the edge. Below, Eli's body lay on the rocks, arms and legs outflung. "Hurry! We must hurry!" she exclaimed, turning to Wenonga, who stood beside her, gazing down.

Slowly, he turned to look at her, his eyes fierce, his mouth grim.

"He's alive!" cried Supaya. "I saw him move!"

But Wenonga stared at her, unbelieving.

"He moved, I tell you!" Supaya insisted frantically. "He moved his head! Ah!" With an impatient gesture, Supaya spun around and began running. She would get George and Gerald Toomis to help! They would go with a stretcher and a wagon!

Wenonga looked down once more. This time he saw Eli lift his head. Instantly he turned and raced for home.

CHAPTER
FIFTEEN

Jules received Supaya's letter and left the next day, catching the steamer on its return trip. He rode out from Wellston to the reserve with Jess Fallon. Nonen met them at the door. Supaya came quickly from Eli's room to greet her father.

Jules was shocked to see her face. As Supaya had grown into womanhood, he had watched with pleasure and pride her increasing beauty, heightened beyond that of her mother by the subtle admixture of his own features. Now he stared in anger at the ugly, greenish-purple bruise and the still-livid welt disfiguring her face. "What happened?" he demanded.

"Oh, Father!" Supaya leaned her face against his shoulder, hiding the tears of gratitude for his coming that rose in her eyes. Jules held her silently for a moment, then asked in a dangerous tone, "Why has Wenonga not . . .''

Supaya raised her head. "Father, he is not to blame." As Jules continued to look searchingly at her, she touched her face as if to brush away the blemish. "It is nothing now. I am all right. It's Eli who needs help! Father! I'm so glad you have come!"

"I am glad to be here," said Jules, accepting her word and putting aside his anger. "Where is Eli? May I see him?"

As they entered the bedroom, Eli was speaking in a breathy, gasping voice. "I'm hot! So hot!" He lay flat on his back, his body bare except for a loincloth. His arms and legs, unnaturally still, were swollen and splotched with deep bruises. One leg was crooked, the skin torn open where a jagged point of bone pierced through.

Though the window was open, Jules could smell a faint odor of putrefaction. Wenonga sat by the bedside, bathing Eli's head and chest.

"I'm hot! Give me a drink!"

Wenonga slid an arm under his head and held a cup to his lips.

Jules, observing that Eli did not move, went around to the other side of the bed. He nodded a silent greeting to Wenonga, then bent forward, putting himself in Eli's range of vision, and spoke softly. "I am Jules, Supaya's father. I have come to see you, Eli, to help you."

Eli's eyes were shiny with fever. He focused his intense gaze on Jules. "I am glad you came." His voice was hoarse. A faint smile crossed his face. "But you cannot help me."

"We will try," said Jules.

Eli appeared not to have heard. His gaze wandered, then his eyelids drooped and he drifted off into sleep. As he slept, Wenonga and Jules examined him, consulting together.

"His back is broken," said Wenonga. "That is why he does not move. He feels nothing."

Jules' sensitive fingers moved gently over Eli's body. "Both his arms are broken. And his legs—here, and here." He raised Eli's body to one side, then laid him back, sickened by what he'd seen. "It is good he can feel no pain," Jules said grimly. "His back is mangled. But he must be bathed."

Wenonga agreed. "He cannot control his body. Let him sleep now. When he wakes we will treat him."

In the outer room Jess Fallon was speaking with Nonen, asking if there was anything they needed that he could bring. "I'd be glad to get medicine from town or a doctor. Do you want me to go now and bring a doctor?"

"You are kind," said Nonen stiffly, trying to hide her grief, "but they," nodding toward the bedroom, "*are* doctors. They make their own medicine. If they need help, they will call on their *midé* brothers."

Jess nodded. He was familiar with the general reluctance to call in a white doctor. And he partly understood, knowing Indians could rarely afford the fees. Determined to help in some way, he brought in supplies from his wagon and, over Nonen's protests, left them on the table. Last, he carried in a rocking chair Jules had made as a gift for Supaya.

179

When Jules and Wenonga came from the bedroom, Jess shook hands with Jules. "If there is anything at all I can do, please let me know."

When he had gone, Nonen lit the lamp and brought tea and food for Jules, who had not eaten all day.

Supaya was surprised and pleased by Jules' gift. She admired the chair's high curved back of ash and maple and its closely woven ash splint seat.

"My daughter told me I must keep my fingers nimble," said Jules, smiling at her. "That chair tells you I will never forget what you did for me."

Supaya leaned her head back. "It is a comfortable chair, Father. I will rest in it always." But weary though she was, Supaya was too distraught to sit still. "Is there nothing you can do?" She appealed to the men, their faces grave in the lamplight.

"He is asleep now," said Jules gently.

"You must rest too, Suppy," said Nonen. "You haven't slept for two days."

"We will hold a *midé* ceremony," announced Wenonga. He saw them all turn toward him and was conscious of Jules' surprise. But he chose to ignore it, refusing to acknowledge the hopelessness of Eli's condition. "Tomorrow," he insisted, "I will call our *midé* brothers together and send to the other reserves. . . ." He broke off at a cry from the bedroom.

Eli had awakened and found himself alone in the dark. When they entered, his frightened eyes strained sideways, toward the doorway.

"We are here, Eli. We are here with you," said Supaya, stroking his head.

"Now you are awake, we will treat your wounds," said Wenonga.

Eli whimpered, "No, no, I can't. . . ."

"You must be cleansed," said Supaya soothingly. "You don't need to move. They will do it for you."

Wenonga prepared his medicines while Jules and Nonen arranged boards on two chairs and spread over them a clean quilt. When Wenonga was ready, the two men lifted Eli and laid him face down on the quilt, his head turned to one side. Quickly Nonen and Supaya gathered up the soiled bedding and carried it outside to be boiled clean.

Together Wenonga and Jules bathed him, then with scented

herbal water they cleansed his lacerations and applied medicinal pastes. Jules offered some of his own preparations, which Wenonga gratefully accepted, acknowledging Jules' talent as a healer.

When they could do no more for him, they moved Eli back to his freshly made-up bed and covered him with a blanket, for the night air was chill, and Eli, his fever down, felt cold.

Jules drew Wenonga aside. "Our prayers cannot help him. He has already gone beyond us."

But Wenonga, the astute, perceptive healer, could not face such judgment for his own son. He gestured impatiently, insisting, "There is a chance! We will try! We must try!" Then Wenonga pressed the women and Jules to go and lie down while he sat with his son.

He turned the lamp low and pulled his chair close to the bed. He laid his wide hand over Eli's nerveless one.

"You feel better now, Son?"

Eli smiled faintly. "I feel only hot and cold, Father." In the dim light his gaze rested on his father's face, the bones of forehead, cheek, and jaw strong as carved wood. The tension between them, the smoldering antagonism that flared up at a word and made it impossible for them to speak except in anger, was now gone. Looking openly, deeply, into his father's eyes, Eli rested on the love he saw there. Here was the father he had cried for those first frightening, lonely months of separation so many years ago. Feeling the strength of the cords that bound them together, Eli struggled to speak what he had long ached to say but had shut away within himself.

". . . and I feel . . . sad, Father, that I have not . . . been a good son to you."

Wenonga leaned closer, his wide, strong face soft and gentle, his broad hand gripping Eli's. "My son, rid your soul of regret. The fault was not yours. You were deprived of the dream that every man must have. You were driven down a path that led to a barren wasteland, and you could not find your way back. But have courage. Tomorrow I will call our *midé* brothers together, and we will hold a ceremony for you. When you are well again, you may yet find your way."

Eli wanted to say no to the ceremony, but was ashamed of his reasons. He could only smile, his eyes on his father's face until his lids grew heavy and he drowsed off.

Before dawn Jules came and relieved Wenonga, who reluctantly agreed to rest. Eli was feverish again and delirious, breathing in quick, shallow gasps. His lips quivered, and he uttered small mournful cries.

Jules was gently bathing his head and chest when Eli suddenly started awake. Jules gave him a drink of water that George had brought for him from the spring. When the water had eased the dryness of his lips and throat, Eli said, "I had bad dreams."

"You have a fever. Fever brings bad dreams."

"A man was chasing me! And when I fell, he stopped and waited for me to get up. Then he chased me again, and I fell! Over and over!"

Jules pressed a damp cloth to Eli's temples. "But now you are awake."

"Yes, but I can smell him! I smell Death! He touched me! I can't ever get away!" His mouth twitched. He spoke sharply under his breath. "You know I will die, don't you! I see it in your eyes! I will, won't I!"

Meeting Eli's piercing gaze, Jules nodded soberly, once.

Eli immediately looked away and spoke rapidly. "I am glad you are here. Without the others. I can speak to you. My father . . . wants to hold a *midé* ceremony. You must tell him no. No, I say!" His glance flashed at Jules, then away. "I do not wish it. It would do no good." He frowned. "I wish to die . . . I mean, I don't want to live as . . . as I have! You must help your daughter! I was no . . . fit husband for her!" His eyes pleaded with Jules for understanding.

"I will help her," said Jules quietly. "We all will help her."

"You . . . you are kind to me." Eli's face crumpled. Tears filled his eyes, and his words spilled out in a whisper. "I . . . I don't want to live! But I'm afraid! I can't speak of fear to my father! He thinks I am brave! But I'm afraid! I don't know his spirits! I don't know any . . . oh! what will happen? Help me! Please, help me!"

Jules put aside the basin and cloth. He rose, turned out the lamp, and stood in the gray morning light, by the window. "See, the sky lightens. The sun rises. The day has been born again." He sat down and gazed hypnotically into Eli's eyes. "Death has touched you, as he touches all things. But he cannot take. Our Father, the Great Spirit who causes this day to be born, who gives life to every living thing, also gave you life. Though you know him not, He knows you. The great Giver-of-Life, He it is, and only He, who will take you." Jules bowed his head and extended his arms over Eli.

182

"Oh Great One who watches over us! Hear me! I who
    know nothing beg of you who knows all! Take up
    this lost soul! He is blind and cannot see his way!
"Oh Great Spirit! You who cause the earth to spring with
    eternal life! Guide this soul back to you!
"Oh Great Spirit! Father of all life! Fill his soul with joy!
    Guide him back into the river of eternal life!"

Slowly Jules lowered his arms. His eyes met Eli's and held in silence. After a time, Eli asked, "Will you stay by me? Help me
when . . . when I need it?"

Jules smiled. "Yes, Eli. I will stay by you."

That morning friends and neighbors began coming, bringing
gifts of food. Some stayed, sitting on the floor, backs against the
wall, silently concentrating, striving to bring the force of their ener-
gies and that of their spirit helpers to the aid of the sick one.

Wenonga, whom Jules finally brought to understand Eli's
wishes, sat near his son as Supaya combed his hair and coaxed him
to drink some broth.

Eli's sleep grew more disturbed, his waking periods less lucid,
more feverish. Toward evening, after Wenonga and Jules had
treated him again and his bedding had been changed, Wenonga
went to his own home. Jules, Supaya, and Nonen sat with Eli while
old women in the outer room began to wail softly, their shawls
pulled forward over their faces.

At home Wenonga did not light a lamp, but entered his own
room and pulled the curtain. From his trunk he took out his ceremonial pipe, carved out of grayish pipestone, with a round bowl and
a straight stem, seven inches long. The mouthpiece, nine inches
long, was carved of wood. Hanging from the long stem were pieces
of beadwork, a fur talisman, and offerings, little bundles of cornmeal
wrapped in rawhide. Filling this pipe, he sat down cross-legged on
the floor and smoked quietly, composing himself. In the still air of
the dim, closed room, the smoke curled up from the pipe and
spread out, hanging like a thin, blue-gray cloud in the growing dusk.
Gradually night filled the room until only the red glow of the pipe
shone out at intervals, a red eye in the dark.

Much later, when the remote stars moved silently across the
heavens, Wenonga put away his pipe and took from his trunk a
bundle of mink fur. Carefully, needing no light, he unrolled it and
took out a long, delicate whistle made of a wild goose bone which
was suspended from a rawhide thong. He put the thong over his

183

head so the whistle, smooth as ivory, hung against his chest. Kneeling, his hands raised, palms outward, he rocked back and forth, chanting softly until his eyes, opened wide in the dark, saw beyond the dark, and his spirit floated up from his body.

Then, lifting the whistle to his lips, he blew four high, piercing blasts, and called out in hollow, nasal tones:

"Great Spirit Dog! You who are great in heart and
strength! Hear me! Come to me!"
"Great Spirit Raven! You whose shadow and keen eye
strike fear in all men! Hear me! Come to me!"
"Great Spirit Turtle! Whose wisdom knows no end!
Whose thought circles the world! Hear me! Come to
me!"

Slowly, rhythmically, he rocked, back and forth, back and forth. Then he blew the whistle again, four shrill blasts.

"Great Spirit Dog! Help my son who lies still and dying!
Give him of your strength and endurance!"
"Great Spirit Raven! Help my son! Fan him with your
wings! Frighten off Death, who sits at his feet!"
"Great Spirit Turtle! Help my son! Breathe on him that he
may live to thank you for long life!"

Again he blew four times, four long, high notes that sounded far beyond the walls of the house, that pierced the breathing night, startling creatures in the woods who paused to listen. Then Wenonga closed his eyes and with hands resting on his knees, knelt motionless, entranced.

As night faded, the soft white of the bone whistle appeared, emerging out of the dark, alone and glimmering, suspended in midair; then Wenonga's rapt, uplifted face, his broad forehead and wide cheekbones rising out of the night as out of dark water, his closed eyes and all about him still in deep shadow.

In the east, a blood-red sun tipped the horizon, staining the rippled surface of the lake a shimmering rose and reddening the tops of trees. Soos, her shawl around her head, crossed the damp fields, and entering Supaya's house through the lean-to, began preparing food for the family, and those who had come to mourn.

In the bedroom Nonen turned out the lamp. Silently, Wenonga entered and took a seat opposite Jules. The stench of rotting flesh, like a pall on the damp morning air, assailed his nostrils. Relinquishing at last all hope, Wenonga sat stolidly, his head sunk on his chest, watching his son.

Eli's breathing was irregular. He muttered and cried out, startling himself into brief consciousness. He stared at Supaya or Nonen when they wiped his forehead, with glazed, wild eyes, the glimmer of recognition coming slowly or not at all. Finally he fell into a less troubled sleep, so deep that they could scarcely discern his breathing. Suddenly, with a gasping cry, his eyes opened wide in horror. Jules leaned forward, and Eli, seeing him, whispered, "Help me!"

As the others watched, Jules took from his bag a powder he had prepared during the night and stirred it into a cup of spring water. Lifting Eli's head, he held the potion to his parched lips. "This will give you sleep without dreams."

Eagerly Eli drank. For a time he gazed wearily at the morning light shining in at the window. Then, smiling faintly, he fell asleep.

Silently they sat with him, their faces drawn, their eyes burning from sleeplessness. In the outer room the wailing of the old women rose and fell, an unceasing, mournful expression of all their grief. George had already gone for the coffin.

By midday Eli's face was no longer flushed. His expression was calm. All at once his lips parted on a sharp intake of breath, then he sighed, and his face went slack.

Wenonga raised his head and gazed on his son. Without a word he rose and walked out. Quietly, sadly, Jules followed. When the old women saw them coming out, they raised their arms, their lamentations increasing in volume and intensity. As the men left, Nonen began to keen, beating her clasped hands against her knees, and Supaya started to her feet. Seeing Eli's lifeless face, she cried out, in long, bitter wails. Bending over him, not knowing what she searched for, she gazed down at him through a blur of tears, filled with a deep, aching sorrow for his lost and wasted life, for the life they could have had together. Overwhelmed with a numbing sense of defeat, she turned away. Mechanically, she undid her hair, shook it down, and taking the scissors, cut it off, a handful at a time until it barely reached her ears. Then she took Nonen's arm and, helping her to her feet, led her out into the other room.

The old women, long-time witnesses of death, were ready to lay out the body. They carried basins of sweet-scented herbal water into the bedroom. Carefully they washed Eli's body, combed his hair, and dressed him in clean clothes.

In the kitchen Supaya and Soos put cedar boughs and water into an enameled pan and heated them until they were hot and smoking. The branches exuded their oil into the water and filled the house with their aromatic odor.

When George returned with the coffin, Jules helped him

place it on two chairs in the living room. Nonen lined it with an old, clean, brightly colored quilt she had made years before which included many patches from clothes Eli had worn as a child. The men carried Eli out and placed him in the coffin; thereafter he would not be touched again. Then Wenonga and Jules, Supaya and Nonen, and the two old women dipped their forearms in the hot, oily cedar water and wiped their faces and hands with the hot boughs.

They were shaking the wet boughs around the coffin when Gerald Toomis and Reverend Crowell came in. The two men nodded gravely and exchanged greetings with the assembled mourners, then turned toward Supaya.

She paused, holding the hot, wet boughs, to accept their sympathy. But Nonen and the old women carried theirs into the bedroom, where they waved them about the room and brushed them over the bed and chairs.

"What are they doing?" asked Reverend Crowell, looking after them, a faint frown on his long, thin face. His eyes rested suspiciously on the boughs in Supaya's hand.

"It is our way," said Supaya, "of disinfecting." She spoke quietly, choosing her words carefully to allay his suspicion. "The hot cedar oil takes away infection."

"Ah yes. I see." His face relaxed. "Our doctors use peroxide or alcohol for the same purpose."

And Supaya, continuing with the ritual of cleansing away the pollution of death, let him think what he wished.

Everyone came to the wake: Nonen's friends, Eli's friends, those Supaya had treated, and all the others who knew Wenonga's power and would not risk offending him. They came bringing food and tea for the wake, and they filled Supaya's house. They stood against the walls and sat on the floor until there was little room to move about in. Soos and Sarah and neighbors helped with the cooking. Sarah, solemn but excited by her first experience at a wake, asked her mother in a whisper why Supaya, pale but dry-eyed, didn't cry more.

"Hush," said Soos. "You do not understand. One does not always cry."

Reverend Crowell, holding his Bible, stood by the coffin. He cleared his throat and when all were silent, he spoke of the young man he had married with such hope for his future, and of his bravery in confronting on behalf of them all the wild beast that was ravaging the countryside. He read a passage from the Bible, then asked all to bow their heads in prayer. After leading them in singing a hymn, he accepted a cup of tea and some scone.

A few of the mourners joined him out of politeness, so he should not eat and drink alone. But they did so with decorum. Not until he and Gerald Toomis had shaken hands with the principal mourners and left did they relax, and then the real wake began.

Lamps were lit, and food was passed around. Those who wished to place something in the coffin for Eli came forward. Wenonga, hiding inside his shirt a toy bow and arrow he'd made which Eli had prized, bent over the coffin. Not wanting anyone to see he surreptitiously slipped the bow and arrow under Eli's arm, alongside his body. Supaya brought one of her embroidered birch-bark boxes, but was not satisfied. Getting some of Quayo's medicine that glowed in the dark, she wrapped a pinch of it in paper-thin birchbark and slipped the little packet into the pocket of Eli's shirt so it might guard him against perils on his soul's long journey. Several of his friends left tokens in the coffin, one, his prized penknife, which Eli had once admired.

A group of old men, sitting on the floor in a semicircle, began an old chant, a song of loss. Their voices rose and fell in cadence to the slow clapping of their hands. The other mourners, sitting and standing, swayed to the beat, as the strong, deep voices chanted their dirge for the dead, expressing the bereavement of all those left behind. After the last, long, atonal note died away, all joined in singing hymns in Ojibwa.

All night long the wake continued. Children fell asleep, their heads in their mothers' laps, while their parents sang. Nonen sat in the rocking chair, Supaya and Jules on the floor beside her. Wenonga stood apart, by the fireplace, his face in shadow. Supaya thought she could not sing or eat or drink, but as the singing continued, she was caught up by it. Stirred by the music, she sang with the others, finding in this communal expression of grief an unexpected solace. Almost unthinking, she ate when food was put in her hand and drank when given a cup, then sang again, eased and comforted.

When the lamps paled in the morning light, the mourners began to depart, in twos and threes, walking slowly back to their homes in the fresh dawn air for a rest before the church service and burial.

Eli was given a fine funeral. Everyone attended, filling the church so that it was necessary for some to stand at the back. Gerald and Lizzie Toomis came, and Jess Fallon and his wife with her thick yellow braids like a crown on her head. Even the schoolteacher, whom Supaya scarcely knew, came. Amy played for the service, and afterwards a group of Indian men playing trombones, cornets, and trumpets accompanied the coffin from the church to the grave and played one last dirge at the graveside.

A week later Supaya and Jules walked to the cemetery. At the head of the mound of raw earth was a flowerpot holding a flowering plant, put there by Amy Crowell. Stooping, Supaya tucked under its leaves a bundle of dried meat and bread, food for Eli's soul on its journey. Should Amy discover it, Supaya knew she would say nothing.

Nonen had gone back to Wenonga's house so he would not be alone, and Jules stayed with Supaya. She was grateful for his company, and able to speak more freely to him than ever before. She showed him her garden, told him of her plan to fatten a pig and raise chickens, and showed him the ash splint baskets she had made during the winter months. But she took no time to sit with him, going about her work with a driving intensity. Observing this, Jules went hunting with Wenonga and brought her porcupines, went fishing and brought his share back for her to split and dry. He spent hours in the woods, stripping birchbark. He cut ash wood and pounded it into splints.

After a week of this, Supaya gently admonished him. "Father, you need not work so hard. When you go home they will say you tired yourself taking care of your foolish daughter."

"Very well, Foolish Daughter, I will gladly sit and smoke my pipe if you also will sit for a while. Otherwise, I will think the chair I made for you was a useless gift."

Supaya laughed and sat down at once. She realized how tense and tired she was and how reluctant to face the time when her father would return home and she would be left alone.

Jules filled his pipe, lit it, and leaned back against the table. "This is a fine house, Daughter. Is it still yours to live in?"

"Yes, Father. Nonen gave it to me. She calls it her little hut. When her daughter moved away, she had the agent register it in my name."

"Then you have your own home. That is well. You have good friends here, and also the friendship of the whites."

"All the same, Father," said Supaya, a bit shamefaced, feeling like a child again, "I will miss you."

Jules was deeply pleased, but he laughed.

Supaya looked up quickly. "Why do you laugh?"

He pulled on his pipe before answering, and his eyes were amused. "Daughter, you won't have time to bother about your old father. You'll have a garden, a pig, chickens . . . and suitors."

"Father!"

Jules chuckled and gazed at her appreciatively. He was quite aware of her attraction for men. He had seen it in the eyes of men who looked at her, both Indian and white. "I am sure any man would welcome a wife, no matter how plain, who came with a house and chickens. That store owner, the one who drove me here," he said shrewdly, "he would admire a house like this."

"Oh, Father!" Supaya laughed. "He's white! Besides, he is married."

"*Is* he," said Jules musingly, seeing her blush. "Well," he said, seriously, "you have a year of mourning. Then there will be time for suitors. You will be busy also with healing. You are much respected here for your skill. Do not shake your head. Many have spoken to me in praise of your healing." He paused again and frowned. "You have had a difficult time here. I know that, and I am sorry for those times. Even so, you have brought only honor to your family. We are proud of you."

Supaya was rendered speechless by his praise, and Jules smiled at her fondly. But he was saddened. "Like your mother— and your grandmother—you are a strong woman. You no longer need a father to tell you what to do." He rose, and getting his medicine bag, took out of it the bear claw necklace with the blue stone. Remembering the old, deep wound he had dealt her, he held it out, and uncertain of her reaction, lied tactfully.

"You forgot it," he said. "If you don't want it, I will take it back."

At sight of it, tears filled Supaya's eyes. "Father!" She reached out and took the necklace, holding it with both hands. "I am glad you brought it!" She pressed it against her chest. "I have wished for it. It gives me strength. And I will need strength now that . . . that I'm to be alone."

Jules heard the fear in her voice and thought of Kineu, who had carefully stayed away. But he could not yet speak of Kineu, not for a year. "You should not live here alone. Could that child, Sarah, come to stay with you?"

"Maybe. But it isn't just that I'll be alone! Oh, Father, I'm afraid of Wenonga! He . . . he comes too close! He. . . ." She thought of the huge white dog, padding through the woods, waiting for her on the road, or at night, standing in the snow, staring upward, eyes flashing in the moonlight. "He . . . he is a powerful doctor! He pursues me!"

Jules frowned. "But you must not be afraid! Or do not let him know you are! He knows you are the daughter of a powerful doctor. And he knows you dreamed and have a powerful guardian. Do not forget, you can always call on him for help. Wenonga knows that and will be cautious. Also, you have friends here. The white women will be your biggest friends in this matter. They will have no patience with Wenonga. If you tell them of him, they will be angry and will tell their husbands to speak to him. The agent could take away his right to cut wood. Wenonga would not want that."

Supaya, relieved to have voiced her fear, put the necklace around her neck and thanked him. "I will remember what you have said, Father. And I will try to be strong. You must not worry about me."

Before Jules left for home, he visited Nonen and Wenonga. Nonen was dozing in her rocker by the stove. The two men walked together down the dirt road.

"Tomorrow I return home," said Jules. "I am sorry I was of no help."

"You did what you could," said Wenonga. "I am grateful. I regret that I have no grandchildren. But do not worry about your daughter. She must come back and live in my home, where she belongs. My sister and I will look after her."

"No," said Jules flatly.

Wenonga halted, surprised by an answer he clearly had not expected. Jules looked him in the eye and spoke quietly, but his words were commanding and final. "She has made a home for herself. She is to stay where she is."

Wenonga's face suffused with displeasure. He glared at Jules suspiciously, debating whether he should consider himself insulted or not. He answered angrily. "There is the period of mourning to be considered. She has a duty to her husband's family."

Jules' narrowed eyes and cold, haughty tone were a warning. "I am sure my daughter will perform her duty as she has always done. I no longer hold you responsible for her welfare. She is a strong woman, able to look after herself."

Wenonga restrained his peevish temper, and the two men parted.

The next morning, very early since Jules was riding into Wellston with Jess to catch the morning steamer, Supaya prepared food for him to take on the journey and made some bannock to have with their morning tea. She wrapped up dried berries and soft white cheese as a special gift for Quayo.

"Tell Grandma she is often in my thoughts," said Supaya, "and greet Rhea for me."

Jules nodded. "Life burns strongly in Quayo. But, remember, she is old and her body is weak. You must come soon to see her. Perhaps," said Jules slyly, amusement in his voice, "next spring. There will be a birth. You will have a half-brother or half-sister."

"Father!" Supaya smiled with surprise, then, seeing the mixture of embarrassment and happiness in Jules' face, she laughed. Their eyes, so much alike, met in an understanding that needed no words, and he laughed with her.

"Life has been much better since your visit," said Jules. "She has learned how to be a wife." He paused thoughtfully. "I think someone must have spoken to her."

"Very likely," said Supaya soberly.

"I must go now," said Jules. "It has been good to see you. I have spoken to Wenonga. He understands that you are to remain here in your own home." He gazed at Supaya fondly and gently touched her cheek where the bruise was rapidly fading. "You are looking better now. I am sure you will be all right."

"Let me know when, Father, in the spring!" called Supaya after him.

He raised his hand in salute and strode down the lane to the road. She stood in the doorway and watched him go, his banded, black hat at a jaunty angle, his bag slung over his shoulder, walking with his usual faintly arrogant swagger.

PART THREE
1907–1909

CHAPTER SIXTEEN

Supaya, working in Nonen's garden, felt oppressed and weary. She thrust the spade into the hard, sun-baked earth, loosening it, turning the clods over and breaking them up, working one row after the other. She longed for a good soaking rain, but the cloudless sky glared with a brilliant, almost white light. Her back and shoulders ached from spading Nonen's garden as well as her own and from carrying pails of water to the drooping, wilting plants, inadequate but enough, she hoped, to keep them alive. She paused to drink at the pump, holding her dusty arms under the cool gush of water and splashing it over her throbbing forehead and smarting eyes. Hearing Nonen call, she went inside.

Nonen sat in her rocking chair, her head leaning back. The bones of her wide face were more prominent than they had been; her once vigorous body had shrunk so that her dress hung loose from her shoulders. A cold, contracted in late spring after Eli's death, had debilitated her and developed into a wracking cough, and though Supaya tried, she could not coax her out into the sun. Knowing she grieved for her daughter who never wrote or visited her and for Eli, the little boy child she had mothered for his first six years, Supaya tried to pamper her, visiting her as often as she could, bringing special, tempting dishes. But Nonen waved the food away. Content to sit and rock, she steadily lost weight and strength, and only occasionally would she take the medicinal drinks Supaya prepared for her. A coughing fit left her exhausted. Still she would smile and say it was nothing.

Now she wanted Supaya to keep her company. "Sit down and rest. You work too hard."

Hearing their voices, Wenonga came from his room. The sight of Supaya, her face flushed, the curve of her throat exposed by her opened collar, drew him close to her. He sought to compel her by his eyes, soft and suggestive. "Nonen is right. The sun is hot. You should come with me to the spring. That would refresh you." He slid his fingers around her upper arm, pressing the back of his hand against her side.

Supaya pulled her arm free and turned away. "I am too tired to go anywhere."

"Then you should lie down. Your room is here, waiting for you." His tone was ingratiating, and he laid his hand flat against the middle of her back.

Through her damp blouse, his hand, heavy and warm, seemed to lie directly on her bare skin. After a brief, almost numbing shock, she stepped away. "No, I must go home."

"Let her be," said Nonen with an impatient gesture. But her voice was weak and testy, not firmly protective as in the past. The other two heard the difference and understood instantly.

"This is your home," said Wenonga smoothly, perceiving that Nonen would welcome Supaya's living with them and pressing his advantage.

Panicked, Supaya backed away. "No . . . no! I have my own home. I will stay in the old hut." She left quickly, half running despite her weariness and the heat. She saw now that Nonen, growing weaker and needing support, could easily come to overlook Wenonga's advances, even, she thought with dismay, to accept their living together in order to keep Supaya near. But however weak, Nonen was some protection. Should she die, unexpectedly soon, as could happen . . . Supaya thought of her sister, Neegonas, of her unexpected death in childbirth. Jacques had written a short time ago to say that Neegonas had died, and that Aunt Hettie was caring for the infant. Should Nonen die, there would be no one to stand between her and Wenonga.

She thought of her father's suggestion that Sarah come to live with her, but she hesitated to ask Soos for Sarah. Soos' second child still needed much attention and nine-year-old Sarah looked after her, freeing Soos for other work. Supaya, placing Quayo's glowing medicine near her bed, thought of Kineu, as she now so often did. She had not seen him since their encounter in front of

Amy Crowell's house. His uncle had come to Eli's funeral out of fear and respect for Wenonga, but Kineu had tactfully stayed away. Nor did she see him at church on Sundays, for Kineu had refused since boyhood to attend the white man's church. Should she marry Kineu, she would be protected from Wenonga, but that was not to be thought of for months—long, frighteningly lonely winter months.

When she looked in her mirror, she saw that her face was healed. The swelling and discoloration were gone and even the gash, treated by Wenonga's paste, had healed without blemish. As she combed her hair, now grown almost to her shoulders, she studied her reflection. At twenty-two, Supaya was unaware of the strength in her face, but she knew of her attractiveness for men. On the street in Wellston and on the steamer, she knew white men had turned to stare at her, their eyes speculative. And when she went to the general store, conversation among the Indians lounging outside stopped as they eyed her approach and turned their heads to keep her in view. Even in church, while Reverend Crowell was striving, with outflung arms and earnest words, to move the hearts and minds of his congregation, she had found herself under sly, irreverent observation.

Wenonga's persistent pursuing of her focused her thoughts on what she constantly tried to put out of mind. Eli had not slept with her for months before his accident. Though she had often hungered for him, he had revenged himself on her by staying out all night, then stumbling home in the early morning to jeer at her before falling asleep. Since his death, she had worked herself to exhaustion, partly out of desire to help Nonen and partly from the necessity to pay her debt to her husband's family, but also to numb her brain and her senses, so at night she could fall asleep. But for all her weariness, her body was restless, her breasts and thighs painfully sensitive to the feel of the quilt against them, and her sleep was troubled. Her patience stretched thin. She had to catch herself from giving Nonen, Soos, or Sarah sharp answers, and whereas she had taken pleasure in her home and work, she now found pleasure in nothing and was, to her dismay, inclined to sit down and weep for no reason whatever.

One day in late summer, Supaya returned from splitting wood for Nonen's winter fuel supply and found Wenonga working in her backyard. He had hung the door on the shed, put up the fence for the pigpen, and was finishing the chicken roosts. He saw her coming across the meadow, but went on sawing and fitting the boards together, giving her only a side glance when she stopped in surprise.

Waiting for the bear to be caught, Supaya had postponed getting a shoat and chicks and so had put off asking George to finish the shed. The bear, apparently driven away, had never been caught, but since it was then too late in the summer to fatten a pig, she had not bothered about the shed. Now, however, it was done, and she knew Wenonga would expect to come in and be fed as payment.

Blandly ignoring her angry stare, he went on with the work, his matter-of-factness intended to show her how right, how natural it was that he should be there.

Angry at his smugness and his forcing her to give him hospitality, Supaya did not speak, but went inside and began swiftly preparing a meal.

The slam of the oven door and the bang of pots sounded in Wenonga's ears. He knew her wrath. He had expected it, enjoyed it even, as a mark of her strength and of the contest between them, a more exciting contest than he had ever experienced with any other woman. When he had nailed the last board in place and fastened the catch on the henhouse door, he carried the tools into the lean-to and made a great fuss at the wash bench, splashing water over his face, blowing and scrubbing. He wet his ragged hair and combed it into shining black neatness. Pleased with his entire maneuver, his eyes alert with anticipation, he presented himself, massive but meekly awaiting her invitation.

"Sit there," said Supaya ungraciously, pointing to a chair. Obediently he sat, showing his willingness to be ordered about by her. Supaya avoided looking at him as she dished up the food and brought it to the table. But she felt his eyes steadily on her and was acutely uneasy at their being alone together in a domestic situation.

Seeing her cheeks flush, he sought to disarm her with praise. "The fish smells good," he said politely. "You are a fine cook."

"Thank you," said Supaya shortly, cutting off conversation. She brought a bowl of boiled potatoes and beans and a plate of scone to the table. Her nearness, as she set them down, was irresistible to him. He had to touch her. Forgetting for the moment everything but his passion for her, he reached out his arm, encircled her hips and drew her close against him. Holding her thus, he looked up, devoid of guile, his emotion frank and open. "Sit down," he urged softly. "Eat with me."

Supaya stood rigid. She forced herself to look at him. "Let go," she said coldly. "Your fine dinner," she added sarcastically, "is before you."

Slowly, his expression hardened. He removed his arm. Supaya went to stand beside the stove. She folded her arms and watched him eat.

He ate leisurely, his arms braced on the table, contemplating her thoughtfully as he chewed. Then he spoke, with a thinly veiled antagonism.

"You look very well. Not like a woman in mourning. Too neat! Too clean! Your hair not hanging! One might," he sneered, "think you a white woman!" Then, sharply, "When are you going to move back to your husband's home and work for his family as you should!"

"I *do* work for you and Nonen! Every day I work and you know it! But I will stay in my own home!" Supaya declared flatly.

"I understand you," he said musingly. "I know you need a man!" She raised her head haughtily, and he smiled faintly. "Ah! I know I am right. You wish to marry again! Perhaps you think of your cousin. That would be a bad mistake! Remember! You are not free! You are still in mourning, though one must look hard to see it!"

"Yes," said Supaya angrily, "I am in mourning! But not because you say so! For the white reason! As Mrs. Crowell says, out of respect!"

"Respect!" Wengona's white teeth showed in a rare grin, his large, gleaming eyes lit up with a vast amusement. "You, the daughter of a doctor, a woman who has dreamed! Who wears a necklace such as that! You, respect a weakling! You would respect only a strong and powerful man! *I* am such a man!" He hit the table with his fist. "*I* am what you need!" As she was silent, his face sobered in mock solemnity, his eyes grew cunning. "Strange, he who could not hunt went hunting bear! Strange, the bear did not claw him!" Seeing her face, pained by the memory, he mistook it for an admission of sorcery and grinned again, triumphantly. "I saw the bear spare you! I was behind you, and I saw! But," he held up his hand to reassure her, "I will say nothing of it. Once we are together, you and I . . ."

For a moment Supaya was too aghast to speak. Then, suddenly furious, she snatched up his plate and, rushing to the back door, threw plate and all out into the backyard. Turning, fists clenched and shaking with rage, she exclaimed, "Get out! Get . . . out!"

Slowly Wenonga rose, no longer grinning. No one had ever dared to so insult him. He burned with anger, but anger mixed with a fierce elation. He was stirred by combat. This was a contest worth winning! He could allow an insult when the end was certain.

As he came toward her, Supaya felt the violence, the menace in his powerful shoulders and hands. She thought he would hit her and she raised her head arrogantly. But he stopped, facing her, his eyes burning, his whole body tense with restraint. He made no move toward her, but his eyes rested on hers, then moved slowly, deliberately, to her mouth and down over her body. In spite of the repulsion she felt for him, her body responded to his gaze as though he had possessed her. Giddy, she leaned against the door for support.

Seeing this, Wenonga smiled and spoke with malicious pleasure. "You are a woman of much strength, but you do not understand yourself. I see you are learning. I will wait. One day you will want me!"

The dry heat of summer persisted into fall, giving Supaya hope for Nonen, whose coughing diminished. Day after day as the air grew cooler, the sky remained a clear brilliant blue. The maple trees flamed with color, and the aspen and birch glowed like gold among the dark cedar. With two gardens to harvest, Supaya was grateful for the prolonged drying period. Sarah had come to live with her, and together they dried and stored vegetables and fruit from Nonen's garden and her own. She also had to dry the meat and fish given to her by Kineu and his uncle, John Bruley.

They came together, John and Kineu, John doing the talking, offering her the meat or fish, saying they had been fortunate in the hunt or with their nets and wished to share with her out of respect and sorrow at her loss. Kineu said little, accepting politely the tea and food she offered them. And he ate little. All his attention was for Supaya. He had agonized over the injury she had suffered on his account, and from across the table he scrutinized her face carefully until he satisfied himself that she was well. Single-mindedly he noted every detail of her appearance, caught every inflection of her voice, every change of expression. He recognized the irregularity under the neck of her dress as that made by the blue stone necklace and was glad, taking that as a sign that she was as she had always been. The meat and fish his uncle presented were of his, Kineu's, catching. He wished to provide for her, even indirectly, as well as he could, and also atone for bringing harm upon her.

Supaya, surprised by their first visit, came to look forward to their coming, though they stayed only a short time and she and Kineu had no opportunity to speak together alone. She responded politely to John, an elderly, gentle man who, with his wife, lived apart from others, depending almost solely on fish for their livelihood. She understood Kineu's sober observation of the mourning period: he would not make the mistake of endangering her again. Touched by his remorse for what she had already forgiven, Supaya stole admiring glances at him.

She missed the lighthearted, carefree spirit of his boyhood, but she thought him grown more handsome. His lean face had lost its youthful delicacy; his aquiline nose and straight black brows combined with an unsmiling expression to give him a stern, somber look that struck Supaya and other young women on the reserve as romantic. Contrive as they might, the others had small opportunity to pursue him, for he attended no parties, no dances, only meetings of the council. On the rare occasions they encountered him at the general store and, giggling and nudging one another, attempted a flirtation, his cool gaze passed them by.

Now she was free; perhaps next spring, when her obligation to Nonen and Wenonga ended, then what they had planned so. . . Supaya, lost in her own thoughts, realized with a start that John had spoken to her. Kineu answered, saving her embarrassment. When they left, she longed to call him back, and stood at the door watching as they walked down the lane. At the road he paused, not to wave, but to look back once before going on.

One morning Supaya wakened to hear rain drumming on the roof. It fell from the eaves like a moving curtain and sluiced down the windows, blurring the outside world. The temperature had dropped sharply overnight, and she and Sarah welcomed the heat from the stove when they made their morning tea. The heavy rain, blown by a gusty wind, fell for three days, stripping the trees bare and turning roads into muddy streams. Sarah wore gum boots as she splashed to school, and the house smelled of wet clothes hung up to dry by the stove.

As the temperature continued to drop, the rain turned into a mixture of sleet and snow. Roads and fields were sheeted with ice. As Supaya walked to Nonen's, her boots cracked at each step as though she stepped through thin glass. The damp, penetrating cold made Nonen's coughing worse. She tired quickly, and scarcely had the energy to stir a pot of stew. Generally listless, she grew animated only when Supaya came or when speaking of the past. More and more she lost herself in happy memories of her life with her husband, when her daughter Mary and Eli were small children. Supaya listened as she combed and braided Nonen's hair, built up the fire, or cleaned the house. Often she cooked dinner for her and Wenonga, though she always tried to leave before he returned home.

When they did meet, he spoke smoothly to her, a knowing glint in his eyes recalling their past meeting, his whole demeanor one of amused forebearance as if the breaking down of her resistance to him were assured, were only a matter of time. Aware of Wenonga's power over mind as well as body, Supaya was wary. Remembering her father's advice, she faced him boldly. When he once remarked, pointedly, that he had seen her cousin entering her house, she answered sharply, "He came with his uncle, who brought me meat," adding pointedly, "if it were not for John Bruley, I would have none." Hearing that, Nonen fretted, insisting querulously that Wenonga give her some. Supaya soothed her, and Wenonga said nothing further.

But always, after John and Kineu's visits, the white dog appeared like a warning. She would see him, not in the open, but paralleling her path, dodging in and out of the underbrush as if accompanying her or checking on her destination. At night when she turned off the lamp and went to bed, she could hear his bark, first at a distance, then closer, as he circled her house. Getting up and standing at the corner of her window, she would see him, a pale shadow pacing restlessly in the night, and catch the glitter of his eye as he raised his head and uttered one short bark before disappearing into the darkness.

The long winter was dreary, not crisply cold as other winters, but wet. Raw damp penetrated houses, clothes, and bones. There was much sickness, and Supaya was kept busy treating colds, sore throats, and chills. Sarah, watching Supaya prepare medicines, took a deep interest in them. She was quick to learn, and Supaya began teaching her, hoping Sarah would become her apprentice. When she wasn't in school, Sarah accompanied Supaya on visits to patients. Supaya was glad for her company, especially on walks to homes at distant points on the reserve. Without Sarah's cheerful presence, Supaya would have found the winter unbearably lonely. Caring for Nonen, who grew steadily worse, and her other patients left her little time to visit friends. What little free time she had, she spent making baskets, saving what money she could for the trip home in the spring.

Kineu and John continued to bring her meat and fish, coming every two or three weeks, visits Supaya eagerly looked forward to. Grateful for the food, she was still more grateful for their company and pressed them to stay, though after they had gone she was more restless than before. During the worst of the winter weather, John needed no urging to stay, for he had a cracked stove in his small house and could make up only a small fire. He enjoyed sitting close to Supaya's fireplace and smoking his pipe. And Supaya was happy serving them hot soup or tea and bannock. Always she gave them something, dried berries, strings of dried apples, or scone, to take home.

Sarah, too, was delighted when Kineu and John came. Once Kineu whittled a bird out of a piece of wood and gave it to her. The next time he came, she coaxed him to carve something else.

"A bear! Make me a bear, please, Kineu!"

"A bear? Very well, a sitting-down bear, fat and full of berries." He began to whittle, while Sarah watched, fascinated. 'I came upon a bear once. Not a real one," as Sarah gasped. "A stone bear," he said, glancing sideways at Supaya, "washed up by the lake. I gave him to a little girl not much older than you."

"And what happened?"

"She kept him for a time. Then she threw him away."

"Oh, I would never do that!" exclaimed Sarah.

"She did not!" said Supaya, indignantly.

"Did you know her too, Aunt Suppy?" asked Sarah.

Kineu, shaping the bear's ear, shook his head solemnly. "When she grew up, she threw him away. I am sure."

"And I," said Supaya, vigorously poking the fire, "am sure she did not!"

Sarah, looking from one to the other, opened her eyes wide. "How do you know, Aunt Suppy?"

Exasperated, Supaya looked at them both. Seeing the amusement in Kineu's eyes and the puzzlement in Sarah's, she said tartly, "I did know her. And I know she kept it."

"I am glad to hear it," said Kineu, head to one side as he inspected his work.

"I will keep this one always," said Sarah positively, no longer interested in another girl.

Supaya stopped behind Kineu's chair and rested her hands on his shoulders. It was the first time she had touched him. John, gazing into the fire, appeared not to notice. Kineu half turned his head, then went on with his carving. Irritated by his teasing and impatient of the restraints imposed on them, she almost wished they would leave. Kineu now lived by himself in a small abandoned house at the head of the north inlet. Knowing he must do all his own cooking, she would set aside a pie or dish of stew just for him. Going briskly to the stove, she spooned out a potful of vegetables, banging the spoon unnecessarily hard against the kettle. John, recognizing the signs of woman's impatience, tapped his pipe against the fireplace as a signal they should go.

After they left and Sarah had taken her wooden bear and gone to bed, Supaya went upstairs to her room and opened her trunk. The stone bear was where it had always been, in the leather pouch that hung from her waist. But now from the bottom of the trunk she took out the shawl she had put away with such confusion of heart, the shawl Kineu had given her before she left Stone Island. She unfolded it and drew it about her shoulders, wondering, resentfully, at Kineu's staying away from her for so many months. She knew why, but for once her mind refused to accept reasons, skittering perversely away, leaving her only the bitter conviction, born of loneliness and exhaustion, that were she Kineu, she would have contrived long before now . . . that despite Wenonga she would have found a way. . . . She pulled the ends of the shawl tightly about her. Tomorrow she would see where he lived. She would go and see.

But she did not go close. She stood well back in the trees. She stood in the snow, her shawl pulled forward, shielding her face, and saw Kineu come out. He wore snowshoes and carried a gun and traps. When he moved out of sight, she retraced her steps. And although she had not seen the white dog, she broke off pine branches and smoothed out her footprints as she went.

Several weeks later she came home late. She had worked all morning at Nonen's, cooking and washing clothes, boiling them clean. She had walked to the store to sell baskets and had carried back supplies for Nonen, who sat wrapped in her blanket, unable to get warm and stubbornly refusing all medicine. The rest of the day she had visited patients who lived at a distance from her house.

At her last stop she treated a child, a little girl so thin that her bones showed through her delicate skin. Her eyes were dull, she had no will to move, had scarcely the strength to breathe. Supaya applied a paste to her narrow little chest and helped her swallow medicine to ease her breathing. She gave the mother, who was pregnant, medicine to be administered during the night and promised to return the next day. But she saw her own hopelessness reflected in the mother's eyes. She left fearing that by tomorrow the child, already dying, would be dead.

Outside Supaya bent her head and pulled her shawl forward to shield her face from the icy, stinging flakes that came swirling down the wind. But a depressing sense of helplessness and sadness numbed her more than the cold. For once she was indifferent whether the white dog trailed her steps or not. She plodded along in boots that grew heavier with each step. As she turned down the lane, Supaya was thankful to see the lighted windows and smell, as she entered the house, the soup that Sarah had heating on the stove.

Sarah rushed to greet her, taking her coat and shawl to spread out over a chair to dry. Supaya was removing her boots when Sarah exclaimed, "Oh, Aunt Suppy, I forgot! Mr. Bruley and Kineu were here! They said to tell you. They brought some fish. They couldn't stay though."

"Kineu was here?"

"Yes. You just missed them. Aunt Suppy! What's wrong?"

For Supaya, to her own surprise as well as Sarah's, began to weep. She leaned her head back against Jules' chair and wept tears of weariness and disappointment.

Sarah was frightened. "Aunt Suppy! Don't cry! Please! Did I do something wrong?"

"No, Sarah, no. It's all right." Supaya wiped her face and smiled ruefully at Sarah, standing close beside her. "It's the winter, Sarah! If only it would end!"

Several weeks later, when she was in the woods gathering elm bark for medicines, Supaya surprised a porcupine climbing about in a poplar tree, browsing on new, tender buds. And she found the morels had thrust up through the dead leaves and the trilliums were in bloom, their large white or maroon flowers strikingly bright and fresh. Elated at these signs of spring, she searched for leeks and found enough to fill the rest of her basket.

Cheerful for the first time in many days, Supaya boiled a potful of leeks for herself and Sarah and took some to Nonen, as a good medicine for her cold and encouragement for her flagging spirit.

When Supaya next went to the store, there was a letter from Jacques. Rhea had given birth to a son. All were well. They hoped she could come. And come she would! The arrival of the letter meant the steamer was running! The lake was open at last!

CHAPTER SEVENTEEN

Supaya's second homecoming was a happy occasion. Everyone was there to greet her—Quayo, Jules, Rhea, Jacques, and Maud, all in a festive mood. A fire crackled in the fireplace, food waited on the table, and Quayo, in her chair by the fire, held up her frail arms to embrace her granddaughter. Then Rhea proudly brought forward the baby for Supaya to hold, and they all gathered round, smiling, as she admired Wagash, the little fox, sleeping on his cradle board.

After they had eaten, Supaya gave them the gifts she had brought—tobacco, food and clothes she had made, including some garments for Wagash, and Jules' gift from Kineu.

Jules, happier than he had been in many years, accepted Kineu's gifts, a package of tobacco and a box of ammunition, with pleasure. "He is a good man, faithful and patient." Standing with his back to the fireplace, he filled his pipe with Kineu's tobacco and smiled down benignly at his daughter. "Like us, he lives according to the old way. He will make you a fine husband."

Supaya, sitting on the floor beside Quayo, was struck by his smug satisfaction. That he could speak as if events of the past seven years had never occurred pained her. Unable to smile back, she answered sharply, "Yes, Father, I had always believed so."

But Jules was not to be drawn from his good temper. Seeming wholly absorbed in contemplating Rhea, whose face and figure were more sensuous and seductive than before, and Wagash, who had just finished nursing, he commented simply, "The year of mourning and your duties to your husband's family is nearly over." Then he asked complacently, "When will you marry?"

Piqued by his easy acceptance of matters that for her had been the source of much grief and sorrow, Supaya stood up and moved restlessly about the room. She was irritated by his assumption, which robbed her of making her own decision. She felt as she had at sixteen—controlled, manipulated. Because of that, she felt inclined to be impudent, to say something to shock him, such as, "I may choose not to marry at all. Ever." But she was a guest in her father's house. He was happy with his newborn son. She did not wish to be unpleasant, and so she said, easily, since his attention seemed to be all for Wagash, that she didn't know.

That night, lying under the eaves in her old bed in the loft, Supaya relaxed, mind free of problems for what seemed to her the first time in months. Wenonga, Kineu, even Nonen's illness, all fell away, their immediacy, their importance diminished. Secure in her childhood refuge, she had nothing to fear, no decision to make. Her mind blank, she sank into a deep, restful sleep.

She woke early, and going downstairs found Rhea up before her. She had already made up the fire and fed Wagash. Now she poured cups of hot tea for Quayo, Supaya, and herself.

Supaya talked to Quayo of her patients, of Nonen, and of the child who had died. "I need more knowledge, Grandma, more medicines, more cures!"

Quayo, although physically frailer than when Supaya had last seen her, still spoke vigorously and with complete presence of mind. She said, "There is little more I could tell you that you don't already know. But," she added thoughtfully, "there are two women, both very old, who are fine healers. One of them, Beedaubun, is wiser than the other. You should visit her. She lives alone and has no one to leave her medicine to. She was fond of your mother. Tell her who you are and why you need her knowledge. She may help you. But you should go to see her at once because of her age. Besides, I think you will not want to stay here too long."

"I will go soon, as you say, Grandma, but why won't I want to stay?"

Quayo smiled but would not explain. She stroked Supaya's cheek and leaned back in her chair, saying only, "Speak to Beedaubun soon."

Supaya went the next morning, taking with her one of her

finest quill boxes, a pot of stew, and a package of dried berries from last summer's harvest. She found Beedaubun standing outside her house, straight and very still in the bright sunshine. The air was cold, but her shawl hung loosely about her shoulders, as though she were indifferent to the weather. Her whole attitude gave the impression of energy restrained. Her head was cocked to listen and her eyes, squinting into the sunlight, disappeared amid the fine lines and deep creases that marked her wide, rather flat face. Her sharp eyes had seen Supaya coming, and now she motioned for her to approach. Quietly Supaya came and stood beside her.

Though the sun had warmth, patches of snow still lay under the trees, whose budding branches stirred slightly in the faint morning wind. Together they listened, but Supaya heard only the silence of a spring morning. Then, tearing the silence, a pair of blue jays shrilled to each other. At that Beedaubun smiled and turned to Supaya.

"I was listening to the trees. One must be very quiet to hear them. Now they speak," nodding toward the jays flashing about the fir trees, "the trees are silent." Her attention narrowed to Supaya's face. "You look familiar. Come inside and tell me who you are."

When Supaya told her she was Shooskonee's daughter, Quayo's granddaughter, Beedaubun took her face between her hands and said, "Ah, ah, it was Shooskonee I saw, looking out at me through your father's eyes." Then, mischievously, "The trees spoke of spring. They did not tell me you were coming."

Supaya smiled. "Perhaps they wished to surprise you."

Beedaubun laughed silently, showing her almost toothless gums. "I see you come with gifts," she observed shrewdly. "What is it we are to trade, you and I?"

Supaya described the illnesses she had treated, the child whose life she had not been able to save; she explained her need for more medicines, more knowledge. Finally, she spoke of Nonen, who sickened but refused to be treated.

Beedaubun listened attentively, rocking in her chair. When Supaya finished, Beedaubun studied her, eyes narrowed to slits. Suddenly she leaned forward, bracing her arms on her knees, and spoke sternly. "I hear your deep concern. Because of that—and because of my fondness for your mother—I will entrust to you what little I know. It is good you have come now, for I have little time. But you must understand certain things." She paused, then began again as if teaching a lesson. "For some ills, of body or spirit, there are no cures. When your patient has no will, you cannot cure. When you contend with Death, you must be strong and clever, for he will challenge you again and again and you must not let him win too easily. When he does win, you must not lose heart. To be a good healer, you must first be a good fighter."

After their first meeting, Supaya went every day to Beedaubun for instruction. One day she returned home to find James sitting smoking with Jules and Jacques, while Maud helped Rhea with the cooking. Wagash slept, snug on his cradle board, his thatch of black hair standing up on his head, his closed eyes mere slits in his plump little face. Supaya thought them all unusually quiet, though both Maud and Rhea appeared to be smothering a fit of giggles. Supaya had not seen James since her last visit, when Neegonas was pregnant. He appeared to her not much changed by Neegonas' death. His long, dour face and large humorless mouth were as empty and uninteresting as she had always thought them to be. She greeted him and inquired politely about his children.

"My children," said James, "are well but they lack a mother. That is why I have come to speak to your father."

Instantly alarmed, Supaya glanced swiftly at Jules, then at the others. Jules puffed placidly on his pipe, his attention focused on a distant point. Quayo rocked gently, her hazy eyes straight ahead, as if she were not listening. Jacques was overly preoccupied with sharpening his knife, a slight frown creasing his forehead. Rhea and Maud glanced at each other, then rushed into the lean-to.

"It is a year since your husband died," continued James, not recognizing Supaya's consternation. "It was right that you stayed to pay your debt to your husband's family. And it is right that now you have come home where you belong, to do your duty to me, your dead sister's husband."

Supaya exclaimed, "My duty to you . . . !"

James raised his eyebrows haughtily. "You have no husband now. I need you as a wife and as a mother for your sister's children. It is your duty to take her place as it is my right to become your husband."

Supaya was struck dumb. The others looked slyly at her as she stared amazed at James and sought for the right words. Trying for courtesy, she said, rather stiffly, "I am sorry, James, but you speak of the old way of doing. I am no longer bound by that. I have come only to visit, to see my new brother. I have not come to stay. This is no longer my home. I must return to Two Bluffs. My life now is there."

Her answer brought a spark of anger to James' otherwise dull eyes. "You are mistaken! You are a woman and must be reminded of your duty. It is as I have said!"

A muffled sound came from the lean-to. Jules and Jacques didn't stir; only Quayo stopped rocking and sat perfectly still.

Supaya eyed James with distaste. Hoping to avoid an unpleasant family quarrel, she tried to conceal the angry contempt she felt and chose her words carefully. Coldly, with more arrogance than she realized, she said, " I *am* a woman. But I am not the woman to be *your* wife. You must look elsewhere."

Despite her intention, he heard the edge of scorn in her voice and turned at once to Jules. "Speak to your daughter! Explain her duty to her!"

So addressed, Jules gave James a hard, warning stare. "You are angry," he said sharply, "and your anger has made you forget yourself. You do not give orders to me. Or in this house. Because you were my daughter's husband, I will trouble to explain to you what you should have seen for yourself. My daughter is no longer a girl to be ordered about. She is a strong, powerful woman, a doctor of reputation on her own reserve. Once I had to tell her her duty. It is no longer necessary. Now she sees for herself and follows her own will."

James rose, scraping back his chair. "But you owe this to me!" He looked at them all resentfully. Getting no reply, he cast about for some sort of threat and finally in his frustration foolishly blurted out, "I will speak to Reverend Harris!"

They all smiled. "Do so," said Jules. "As we all know, Reverend Harris is always ready to support our oldest traditions."

Incensed, unable to speak further in the face of their amusement, James left. But every evening he came and sat, glumly watching Supaya, and speaking, when he could find an opportunity, of his need for a woman in his house. Once Quayo asked him with mock innocence if he had asked the preacher for a list of eligible girls. After that he stopped coming to the house, but one day, having observed Supaya's daily visits to Beedaubun, he waylaid her on her way home.

She tolerated his walking beside her, even his bullying words, but when he grasped her arm and attempted to pull her in the direction of his house, she lost all patience. Twisting free, she faced him with the accumulated exasperation of days past.

"Understand me! I will not be your wife! Not ever! And do not touch me again. If you make it necessary, I will speak to my brother." James was shocked by the vehemence of her reaction. Seeing this, Supaya followed up her advantage and took a threatening step toward him. "Do you see? I am not like Neegonas. You would not find me suitable. Do not speak of this ever again."

Dumbfounded, James drew back as from a stranger, and she left him standing there. After that, he resumed his evening visits to Jules' home, sitting silently as the others talked, staring spellbound at Supaya.

His sulky presence was displeasing to them all. Supaya now understood what Quayo had meant and knew that the only way to improve the situation was for her to return home as soon as Beedaubun finished her instruction. Before Supaya left, Jules gave her a pipe of hawthorne wood he had made for Kineu.

"Tell him," said Jules, "that as my sister's son he is dear to me and that it would give me great pleasure to have him as my son-in-law. Give him this as a token." Then he added, with a sly smile, "Even if you don't marry him."

Realizing he had noticed her irritation with him and understood it, she took the pipe and laughed with him, at his slyness and her own foolishness.

The sap was running when Supaya returned to Two Bluffs. Wenonga had already tapped the maple trees and hung the pails. With bedding and supplies for a two-week stay piled in the back of the wagon, he and Nonen, who had not the strength to walk, rode out to the maple bush, Supaya and Sarah following along behind. Supaya, fearing the effect of the damp, cold air on Nonen, had urged her to stay home, promising that she and Sarah would gather the sap and tend the fire for the two weeks. But Nonen insisted on going. For years past, she had gone every spring, and after the long, confining winter she had a sudden strong longing to be in the open once more. A blanket wrapped around her shoulders, she enjoyed the ride, jouncing along behind Nellie, whose shaggy red-brown rump moved rhythmically as she plodded through icy puddles and the soaked, matted leaves that hid the rough path.

When they reached the site, they found the lean-to of un-

211

peeled saplings still standing except for the roof which had fallen in under the weight of winter snows. Quickly Wenonga cleared away the branches, uncovering the huge iron kettle that had been left there, upside down, and the two rough bed frames where he and Nonen would sleep for the next two weeks. Swinging his axe, Wenonga lopped off fresh balsam and cedar boughs. Using the larger ones for a new roof, he fastened them to the frame that was just head-high at the front opening and slanted to the ground at the back. Wanting to help, Nonen carried smaller boughs to Supaya and Sarah, who arranged them on the bed frames, making thick, springy mattresses, which they covered with quilts and blankets. The beds were set as far back in the sharp V formed by ground and slanting roof as they would go. In front of them, under the shelter, Wenonga erected a tripod and from it suspended the kettle.

Every morning Supaya and Sarah walked from home to the maple bush and collected the sap while Nonen tended the fire under the kettle. In the evening Wenonga returned, and together he and Nonen kept the fire going through the night.

Nonen became more animated than she had been in months, taking such pleasure in being out in the woods that Supaya was glad she had come. While the others collected sap, Nonen sat on a pad by the fire, moving only when she needed to put on more wood. She basked in the sunlight that tempered the spring air. She listened to the clear, piping calls of the birds flashing in and out of the thicket and watched the flight, high above the trees, of flocks migrating north, their swift, tireless wings dark against the sky. So absorbed was she into the flow of life about her that the squirrels and chipmunks ceased to eye her. A thin, foraging porcupine sniffed close by, ignoring her presence. A deer, stepping into the clearing, paused to regard her with calm eyes, alert ears, then, unconcerned, moved on past her.

Occasionally the morning sun shone fiery red across the surface of the lake and straight into the bush, lighting up the trunks of trees before disappearing under heavy dark clouds. Then a cold rain fell, glistening on the budding leaves and dripping from the roof edge of the lean-to, forming a row of puddles before the shelter opening. Nonen could pull down the piece of canvas to cover the opening and keep out the mist but she didn't, preferring to sit and watch the drops that sparkled like strings of crystal beads and breathe in the rich, wet smell of the earth.

When Supaya and Sarah came hurrying back with their pails,

shook the rain off themselves, and knelt by the fire to warm their cold, chapped hands, Nonen would rouse herself, greet them, and dish out the food that had been kept warm beside the fire. Whenever Supaya asked how she was, Nonen smiled and insisted she was fine. That the damp air cut her lungs with each breath and fits of uncontrollable shivering seized her when her very bones ached with cold, she did not say but simply pulled her blanket closer to hide her tremors.

At evening when Wenonga returned, he lowered the canvas across the front of the lean-to, and the air in the small, enclosed space grew warmer and eased her breathing. Huddled in her blanket, Nonen watched the red eye of the fire, thrusting on more wood to keep the tongues of flame flicking upward against the bottom of the kettle and dreamed of the past when she and her husband William had tended the kettle through the cold spring nights.

While Supaya was away at Stone Island, Kineu had kept watch on her house from the wooded slope behind it. One evening, sooner than he had expected, he saw lighted windows and Sarah in the backyard drawing water from the pump. The next afternoon he and Uncle John came with a bundle of fish to welcome her back. Supaya gave them greetings from their relatives and then brought out the pipe Jules had made for Kineu.

"My father also sends you greetings. He thanks you for your gifts and says you are dear to his heart. He sees that you do things the old way and sends you this pipe as a token of his affection." As both John and Sarah were watching and listening with interest, Supaya was embarrassed to give Jules' entire message. But Kineu understood and was delighted with the pipe, turning it about and cupping it in his hand. He got out tobacco, filled the pipe, and as he puffed on it, looked across the table at Supaya, his eyes questioning.

Supaya knew he was waiting for her to speak, to say that now her obligation to Wenonga was ended. But she said nothing, pretending not to see his question. She would not have spoken before John and Sarah, but why she continued to hang back now that she could do as she wished, she didn't know. She felt suddenly shy of action. Her thoughts were confused, uncertain. She wanted Kineu, yearned for him, yet she also wanted. . .she was not sure what. She thought surprisingly often of Eli and always with a peculiarly painful sadness for a life together lost to them both. Though he had been dead nearly a year, she felt obscurely that something was not yet concluded, that she had failed to understand some essential fact.

During the year she had visited Eli's grave frequently, placing small packages of food there except when snow had completely filled the cemetery in great curving drifts, leaving only the tops of the painted wooden crosses showing. Now the cemetery was muddy, many crosses were askew, tilted by winter winds and loosely held by the thawing earth. Supaya carried a small shaping axe of Eli's. As she leaned over to straighten the cross and tamp the softened ground firmly about its base, she placed the axe on the ground behind Amy's flowerpot so that the tangle of dead brittle stems hid the axe.

On her way home she stopped to see Nonen, home now from the maple bush. Finding the back door ajar, she entered, but Nonen's chair was empty. Supaya called out but got no answer. With growing anxiety, she looked in the bedroom, the loft, the backhouse, even, though it was unlikely, the barn. The wagon was there, but Nellie was not in her stall, nor was she out grazing in the meadow. Alarmed, Supaya ran down the lane. To the left the road led straight away, empty as far as she could see. To the right, it curved. Running in that direction, Supaya rounded the curve and saw some distance ahead Nonen walking along, leading Nellie by the halter.

When Supaya reached her, she had stopped and was looking about, her eyes blank, withdrawn. She seemed not to recognize Supaya, but handed her the halter, saying only, "I must rest."

Seeing she was about to faint, Supaya put an arm around her and guided her to the side of the road where there was a stump she could sit on. "Where were you going, Nonen?"

"Where?" Nonen was vaguely puzzled. "You know. We must leave. William says we must go to Two Bluffs."

"William is right," said Supaya gently. "You *have* come to Two Bluffs. You are almost home. When you have rested, we'll go on."

"But it is such a long way," protested Nonen, her eyes filling with tears.

"I know," soothed Supaya, understanding what she meant. "But you will like it here."

"It is not home," said Nonen sadly. "We have deserted the bones of our dead."

For that Supaya had no answer, and Nonen, her head bowed, expected none. She wore no coat or shawl, and Supaya

214

could see her shivering. She looped Nellie's halter around a fence post and said, "Come, Nonen, we must go now." She helped her up and, supporting her as much as she could, led her home. Nonen made no further protest, but when they reached the house, she refused to lie down, insisting on sitting in her rocker by the stove, where she fell asleep almost at once.

Supaya wrapped a blanket around her and added wood to the fire. Not daring to leave her alone, she sat and waited for Wenonga to return. Soon she heard the clop-clop of hooves, and after a moment, Wenonga entered, angry at finding Nellie alongside the road. Someone, he suspected, had been using her without paying.

When Supaya explained, he leaned over Nonen, listened to her breathing, felt her forehead. Then he turned accusingly to Supaya. "She must not be left alone. If you had been here in the house . . ."

"I have given her what care she would accept," interrupted Supaya. "I cannot leave my own home, but I will find someone to come and stay with her."

Supaya asked Alma, one of Nonen's old friends and one who had helped lay out Eli, to come and live in Wenonga's house. Alma had no family left and she was not afraid of Wenonga. Occasionally she was able to coax Nonen into taking medicine Supaya prepared for her, but, most important to Nonen, she talked of old times. Nonen so lived in the past that she often mistook Supaya for her daughter Mary, and Supaya, seeing that Nonen was growing weaker, got Mary's address from Gerald Toomis and wrote her a letter.

That spring Supaya bought four hens and a rooster from a white farm woman Lizzie knew, and being determined to provide some of her own meat supply for the winter, she asked Jess Fallon to get her a pig if he heard of a farmer with pigs to sell.

It was the first time she had asked Fallon for anything. She had bought supplies from him, sold baskets and birchbark boxes to him, and even taken his suggestions, but she had never asked a favor of him. Somewhat to his own surprise, he found that getting a pig for Supaya was of more immediate importance for him than anything else. He made a show of needing to visit several farms on business, but his real purpose was to find a healthy young pig. He inspected pigs of various sizes until he found one whose size and condition pleased him. He bought it, put it in a burlap bag in the back of his wagon and, with an eagerness he seldom felt, drove to Supaya's house.

As he turned into the lane he saw her out in the field speaking with George, who had taken advantage of the breezy, sunny day to come with his horse to plow the garden. Fallon raised his arm in salute and watched her as she came toward him across the field. The sight of her, walking swiftly and gracefully in the sunlight, her skirts blowing about her, filled him with pleasure, as the sight of her invariably did. It was a deeply private pleasure, one he had never troubled to explain to himself. As she approached, his smile deepened. "Morning, Mrs. Red Sky," he called, flicking his hat brim.

"Good morning, Mr. Fallon." Her response was reserved, as always, but cordial. Though Supaya never forgot that he was a white man, she had come to have confidence in his judgment and to rely on his good will. Often something in his expression puzzled her, but she was less shy in his presence than she had been.

He swung down off the wagon and hauled out the burlap bag, which bulged and squirmed in his grasp. "I've got a fine pig here, Mrs. Red Sky. Where would you like him?"

Supaya led him back to the pen at the side of the shed. Jess leaned over the fence and upended the bag. A squealing black and white pig tumbled out, righted itself, and trotted about on short, stiff legs, snuffling out its new quarters.

They stood together watching the pig. Supaya was delighted and amused by it. She noted its plumpness with satisfaction, thinking of the meat it would yield by late fall.

"It was kind of you, Mr. Fallon, to find one so soon, and such a fat one."

Jess didn't hear her. His attention was arrested by their hands, resting side by side on the fence rail. He had counted out change and dropped it into her outstretched palm many times, but this was different. This was not a transaction across a counter, but a natural being together, a sharing of purpose and interest. Staring at her hand, so close to his, he felt a sudden compulsion to put his hand over hers, to curl his fingers over hers and hold them firmly. Startled by the strength of his desire, he thrust both his hands into his trousers' pockets, realizing as he did so that she had turned toward him and was waiting for an answer to something she'd said.

216

To Supaya, he appeared intensely preoccupied. Obviously, his thoughts were elsewhere. She realized that her fattening a pig was of no importance to him, and politely repeated her remark that by fall this pig would yield a great deal of meat.

But he continued to stare at her abstractedly, even frowning slightly as he murmured automatically, "Yes. Yes, it will," scarcely knowing that he had spoken.

For Jess, it was a moment of shock, as if he were seeing her and himself clearly for the first time. She was no longer a pretty, lively girl whose spirit he admired and whose unconscious arrogance had amused and attracted him. Nor was she the young wife whose struggles to support herself had stirred his compassion and whose battered face had moved him to a deep, secret anger. She was suddenly, more than a beautiful, vigorous woman who happened to be standing beside him. She was a woman whose image he now discovered had become part of himself. That wide brow and expressive mouth, those brilliant dark eyes now regarding him with an amused, tolerant smile, all, he had long and unwittingly carried within him like a lovely miniature. Only now, with the sunlight all about them, did he recognize that she, who had seemed to exist on the fringes of his life, had from their first encounter seized his imagination and lived within it, a precious, private life that had grown and become inextricably woven into the fabric of his own. He saw that she was speaking and heard, ". . .inside, and I will pay you for the pig."

The pig! He wanted to laugh. Impossible that he take money for it! Regaining his composure, he smiled, filled with exhilaration by his discovery, and said jauntily, "There is no charge, Mrs. Red Sky. This pig is free!" Knowing her reaction to anything smacking of charity, he watched for her response and was rewarded by seeing her chin lift and her back stiffen.

"Free!" she said suspiciously.

"A farmer gave it to me," he said offhandedly. "But I don't raise pigs. You'd be doing me a favor to take it." To avoid her sharp scrutiny, he started back toward his wagon.

If a farmer gave it to him, thought Supaya, it was in place of payment. "I can't accept if for nothing," she called stubbornly after him.

He stopped and looked back at her, smiling. His vivid blue eyes had a mischievous glint, and she thought suddenly that he was laughing at her as he had when she ran into him on Stone Island.

As if he too were remembering that encounter, his smile broadened, and he said, "We are old friends, you and I. I choose to give you this pig."

"Then as an old friend," she said arrogantly, "I choose to give you something in return."

He would not hurt her pride, so he said, "I didn't think old friends kept such close accounts, but I could use some medicine for a sore throat." He saw her relax, wonder in her face at this strange white man.

"Very well. I will keep the pig and bring the medicine as soon as I have made it up." Then she politely offered him a cup of tea, which he as politely declined, saying he must return to the store. He flicked the whip over the horse's back, tipped his hat, and drove away, taking with him yet another image of her, standing in the lane looking after him, skirts blowing, black hair lustrous in the sunlight.

CHAPTER EIGHTEEN

Nonen accepted Alma's presence without question. Except for brief, painful interludes, Nonen relived her past, speaking to whoever was present of matters that had concerned her long ago, never waiting for an answer. She talked aloud with her dead and regarded Supaya, Soos, and others who came to visit or help her with the indifferent eyes of a stranger. She also grew sly, tricking Alma into getting her this or that so she was free to wander off, following her own inner promptings. Once she climbed the stairs to the loft. After searching and calling, they found her there, asleep, huddled on the floor beside her old trunk. Other times they found her walking along the road or in the woods hunting for berry bushes.

Supaya was putting in squash and turnip seeds when she saw Alma crossing the field toward her, her gray head, dark clothes, and quick, jerky motions making her look oddly like a large, grounded bird. Coming within earshot, she raised her hands in dismay and cried out.

"Nonen is gone again! I cannot find her, and Wenonga has gone fishing! Please come!"

Hurriedly Supaya came. They found Nonen had not returned to the house or the barn, and Supaya paused to consider in which direction they should look.

"She had been speaking of Eli," said Alma. "Then she fell asleep, and I went out to the backhouse. When I returned, she was gone."

Perhaps, thought Supaya, she had gone to the cemetery, drawn there by thoughts of Eli. "You go through the woods toward Soos' house," said Supaya, giving Alma the shorter route. "I'll go by the road toward the cemetery."

All day heavy, slow-moving clouds had been threatening rain. Now, in the late afternoon, they had gathered together, towering up in great slate-dark masses that glowed intermittently, lit from within by hidden flashes of lightning. Lower ragged clouds streamed eastward, moving fast. Supaya hastened toward the cemetery, hoping to find Nonen before the storm broke. A fresh, cool wind suddenly blew up, raising dust devils in the road and whipping trees about. The lifted dust stung Supaya's eyes and gritted unpleasantly in her mouth. Her skirts buffeted about her, and she began to run as a bolt of lightning cracked overhead, flaring blue-white against the black clouds. A peal of thunder shattered the air, and rain splatted down, marking the dry road with large, dark rings.

Supaya ran through the cemetery gate and paused, her hair blowing across her face. There was no one by Eli's grave. Undecided, she paused, pushing back her hair, and her attention was caught by a movement at the far side of the cemetery, where the older, overgrown graves were. She ran through the wet grass and found Nonen kneeling on the ground, her head bowed to her knees. She had pulled her shawl forward over her head and was rocking back and forth, unconscious of the rain soaking her back. The grave was that of Nonen's husband, William, and when Supaya tried to lift Nonen up, she resisted, clinging to the earth like a stone.

"Please, Nonen! Get up! You're wet! You'll get a chill!"

Then Nonen raised her head, and Supaya saw she was crying. Rain struck her face and ran down with her tears. "Supaya, it's you. I thought it was Mary, but it's you."

"Yes, me," said Supaya gently. Mary had not answered her letter about Nonen or sent any message to her mother. But Supaya's real concern was to get Nonen out of the rain. "Come home now, Nonen, please. For me."

Nonen nodded and made an attempt to get up. Supaya steadied her, and clinging together, heads bent against the lashing rain, they left the cemetery and moved at Nonen's slow pace down the road.

The storm was directly over them. Sheetlike rain obscured the landscape. Lightning split the rolling clouds in glaring, jagged streaks and thunder crashed and boomed, causing the earth to vibrate from the successive shocks. The women were drenched, their soaked clothes clinging to them, hampering their progress. Supaya could feel the water running through her hair and down her neck. She had not been caught out in so bad a storm since she was a child on Stone Island. Now, as then, she was excited by the vast power and violence shaking the land. Despite her concern for Nonen, Supaya was exhilarated by the tearing wind and driving rain. But Nonen was tiring rapidly. She stumbled and leaned more and more heavily on Supaya, going blindly wherever she was led.

Alma, who had returned to the house when the storm began, was watching for them and held the door open. Together they brought Nonen close to the hot stove and removed her wet clothes. Like a child, she submitted passively to their care of her as they dried her hair and rubbed warmth back into her thin, emaciated body. When she was once more warmly dressed, Alma gave her a cup of hot tea.

Supaya, feeling chilled in her wet, clammy clothes and seeing that Nonen, exhausted after her experience, was dozing over her tea cup, left for home.

Rain was still falling, but the center of the storm had moved eastward, out over the lake. Above the gray, wind-lashed water, lightning crackled, its lurid flashes vivid against iron-gray clouds. Volleys of thunder rolled across the water, reverberating against the rocky cliffs.

Stepping briskly, Supaya crossed the soggy meadow and took a path through the woods. Though the rain beat down on her, trickling in tiny streams down the crown of her head, over her face, and between her breasts, she was warmed by an inner exuberance. The dreary, unhappy winter was at last truly over! She felt washed by the rain, mind cleared, spirit cleansed of all the grief and worry of the past year. Planting time had come, a time of renewal, and, for her, freedom! Freedom to do as she liked, live as she chose! She had her own house, a garden, even—smiling at the thought and tasting the rain on her lips—even a pig and chickens! And her guardian had blessed her with the ability to heal. The Great Spirit had indeed granted her many blessings! Her heart swelled with gratitude toward her Grandfather, the Great Bear. Tilting back her head, she breathed deeply the pungent, earthy smell of the woods. All her perceptions were sharpened. She saw with delight the swift-falling rain slanting down through the branches, the shiny-wet leaves and the soft mist that filled the woods like a fog and gathered on cedar and balsam branches in trembling, glistening drops.

The rising mist muffled all sounds except that of the falling, dripping rain. She had no warning of the figure that emerged on the path ahead of her. Large and dark, he came through the mist like an apparition and struck her with sudden fright even before she recognized him as Wenonga. Involuntarily, she stopped. But he came steadily on, unhurried, until, at a little distance, he stopped and gently, as if not to break a spell, set down his basket of fish.

Silently they faced each other through the delicate mist, rain sliding down over their faces. The glistening black strands of Wenonga's hair shone like a cap. His dark eyes gleamed, lit by an inner fire. She felt his vitality, matching her own, emanating from him like a force, and saw in his wild eyes and fierce smile her own elation of spirit. A current of shared excitement flashed between them. Like a fighter astonished to find common ground with her adversary, she stared at him, transfixed. Carefully, he moved a step nearer.

Supaya could have run, could have dashed to one side and run past him. He would not have stopped her. She knew that without thinking. But she let herself be held, enveloped, drawn as powerfully by his magnetism to him as he was to her.

He came another step closer. A kind of suffocation gripped her throat. She drew a deep, sharp breath, and was instantly conscious of how she stood revealed, her wet clothes clinging to her body, outlining her breasts, hips, and thighs. Prompted, perhaps, by her own sudden self-awareness, his gaze moved slowly over her and his smile deepened. Supaya's shoulders quivered; she almost stopped breathing. Stupefied by her senses' response to him, she stood perfectly still, her eyes wide like those of a stunned animal as he slowly reached out both hands, laid them on her shoulders, drew them caressingly down over her breasts, and encircled her waist. Consumed by his touch, she closed her eyes and would have fallen, but his arms embraced and held her up, close against him.

Half fainting, she was overcome with lassitude, her spirit withdrawn to its innermost center. She was conscious of his face brushing hers, of his mouth pressing hers. Her heart swelled, and she longed, like a tired swimmer, to close her eyes, her mind, forever, to be finally, irrevocably enveloped.

Then, like a clarion above the soft fall of rain, came the loud, raucous cawing of a crow. Its strident, repeated cries as it circled above the treetops woke Supaya's spirit and shattered her stupor. Her eyes started open. Seeing Wenonga's face bending close, she cried out, thrust her fists against his chest and wrenched herself free. Eyes blazing with fury, she stepped warily back, arm raised against him and circled around, ready to run.

Startled at first by her unexpected action, Wenonga made no move toward her, but turned as she circled, his eyes never wavering from hers. "Come," he urged softly, "why delay? You see how it is to be with us. If not today, tomorrow."

"No!" exclaimed Supaya, backing further away. "It will *not* be tomorrow! Or any day! You are clever! And powerful! But you should think twice! You are not the only one with power!" Above them sounded again the cawing of the crow. Emboldened, she spat out, "Stay away from me! Leave me alone!"

As she backed away down the path, rain and mist filled the growing distance between them, gradually obscuring Wenonga until he became again the dark, enigmatic figure she had first seen blocking her homeward path. Turning off, she fled through the woods toward the inlet, to Kineu.

She came out of the woods on a small rise just above the end of the inlet, where she had stood months before in the snow to look at his house. Here by the shore, the mist was thicker. Shore birds mewed plaintively. Feathers fluffed out, they huddled along ledges and perched on rocks, heads all pointing lakeward. The light was fading. Toward the east a pale rose light flared up inside the dark mass of clouds and the soft, retreating rumble of thunder sounded across the lake, the waves sighing endlessly and tumbling stones on the beach.

Supaya crossed the narrow end of the beach to Kineu's house. Though it was small, smoke rose from its stack and there was a door that could be locked. She put her hand to the latch, knowing that Wenonga and her own desire had made her decision for her, that after all, she was not free.

Kineu was sitting by a small iron stove, his uncle's fishing net draped across his knees. He was mending it for John, whose eyesight was poor. Hearing a step outside, he expected it to be his uncle, but when the door flung open, it was Supaya who entered, slammed the door shut, and leaned against it. Surprised by her sudden appearance and wild expression, Kineu dropped the net and came toward her.

"What's wrong?!" he exclaimed. But she only stared at him, and he grasped her arms and shook her. "What has happened?!"

Supaya couldn't answer. Her eyes filled with tears, and she flung her arms around him, pressing her face against his shoulder. Seeing Kineu, so dear to her, so much a part of herself, made even worse the enormity of her encounter with Wenonga. She was frightened, now, by the narrowness of her escape, and she held onto Kineu fiercely.

Kineu asked no more questions, but held her close until he felt her trembling stop and her grip relax. In her own time, he knew, she would tell him what had happened. Meanwhile he could feel how wet and cold she was. He held her off at arm's length.

"Some people know enough to stay inside when it rains," he said, his eyes amused. "Then there are people like you." He spread his arms and looked down in mock horror at his shirt. "Look at me! And the floor! You came here to cause a flood!"

Supaya, entering into his banter smiled and lifted her chin. "If you want me to go . . ."

He seized her wrist and drew her over to the stove. "You'll get a bad chill if you don't get out of those clothes and dry your hair. I think. . ." he paused momentarily, lost in contemplating her up-turned face, then finished softly, ". . .you may have to stay a long time." He bent and kissed her gently. Then, practical again, he went into the lean-to for a towel. "Here, dry with this."

Supaya took the towel but hesitated, looking apprehensively at the door.

"What is it?"

"Lock the door, please, Kineu."

He heard the fear in her voice. Without a question, he shot the wooden bolt on the front door. After another glance at her, he secured the door in the lean-to as well. Still she was uneasy, glancing nervously at the one, uncurtained window as if she expected to see a specter looking in through the rain-washed glass.

"I can hang something over the window," said Kineu. He found an old shirt and fastened it to the top of the window frame. He turned, sobered by the extent of her fear. "Shall I light the lamp?"

"Oh no! Please don't." The smoke rising from the stack would be seen. There was no help for that. But the less light, the less evidence of their presence, the less that could be seen through any crack or chink, the safer Supaya felt.

Kineu brought her a blanket. "You wrap up in this. I'm going to bring in more wood."

Standing close to the stove, Supaya swiflty removed her soaked clothes and wrapped herself in the blanket. She had hung her clothes on a chair to dry and was rubbing her hair with one end of the towel when Kineu finished bringing in the wood and relocked the back door. He stirred up the fire and threw on more wood, which crackled and sent up a flurry of sparks as he shut the iron door. Then he poured two mugs of tea from the pot warm on the back of the stove.

They drank their tea in near darkness, she sitting on the only other chair, he on the floor beside her, the only sounds those of the fire breathing in the stack and the soft ping of rain hitting the windowpanes. A warm contentment enveloped them both. Supaya was remembering another small house on a beach where there had been no need to lock the door. Then they had been together believing they would soon part forever. Now they were together and would never need to part.

"Kineu," she said softly, "remember?"

For answer he rubbed his cheek against her knee where the blanket fell away and caressed her foot and leg. Leaning forward, she took his head in her hands, and turning it toward her, kissed his mouth with all the ardent longing of months past. He rose toward her on his knees, and as she placed her arms around his neck, the blanket slipped from her shoulders. Her body shone soft and pale in the darkness. She drew him close and he kissed her firm-soft breasts and stroked the delicate curve of her waist and back. With one accord they rose and went to his bed. Swiftly, fiercely, he entered her, and they clasped each other tight, mind and spirit annihilated in a kind of death.

Outside there was a deep quiet. The rain had stopped, and the lake, no longer blown by the wind, lapped softly against the rocks. A few tattered clouds, like dirty cotton against the dark night sky, trailed eastward, stirred by a wind that blew high above the earth. There was no moon. A ghostly mist hung among the trees and moved almost imperceptibly across the bare ground, curling over the dark, wet rocks.

Through the mist came the great white dog. Wraith-like it appeared, melted away, reappeared, restlessly circling the house, tail down, head hanging forward. Silently, stiff-legged, it came closer and snuffed about the threshold. Then it swung its head back, snout pointing upward as if to howl, but made no sound.

Toward morning, as the sky paled over the lake and the shirt-hung window let a gray square of light into the dim room, Kineu wakened. He thought he'd heard barking, but as he listened, all was quiet. Just a dream, he thought. Conscious that the room had grown cold, he carefully pulled his arm from under Supaya and got up to put more wood in the stove. His moving and the chink of the stove roused her. When he turned, her eyes were half open, sleepily watching him.

He was lean, as before, but no longer boyish. His shoulders were powerful, his chest broad, and the graceful, sinuous lines of his body and thighs were those of a mature man. Her gaze lingered on him, appreciative. Their eyes met, filled with desire as though their lovemaking of the night before had served only to sharpen their appetite. Smiling faintly, she raised the quilts and held them back for him.

Over the lake a delicate, warm glow suffused a pearl gray sky. The white dog, standing on the rise at the edge of the woods, scented the morning air, and turning, disappeared among the trees.

CHAPTER NINETEEN

That year the harvest was good: beans, potatoes, turnips, squash, and pumpkins, all large and firm. Little rain fell. All over the reserve vegetables were spread out to dry in the warm, autumn sun.

Sleeves rolled up and hair braided back out of the way, Supaya was digging up potatoes to be stored in the root cellar. Kineu had gone fishing with his uncle. Supaya hoped that by next summer they would have saved enough from selling their crops and fish for him to buy his own boat. As she worked, she noticed a woman, well-dressed and wearing a hat, walking along the road. When she turned in at the lane, Supaya picked up the bag of potatoes and went to meet her, thinking there was something familiar about her gait and posture. Suddenly, though the woman's face was shaded by her hat brim, Supaya knew who she was.

"Miss Harris!"

Agatha smiled warmly and held Supaya's grimy hand in both of hers. "Sophia," she said, "it's so good to see you!"

Supaya, who had only occasionally thought of Miss Harris during the past few years, was surprised at her own rush of pleasure at their meeting again, and invited her in for tea.

Miss Harris appeared to be much the same as when Supaya last saw her: a neat, trim woman, with a pale, reserved face, her fine brown hair pulled straight back and knotted. Even her dress might have been the same, and the brooch at her neck certainly was. Sitting with her hands clasped before her on the table, she might have been surveying a class in the schoolroom instead of Supaya's home. As Agatha, an unconscious conjurer of memories, sipped her tea, Supaya saw her standing at the top of the school stairs, her skirts blowing, clutching a shawl about her shoulders as she rang the school bell, and beyond her the long room with the pale winter sun slanting in between the desks, falling in oblongs on the worn floor. But Hiss Harris was saying . . .

". . . sorry to hear of the death of your husband." She spoke seriously and with a slight frown, studying Supaya intently as if to judge the impact on her of that event as she once judged her grasp of grammar.

But Supaya was no longer as easily read as a schoolgirl. She accepted politely Agatha's sympathy, then asked if she were visiting.

"No, Sophia. I have come to stay. I'm the new teacher here. I'm moving into the house next door to the school."

Supaya expressed her pleasure at Miss Harris' coming to live at Two Bluffs. Then an appalling possibility came to mind. "And . . . your brother?" she asked, reluctant even to name him.

Miss Harris was immediately disturbed. She studied her tea cup, turned it about, and seemed at a loss for words. Then it was that Supaya saw she was not quite the same. When her eyes were downcast, the skin below them was smudged and puffy. Lines were apparent in the thin skin of her forehead and at the corners of her eyes. As she answered, an almost pained expression pinched her mouth. "No, I. . .I decided to come by myself. My brother and his wife are staying at Stone Island. I was sorry to leave them. . .and my students. But a teacher was needed here, and I thought . . ." She looked up sharply as though to convey a meaning beyond her words. "I thought it would be an opportunity," she finished, somewhat aggressively. She did not say for what, but added with a peculiar emphasis, "As you yourself know, Sophia, families cannot always stay together. Sometimes it is necessary to. . .to enlarge one's horizons."

"I am sure you are right, Miss Harris, and it will be so good for the children here. They need your encouragement. You see, I have the books you gave me on the shelf there. I read them too, during the winter, when I have time."

Miss Harris admired the flowered wallpaper backing the shelves.

"Mrs. Crowell gave it to me," said Supaya, falling into the old pattern of a child showing her prized possessions to the teacher.

"And Mrs. Toomis, the agent's wife, gave me the curtains and this teapot. They have both been very kind to me."

"I've met them," said Agatha. "It was Mrs. Toomis gave me directions to your house." Her voice turned flat as, glancing about the room, she saw man's clothing hanging from the pegs.

Supaya, seeing the direction of her glance and the lift of her eyebrows, ceased feeling schoolgirlish and said pointedly, "Kineu whitewashed the walls for me, upstairs as well."

"Mrs. Toomis said you had a child, Sarah, I think she called her, living with you." Her inflection made it a question.

"Sarah lived here all last year, when I was alone," explained Supaya smoothly. "Now that my year of mourning is over, Kineu lives here. He is my husband. Sarah lives at home." She met Agatha's gaze squarely, pleasantly, her manner plainly discouraging further questions.

Agatha was struck anew by Supaya's resemblance to her father. It might have been his eyes, looking at her in that cool, challenging way. She was about to venture a comment on Supaya's remarriage when Kineu himself entered the lean-to. He greeted Agatha politely, showing neither surprise nor welcome. He held a fishing net in a basket on his arm and continued to stand as if waiting for her to go.

Agatha was ill at ease in Kenneth's presence. As a child, his manner had kept her at a distance and at a disadvantage. She remembered how she had tried to reach him, to strike a response in those opaque, young eyes, and how utterly she had failed. He had responded only when he wished to, never because of anything she said or did. For her, his face had always been closed, and this she did not understand. Baffled, she had often found herself trying too hard, talking too much and foolishly, which only made Kenneth more withdrawn and mortified herself. Now she knew he wanted her to leave and stood up at once. Putting on her hat, she invited Supaya to visit her and left, politely including Kenneth in her good-bye.

Supaya saw that Kineu was disturbed. As soon as the door was shut, he took the net from the basket and spread it out for her to see. It was ripped, torn into large holes that would require hours of painstaking repair. That the net had been deliberately, maliciously ripped, they both knew, but only Supaya knew by whom. Now she told Kineu about Wenonga. Ever since Kineu had moved into her house, Supaya had been watchful. That she had seen nothing, heard nothing, made her more, not less, uneasy, for she was certain they would be threatened. It was almost with a sense of relief that she saw the ripped net. She cautioned Kineu. "You must be careful. You must always check the boat and when you go into the woods, you must look both ways."

A day later, they found the drying frame broken into pieces, and Kineu had to build a new one. Another time they found the root cellar door open and part of their stored vegetables gone. The shed was broken into and meat and fish were stolen. Then a section of the pigpen fence was thrown down and the pig was gone. Luckily, Kineu found him in the woods nearby. The possibility of losing the pig was bad, but when one morning Supaya opened the door of the chicken roost and found the rooster and all four hens dead, their heads dangling from twisted, broken necks, she was infuriated. She walked to Nonen's, hoping, in her anger, to meet Wenonga face to face.

But Wenonga was not there. He had gone out early, Alma said. She was combing and braiding Nonen's hair. When Supaya told her what had been happening, Nonen raised her hands and moved them slowly back and forth before her face as if to fend off all such acts.

"Ah! Ah! You must be careful, very careful. You have taken a husband! Ah, yes! I have heard! And Wenonga is angry." She thrust her face toward Supaya, her eyes burning, her voice intense. "His anger is like flame inside him! I can feel the heat of it! Always it has driven him to evil! And that evil has turned back on his family! We split apart. We die. His wife, Eli and now me." Her wasted face drew together in a sly, cunning sneer. "But his power will not save him! He will not escape. In the end his evil will turn on him, and he too will suffer! He will be consumed by his own evil!" She laid cold fingers on Supaya's hand. "But you! You must not let him harm you. You are a strong woman. Face him down! Fight him!" Exhausted by her outburst, Nonen's head fell back against the chair. She breathed heavily, eyes closed. As Supaya and Alma watched over her anxiously, her eyes opened again, but she looked at the two women beside her without recognition.

Early one morning Supaya discovered Wenonga sprinkling a powder on the path Kineu took when he left to go fishing. She had been reluctant to speak to Amy, knowing it would upset her, or Lizzie, about a personal matter, but now that Wenonga was threatening Kineu's safety, Supaya resolved to speak to them both. But first she waited, hiding in the brush, until Wenonga had left the woods and turned toward his house; then, taking a cedar branch and following the path he had taken, she brushed the path clean.

When she spoke to Amy, Supaya did not mention Kineu. So far, her white friends didn't know that she and Kineu were living together. Once they did, they would expect her to be married in the church, and that Kineu would not want to do. Nor did she mention the powder, knowing they would not understand.

As Supaya had expected, Amy was appalled. And frightened. She drew closer to Supaya and glanced about uneasily as if Wenonga might be lurking behind the sofa or peering through the curtains. "My dear, my dear! What you must have gone through!" She gave Supaya a timid pat on the arm. "But why? Why would he do. . .oh, I can't think. . . ." She paused, distracted. "It's true, he doesn't come to Sunday service, still . . . and his own daughter-in-law! Why?"

"Why" was a question Supaya had anticipated. She answered carefully. "Because I do not choose to live with him as a wife."

"Well!" exclaimed Amy, scandalized. "I should think not! You just . . . But never mind! I will tell Reverend Crowell about this! He will take this matter in hand! Yes. . . . I am sure he will! He will set everything right!"

Lizzie was outraged. "Killed your chickens! That dreadful man! How dare he!" Angrily, she set a kitchen chair straight with a thud, sharply aligned the dishes on the table, meanwhile darting indignant glances at Supaya as though she were the one to be reprimanded. "Indeed, I will speak to Gerald." Her lips tightened. "He will make this man understand that he cannot act like a ruffian! That he is living among civilized people and must behave accordingly!"

When Supaya told Soos she had spoken to the white women, Soos agreed it was good strategy, but raised the question that was already troubling Supaya: when were she and Kineu going to get married?

"They will protect you from Wenonga, Suppy, but they will expect you to marry in the church." Soos spoke with restraint, wanting only to remind her friend.

"I know," said Supaya. "But it is difficult." She didn't need to explain to Soos the nature of the difficulty. Soos knew Kineu and understood. As Jules had remarked with pride, Kineu did things in the old way. Kineu considered they were already married, had, in fact, been married since before Supaya left Stone Island. It had not been his sweetheart who had been taken from him then, but his wife.

Reverend Crowell spoke to Gerald Toomis about Wenonga. They could not, he said, tolerate such unspeakable harassment of a young woman, not in a Christian community.

Gerald agreed. He found Wenonga in his backyard splitting and stacking wood for winter.

Wenonga greeted Gerald but continued working.

"I understand," said Gerald, "there's been some trouble over at Mrs. Red Sky's place. Root cellar broken into, shed robbed, chickens killed." He paused. Wenonga cast a baleful eye at him but raised his axe and with one powerful stroke split a log in half.

"Naturally, that kind of thing can't be permitted. Everyone on this reserve must obey the law." Gerald paused again. "That's a good stack of wood you've got there," nodding at the fifteen-feet-long stack neatly piled against the lean-to. "Not enough for winter, though, is it."

A statement, not a question, and no response from Wenonga, who set up another log.

"You know," said Gerald, "if the attacks on Mrs. Red Sky's property don't stop right now, all woodcutting privileges will be taken away."

Wenonga straightened and turned to face Gerald.

"That'd make for a damn cold, hungry winter, wouldn't it." Another statement. Squinting into the sun, Gerald looked across Wenonga's fields. "Good piece of land you've got here. Used to belong to the Smiths. The agent before me said old Ed Smith sold you the title to it, but you know, it's a funny thing, but I can't find that contract." Gerald's tone was affable, chatty, but his light blue eyes were as hard and cold as bits of glass, and Wenonga, silently attentive, waited for him to finish. "It may just be that this land belongs to old Ed's son. Not sure, of course." He eyed Wenonga thoughtfully. "I'll have to look a little harder, see if I can find that paper."

Wenonga drew a deep breath and lowered his shaggy head, staring from under his heavy brows at this puny white man with strange red hair and pasty face. His lips curled with distaste, his shoulders bunched with the impulse to crush him.

232

"About that matter of Mrs. Red Sky . . . ." said Gerald coolly. "I don't think we need worry about that happening again, do we. I'm sure no one wants any trouble."

Wenonga, knowing he was trapped, said nothing. He hefted his axe, his eyes full of anger and hate.

After a few other general comments, Gerald left, casually as he had come. He forced himself to walk at a leisurely pace, but Wenonga's deadly eye and powerful throwing arm hung in his mind. As he went down the lane, the back of his neck prickled and his shoulders shuddered inwardly under the imagined impact of that axe.

The harassment stopped. Supaya and Kineu worked hard at gathering and storing food for winter. Mornings now found the ground white with frost. In the garden only withered stems and rotting leaves remained. The last apple had been picked and strung; the root cellar was full and split fish hung stiffly over the smoking rack.

Kineu had gone to set traps in the woods. The day was gray and still, and the slightly misty air was damp and penetrating. Supaya, on her way to Soos' to arrange a time when George could slaughter their pigs, cut across the ridged, frozen garden into the rock-strewn meadow beyond. Her back ached, and though it was not yet midday, she would gladly have rested. She had not yet told Kineu she was pregnant. Preoccupied, she almost passed the large rock outcropping when she realized she had heard a voice. Startled, she paused, then circled the rocks and was shocked to see Nonen sitting on the ground, slumped against the rock. She wore no shawl or jacket. Her eyes were closed and her hands lay limp, palms up, at her sides. She was muttering to herself, disjointed words and phrases.

"Nonen!" Supaya knelt and took her cold hands between her own. "Nonen! Nonen, please! It's Supaya! Nonen, look at me!"

Nonen's lips parted, hesitated, then, "Suppy?" Slowly her eyes opened. "Suppy. I'm glad . . . you have come . . . . help me."

"Oh Yes, Nonen! Here, put my shawl around you while I go. . . ."

But Nonen shrank back and raised her hands in protest. "No! No! Help me . . . move! I want to see . . . my house . . . my old hut." Nonen rolled forward onto her knees, and Supaya, holding her around the waist, helped her get up onto her feet. "Just . . . just around there!" said Nonen breathlessly.

233

Together they moved slowly up the small rise to the top of the outcropping. From there one could see the garden and beyond, the house and shed.

"Here," panted Nonen, sinking down, "just here."

But Supaya, intent on getting her inside, tried to hold her up. "Maybe we can get to the house. Come, let's try."

Frowning, Nonen pulled away. "No! Here! I want to sit here!"

Reluctant to oppose her, Supaya eased her down. Sitting on the ground, Nonen could look straight ahead and see the side of the gray stone house, smoke rising from its chimney and from the drying frame in the backyard. She could see the shed and beyond, the field that sloped up toward the woods. Driven by a longing to be again in this rocky meadow where, as a young woman, she had so often rested, Nonen had exerted her last energy. Now, seeing Supaya's anxious face, she said softly, "Don't worry. You go. I will rest here."

Seeing that she spoke quietly and seemed less faint, Supaya agreed. "All right, Nonen. I'll go, but I'll be right back with the wagon to take you home. You shouldn't be sitting out here on this cold ground."

"Go! Go!" But as Supaya started away, Nonen called her back. "My chair . . . William made it for me. I want you to have it."

Supaya squeezed Nonen's hand and smiled into her eyes. "Not for a long time yet."

When Supaya had gone, running across the field, Nonen slumped back against the rock, her body like an old, half-emptied sack. Content to be alone with her past, she gazed fondly at her old hut, whole and alive, its fires still kindled. A fine sense of weightlessness came over her. Her vision wandered up the slope to where the deep reds and yellows of maple and birch were like brilliant flames amid the dark green of cedar and balsam. She floated above the scene, lost in wonder at its quiet beauty, until the colors faded, the stone house, the slope, the woods, all grew hazy, all finally blended into the soft autumnal mist.

When Supaya returned with Soos and the wagon, they found her so, leaning back facing the house. Her dreaming eyes were fixed. Her gray face and hair seemed a part of the rock against which she rested.

Nonen was buried next to William, her husband, in the old part of the cemetery.

After the funeral, Wenonga began demanding that Supaya vacate her house, insisting the house was now his. He banged on her door and threatened to move in himself; he waylaid her on the road, belligerently accusing her of stealing what was his. Finally Supaya went to Gerald Toomis and asked him to prove to Wenonga that the house really was hers.

Gerald arranged for Supaya and Wenonga to come to his office at the same time. Wenonga came but stood just inside the room, his back to the door. Filled with enmity, he refused to sit down. He glared suspiciously at Gerald, who sat behind his desk, and at Supaya, who sat stiffly at one side of the room, her face averted.

Gerald, a fair man, wanted to be fair to Wenonga. He regretted the animosity that was plain in Wenonga's leathery, lined face. His ragged hair, the forward jut of his heavy head, his very stance, with his blanket hanging rakishly from one shoulder, was aggressive. Gerald saw in him something wild and fierce that stirred his respect and, in the deepest part of himself, almost unrecognized, a touch of fear and awe. He knew other Indians sought this old man's services at the same time that they feared him, and he had met such total, enigmatic silence whenever he mentioned Wenonga's name as to suggest a mystery he could not hope to fathom.

Determined to make this matter of the house clear, Gerald said, very distinctly, "Your sister, Nonen, gave her house—willed it—to Mrs. Sophia Red Sky."

Wenonga answered at once, baring his teeth as he spoke. "I am blood kin. She," with a scornful glance at Supaya, "is not. The house is mine by right."

Patiently, Gerald explained. "If your sister had died without expressing her wishes, Mr. Red Sky, the house would be yours. But she came here, to this office, some years ago when Sophia and your son, Eli, first moved into the house, and she signed over her ownership to Sophia. See, here is the entry. I wrote it myself." He held out the ledger for Wenonga's inspection.

Wenonga, unable to read and contemptuous of Gerald's scratches on paper, would not condescend to so much as glance at the ledger. His face, his voice, expressed his scorn. "I see that you have stolen what is rightfully mine. Soon there will be no place for me to stand. I see that you are against me. I will not listen to more of your false words." Disdainfully he threw open the door and strode out, not deigning to close it behind him.

Annoyed, Gerald thrust his fingers through his hair. Despite his intention, he felt he had failed after all to clear the issue, and he regarded Supaya with some impatience.

Supaya, who remained silent, stood up to go. She saw Gerald's irritation with her and thanked him briefly.

"I hope that will settle it, Mrs. Red Sky," he said dryly. "If he bothers you again, let me know." After the outer door had closed behind her, he thought, irrelevantly, I believe the woman's pregnant, and went to the kitchen to mention it to Lizzie.

Supaya was unprepared for the extent of the pressure exerted on her and Kineu to be married in the church. Shortly after she had been to Gerald's office, Lizzie came to visit. She sat in Nonen's rocking chair and eyed Supaya as she poured the tea.

"When is your baby due?" asked Lizzie directly, never doubting her right to ask. She felt slightly offended that Sophia had not already confided in her.

"In the spring," said Supaya, smiling.

"But you're not married! Who is the father?"

Supaya laughed. "I am married! To Kineu Bruley. He is my father's sister's son. We grew up together on Stone Island," she explained, hoping Lizzie would express pleasure.

But Lizzie frowned. "Your cousin?"

Realizing she had been too open, Supaya said quickly, "It is our custom. Our families approve."

"I see," said Lizzie, still frowning. "He is living here with you now?"

"Oh yes. He is my husband."

Lizzie looked at her sharply, suspecting she was being made fun of. Then seeing she was not, she said chidingly, "He *cannot* be your husband until you've been married. In the church. By Reverend Crowell. It is not right that you live together *until* you have been married. You know that, Sophia! And to have a child, with no true father!"

"But my child *does* have a father. Kineu is its father, and he considers himself my husband; he considers we *are* married."

Lizzie shook her head and smiled. "You know that isn't so,

236

Sophia. Don't you see? It just is not right! Besides, he could leave you any time." She waved her hand. "He could just walk out the door and not come back, and there you would be—with a child and no husband. Really, Sophia, you can't afford to let that happen."

Supaya laughed. "Kineu would never do that. But if he did want to go, why would being married in the church stop him?"

Lizzie set down her cup with a clatter. "Sophia," she said sternly, "you are too intelligent not to understand. You have been educated and brought up in the church. Surely you can see that what you're doing is not right. Tell Kineu you must be married, that's all. It's very simple."

Supaya did not argue. She had few friends. Lizzie was one of them, and Supaya wanted to keep her friendship. It was clear that if she and Kineu did not marry, Lizzie would not continue to be a friend.

Kineu had been hunting, and came home with a porcupine and two muskrats. As he skinned and cut up the muskrats, Supaya pulled quills.

Not looking at him, she said offhandedly, "Kineu, maybe we should be married in the church."

"Why? We are already married," answered Kineu, neatly separating skin from flesh. "You are my wife. I am your husband." He smiled, glancing sideways at her. "Soon we will be a family."

"I know, Kineu. But white people do not believe we are married unless the preacher says we are." She waited, but Kineu only shrugged. Slyly, with mock seriousness, Supaya said, "Lizzie Toomis came to see me today, and she said that if we weren't married in the church, you might go off and leave me."

Kineu raised his head to look at her; his hand and knife were still. "Did you believe her?"

"I don't know," said Supaya, tilting her chin playfully; her eyes opened innocently. "How can I tell?"

"Do you think, then," asked Kineu, his voice hard and angry, "that I have no honor? That my words mean nothing! Or that any words spoken by a white preacher could stop me from doing anything?"

"Oh, Kineu! I was teasing you! Please, don't be angry." Kineu was outwardly placated, but he did not smile or make any gesture toward her. Supaya, surprised he had taken her seriously, said nothing more.

237

As the days passed, Supaya's pregnancy was no longer to be concealed, even by her winter coat. After service one Sunday morning, Reverend Crowell drew her aside.

"Mrs. Red Sky, it is apparent that I must speak to you of a most personal matter. As your spiritual father, it is my duty." His thin lips pursed together; his stern, disapproving expression helped cover his embarrassment at speaking of such a matter to a woman already pregnant. "Do you know who is the father of your child?"

Stung by his insult, Supaya almost turned and walked away. Her face hot with indignation, she frowned at this rash, foolish man and was on the point of reminding him that he spoke to the daughter of a shaman, he, a man who had no understanding of his own wife. But because of her affection for Amy, she restrained her tongue, answering proudly, "Yes, Reverend Crowell, my husband, Kineu Bruley."

But Reverend Crowell was blind to Supaya's scorn, absorbed as he was in his own view of her.

"No, no, no! My child!" he expostulated, "I have not married you since your husband died; therefore you do not *have* a husband. You are living in sin, and that we cannot permit. Bruley—he is not in my congregation, is he? No, I thought not. You speak to him and bring him to me. I must marry you at once."

Knowing the preachers's words would only further alienate Kineu, Supaya did not speak to him. But she began to realize the difficulties that would arise by ignoring Reverend Crowell's order. Not only would she lose Lizzie's friendship, but she would not be able to continue going to Sunday service or to the weekly meetings of the women who met with Lizzie and Amy to sew and drink tea.

The next afternoon, on her way to the store for coal oil for the lamps, Supaya encountered Miss Harris leaving the school building. Her first impulse was to avoid speaking, not wanting to be lectured again, but Agatha came straight toward her, smiling with pleasure, but pleasure tempered by her concern that the coming child be legitimate.

"A child is a blessing, my dear, but only if it has proper parents and a name. Surely, you don't propose that it be born without its father's name. I'm sure Kenneth would not wish that either. It would not be right! Do speak to Reverend Crowell, Sophia."

Supaya was both annoyed and troubled, not least by her own confusion of mind. Deeply proud of her own traditions, she, as much as Kineu, resented being forced into a ceremony that meant nothing to her simply to satisfy the whites. Most of all she resented being robbed of her character, her pride and independence. Nevertheless, she was being made to feel increasingly defensive, as though she were, after all, somehow wrong.

She wanted to turn around and go home. But she needed the oil and her pride would not let her veer from her path though it meant possibly facing still another disapproving white face. One moment she wished Jess Fallon would not be there, that his regal, disinterested wife to whom all Indians were the same would wait on her. The next moment she asked herself what possible difference it could make who waited on her. Certainly, Mr. Fallon would take no interest in whether she was married or not.

Nor did he, greeting Supaya in his usual, half-bantering manner. He filled the tin with oil and remarked that he would be driving into Wellston the next week and would be glad to take any baskets she had ready.

But after Supaya left, Fallon found it difficult, for the first time, to face his wife. Leaving the customers to her, he went out to a small side platform used as an unloading dock. With excessive, driving energy, he carried bushels and kegs into the storeroom, stacking them, slamming them into place. Face set and tense, he wrestled with barrels, straining his back and arms in grasping and lifting, bruising his hands in self-mortification at his jealousy, his shame at hopelessly coveting what was not his.

Kineu, unaware of the pressures being exerted on Supaya, was content. Wenonga's harassment had stopped, and Kineu was living his lifelong dream: making a home and raising a family with Supaya. He took pride in his prowess as a fisherman and hunter, and brought home food every day. Their drying frame was always hung with meat and fish. By spring Kineu figured he would have saved enough to buy his own boat. He was quietly happy, walking his own path, sitting with Supaya by his own fire.

But then he began feeling disturbed without knowng why, as if there were something he'd left undone or forgotten that he should have remembered. Night after night his sleep was troubled, and he wakened knowing he had dreamed but unable to recall anything except the sound of a dog barking. So clear was the barking that when he opened his eyes, he heard it still, and thought it had awakened him. No dog was in sight when he looked out, yet the sound lingered in his ears. Gradually, over a period of days, out of confused and murky impressions, several images came clearly to his waking mind. He associated the first clearly recalled dream with a snowfall because it occurred the night of the first winter blizzard. When Supaya put out the lamp, snow had already blanketed the ground and was still falling. Kineu remembered thinking he must wear snowshoes when he went to check his traps in the morning.

For many nights past, Supaya had been wakened by Kineu's disturbed sleep. He thrashed his legs, threw out his arms; sometimes his whole body gave one convulsive jerk. This night he cried out, inarticulate, frightened. Supaya stroked his head and trembling arms. He shuddered but did not waken, and she murmured soothingly to him until she felt the tension leave his body.

The next morning snow was still falling, small flakes out of a woolly gray sky. Supaya made up the fire and brought out some leftover fish and potatoes to have with their tea. Kineu planned to go hunting and make the round of his traps. He wouldn't be back, she knew, until late afternoon. As she served him, she rested her hand on his shoulder and asked if he were troubled.

Not wanting to worry her, Kineu glanced up and laughed. "Troubled? Of course. I've got a wife who gets bigger every day!"

Supaya gave his shoulder a shake. "And I've got a husband who kicks his legs when he sleeps and cries out. What of that? "

"That's what happens to a man when his wife gets bigger and bigger. It bothers his mind."

"You!" exclaimed Supaya, and made a face at him.

But as Kineu snowshoed into the woods, mysteriously quiet and still in the falling snow, he remembered vividly how, in his dream, as he walked home through the snow, a great white dog had gradually taken shape. First he had heard a breathing, an easy panting that sounded almost in his ear, but when, startled, he turned around, he had seen nothing but fine, whirling snow. After stopping several times, eyes straining, a faint white luminous outline materialized as if the snow itself were forming into the shape of a huge dog. As he stared, the dog turned its head to face him, mouth open in a kind of grin, eyes gleaming red through the vortex of snow. Captivated by those eyes, Kineu watched as the dog lowered its head and moved effortlessly toward him. The distance between them shrank; the dog's head loomed larger and larger. Its eyes started from its head with fury, its black lips wrinkled back from sharp, shining teeth. Paralyzed with fear, Kineu cried out as the

240

dog's low growl rose to a snapping, aggressive snarl, and the dream dissolved.

The snarl and his own cry still sounded in Kineu's memory. A tremor ran through him, and he turned abruptly, searching the path behind him. But all he saw were his own tracks, rapidly drifting over. Feeling foolish, Kineu went on, putting his dream resolutely out of mind.

He returned home earlier than usual because he bagged a deer, quite unexpectedly. A young stag had stepped out from behind a grove of cedars, directly across his path, and had stood there quietly, looking straight at him with great dark eyes, unafraid. . .waiting. Kineu, awed by this gift, took slow and careful aim. Then he knelt by the fallen stag and thanked the great Spirit Deer for his blessing. The deer's body hung heavy but warm across his back, and he carried it home joyfully, taking the deer's deliberate offering of itself as a good omen. That night, his dream forgotten, Kineu fell asleep peacefully.

But the dream came again, a repetition of the one before, and again Kineu cried out in his sleep and Supaya soothed him.

The next morning she did not question him. He avoided looking directly at her, as if he would shield her from what troubled him, but she saw the worry in his face and shared his uneasiness.

Night after night the dream recurred, its dimensions expanding, its violence increasing as the dog came ever closer. Its head swelled, horribly distorted and magnified, stretching forward on a trunklike neck until it filled Kineu's vision. Points of light flashed from its eyes; its slavering mouth and gaping red throat threatened to engulf him. Then, through the never-ending snow, a tiny dark shape appeared from a vast distance, growing swiftly larger as it soared down on powerful wings. Kineu, at bay, recognized his guardian, the eagle, and cried out with relief. Great wings outspread, it floated above the dog, sinking lower and lower in ever-tighter circles. The dog's great head shrank back, its eyes flaming red. Crouching on its haunches, snapping and growling, it slowly backed away and faded into the whiteness. Kineu awoke sweating. Supaya was wiping his forehead and soothing him, and he fell back into an uneasy, restless sleep.

The next night the dog came closer to Kineu, snarling viciously. But the eagle instantly appeared, a black dot that zoomed swiftly down, the wind from its giant wings fanning Kineu's head as it sank low and hovered over the dog. Its black, hooked beak opened menacingly, and the infuriated dog, stiff-legged and wild-eyed, backed slowly away. Kineu's legs jerked convulsively. He groaned and sighed.

Supaya, unable to go back to sleep, watched the darkness fade to pearly gray. The snow clouds had passed on and the sky was clear. When Kineu opened his eyes, Supaya was propped up on one elbow, head leaning on her hand, gazing down at him. Musingly, with light, sensitive fingertips, she smoothed his black eyebrows, traced the pale thin scar from cheekbone to jawline, then, smiling, she leaned down and kissed him.

"Kineu," she said softly, "you must tell me. What is happening? What is wrong?"

Also speaking softly as if in the quiet of early morning they might be overheard, Kineu told her. "It is bad because I am helpless! I can do nothing!"

"It is Wenonga who is doing this!" exclaimed Supaya angrily. "He is using his power to get at you! But your guardian has come to help you. That is a blessing. You must thank him and pray for his protection."

Later, when Kineu had gone to fish with his uncle, Supaya lifted the blue stone necklace from under her blouse. There was now no doubt that Wenonga was bearwalking Kineu with murderous intent, and Supaya was deeply frightened. Clasping the blue stone with both hands, she knelt and, shutting her eyes, prayed to her guardian.

"Great Spirit Bear! Hear me! You who are all-powerful
and know no fear! I who am weak and frightened
bow before you. I beg your help!

"My Grandfather! Hear me! Lend me your wisdom!
Show me how I may save my husband! Teach me
what I should do!

"Great Spirit, Father of all Life! Hear me! Give me of
your strength and courage to keep the life of one
dear to me! Guide me! For without you, I am
nothing!"

That night the great white dog was bolder than before. Defying the eagle, who hovered and dipped above it, the dog circled Kineu, its red eyes glinting, snarling, hungry for the kill. As it circled, Kineu turned, always facing it, one arm raised to shield himself. Enraged by the eagle's threatening dives, the dog lowered its massive head and bunched its muscles for a spring. But the eagle folded its wings and hurtled down, whistling through the air. Pulling up with a great swooping motion, its fanning wings raising clouds of snow, the eagle raked the dog's shoulders with ironlike talons and tore at its head with its scimitar beak. Howling with pain, the dog leaped sideways, twisting, throwing itself into the snow. The eagle lifted off, beating its wings. Regaining its balance, the dog raced away, pursued by the eagle skimming low. Together they disappeared into the storm. Scattered drops of blood stained the snow. Kineu awoke, heart pounding.

He awoke drained of strength, too weakened and inwardly agitated to leave the house. He sat by the fire or strode restlessly about the room, tense and silent, chaffing at his helplessness and dreading the coming of night. Supaya worked steadily at her baskets, saying little because she knew words would not help.

Afraid to sleep, Kineu stared into the dark for hours, exhausted from tension, his eyes dry and burning. In spite of himself, sleep came upon him, and at once the white dog rushed at him out of the snow, head lowered, ears laid back. No longer to be turned aside by the eagle's threatened attack, it dashed at Kineu, hackles bristling, snarling. Its bared teeth snapped at Kineu's leg, his arm. Then it sprang away, only to lunge forward again, driving Kineu back, forcing him to stumble, to fall. Kineu, smothered by the swirling, suffocating snow, stared, mesmerized, into the dog's great fiery, pitiless eyes and saw there his death. Once this giant dog with its implacable hatred leaped upon him and took him by the neck, he would surely die! Kineu raised despairing eyes and saw the eagle, great dark wings beating through the snow. The dog, too, saw the eagle, and with a strangled, enraged snarl, sprang for Kineu's throat. Screaming, the eagle stooped and fastened its talons in the dog's thick neck, thrusting viciously at its head. Thrown off balance, Kineu stumbled backwards, went down on one knee. Terrified, he crouched low, watching as dog and eagle fought. Desperate to protect its eyes and free itself from the eagle's strangling grip, the dog leaped, twisted, flung itself about, but the great bird hung on, flailing its wings and biting ferociously at the dog's head. Frantic, the dog buckled its legs and scraped its flank against the trampled, blood-stained snow. Breaking apart, they whirled to face each other: the dog with bloodied head, threads of spittle hanging from its fell, black jaws; the eagle with wings outspread, head stretched forward, neck feathers raised. Slowly they circled, until suddenly, insane with fury, the dog lunged. The eagle swept its wings forward, and darting its head like a serpent, stabbed for the dog's eyes. The dog veered aside, then lunged again. Again the eagle stabbed, and blood spurted out. The dog barely faltered, but in that instant, the eagle forced it back, arching its great wings over the cringing, snarling dog, forcing it further and further back into the obscuring snow until even its savage, flaming eyes were dimmed and finally vanished.

Triumphantly the eagle lowered its wings and arched its neck, smoothing down its ruffled, greenish-black feathers. Turning sideways, it stood for a moment, proudly, its red-stained beak partly open, its wild, demonic eye staring at Kineu. Then, with a slow, heavy sweep of its glistening, powerful wings, it rose into the air.

Tight bands compressed Kineu's chest, obstructing his breathing. His brain numbed with fear and confusion, he floated in a gray nothingness. From a great distance he heard his name called and struggled to answer. Feeling himself shaken, he opened dazed eyes to find Supaya leaning over him, shaking his shoulders and crying out his name. Gradually, to his stunned vision, the room fell into place—familiar whitewashed walls, beamed ceiling, bare window framing a square of pale sky, and a bed, reassuringly solid, under him. Weak with relief, he smiled faintly at Supaya.

"Kineu! Kineu! You were so cold! And I couldn't wake you! Oh, I was so frightened!" Her eyes brimmed with tears, and Kineu reached up his arms and drew her close. For a time they held each other tight, saying nothing, comforted by one another's living warmth.

Her face against the curve of Kineu's neck, Supaya felt the soft stir of his breath on her shoulder, and suddenly she knew quite clearly what she must do, as clearly as if an inner voice had spoken.

She dressed quickly, leaving her bear claw necklace outside her dress. Wearing snow moccasins, a jacket buttoned up, and a shawl over her head, she walked to Wenonga's house. She had not been there since Nonen died. Resolutely, she went to the front door and knocked loudly.

When Wenonga opened the door, she was pleased to see a flicker of surprise in his eyes, and she almost smiled at him as, uninvited, she stepped inside. The conviction that at last she must face him was so strong that it gave her courage, and she was ready, even eager to confront him. She would not remove her jacket and shawl in a house where she was not welcome, but very deliberately she unbuttoned her jacket and pushed it back so her necklace could be seen.

Wenonga had aged since Nonen's death. There were streaks of gray in his shaggy black hair; his face was thinner, with little flesh between skin and bone. He stood with the air of a tired man, though in the dimly lighted room his eyes still gleamed, this time with no show of friendliness or hospitality. Silently, he waited for her to speak.

Supaya had a sudden flashing memory of opening a door and finding Wenonga, windblown, wrapped in his blanket, standing on her father's threshold. Then, as now, his expression was suspicious and hostile. The tension between them had stemmed from that very moment. Glad to be finally done with pretense, she said boldly, "It is time we talked, you and I. What you did before to me and Kineu was unimportant. But now you are trying to kill him. And that," she said positively, "I will not permit you to do!"

Wenonga raised his eyebrows. "Permit? You speak rashly. You can neither permit or not permit. Besides, I know nothing of what you say."

"Lies will not serve you now. This time we speak frankly. Stop what you are doing to Kineu! Leave his spirit alone! Get out of his dreams!"

"You are a woman," sneered Wenonga. "It is not for you to give orders."

"Then you should remember," said Supaya sharply, "that you are not the only one who has a powerful helper. It is not for nothing that I wear this."

Wenonga's gaze rested for a moment on the necklace. Then, with a show of contempt, he said, "If you had power, you would not need to come here and issue commands, hoping to be listened to."

"Ah!" said Supaya, smiling. Her eyes narrowed with cunning. Daringly, she stepped closer to him. "Beware that you don't misjudge my power! Remember the bear that killed Eli?" She paused and saw a subtle change in his expression. "The men never caught that bear, did they?" she asked, tauntingly. Turning his old accusation against her of sorcery gave Supaya keen satisfaction. She could have laughed aloud, seeing the uncertainty in his eye, the sneer fade from his face. "Some of us who have power do not choose to use it as you do. We do not send our spirits out to murder the spirit of another! But . . ." she lowered her voice and spoke slowly to let her words have their full effect, ". . . that does not mean

245

we cannot." Without taking her eyes from his, she pulled up her jacket collar, buttoning it over her necklace as though to hide it from his view. "If you do not leave Kineu alone, you must be *more* than careful, for there will be a very powerful spirit in pursuit of you! And if any harm should come to Kineu, you will find no rest or refuge anywhere!" She smiled faintly, and pulling her shawl forward over her head, walked out of the house, leaving the door ajar behind her.

Jubilant, Supaya walked home with a light step. She had faced Wenonga! Her guardian had indeed showed her the way, had granted her strength. She had dealt with Wenonga, she thought proudly, not as Jules' daughter or as Eli's wife, but as herself, in her own way! She had tested her power against him and had won! She knew it by his expression of thwarted, baffled hate, by his silence. She was filled with a newfound sense of strength and freedom; the world about her was suddenly, strikingly vivid, the very air she breathed intoxicating. Her heart swelled with gratitude, and she offered a silent prayer of thanks to her guardian.

At home she found Kineu sitting by the fire. "Come!" she cried, insisting he get up and come outside. "We will go together! I will gather bark while you check your traps!" She caught his hands and pulled him. "Come on!"

Kineu, though puzzled, was caught up by her enthusiasm. In her shining eyes he saw reason to hope. Glad to give over his dark fears, he joined in her mood. Happily, their faces tingling with cold, their breaths crystalizing before them, they snowshoed through the woods, across meadows, and along streams where the water ran sparkling cold between overhanging banks of snow.

That night, tired but with a pervasive sense of well-being, they quickly fell asleep, his head on her breast, and their rest was deep and undisturbed.

CHAPTER TWENTY

Reverend Crowell held the reins tight with one hand and shook the other at Amy, standing in the snow beside the buggy. "Remember! This is the last time! You must tell her!"

Amy nodded, face and shoulders drawn together, shivering. She was cold and wished he would stop shaking his finger at her and drive on. She made her way with difficulty through the snow to Supaya's door, fretting to herself, "We never had such winters at home! Never!" And this time her husband was not there to remind her, his voice rising and falling in pious cadence, that this *was* her home and enduring such winters was a small burden to carry in order "to bring the word of God to an otherwise lost people."

When her husband spoke thus of "their" mission, Amy was silent. Foundering through the snow, playing Sunday service with numb fingers in a stone-cold church, rising to an endless succession of bitter cold, snow-filled days, she felt herself a prisoner, forced, like the Indians, to endure. She could remember once, when she was very young, being stirred by her husband's sense of purpose. But the practice was not what she had expected. Often her reactions were quite contrary to those of her husband, and finding it hard to keep her balance in the midst of conflicting ideas, she took refuge in memories and clung to the stability of possessions from home and to her few friends. That her friendship with Supaya was threatened roused a hitherto unsuspected rebelliousness in Amy, for Supaya was secretly her most prized friend, the one with whom she felt most comfortable, and she knocked on Supaya's door like a conspirator.

Supaya knew at once something was wrong. Amy fiddled with her spoon and tea cup, not knowing how to begin, and looked pleadingly at Supaya as if hoping she would fathom the problem without Amy herself having to speak.

Suspecting the reason for her nervousness, Supaya said nothing but smiled encouragingly at her, and finally Amy burst out, "Oh, Sophia! I have to tell you! Reverend Crowell says I must! I can't talk to you any more . . . not after today! He allowed me to come now only to tell you that." She frowned and shook her head in exasperation.

"Did he say why?"

Amy hesitated, embarrassed. "He. . .he *says* you are living in sin!" If it was true, Amy was prepared to ignore it for the sake of her own pleasure in Supaya's company, and her emphasis clearly expressed her impatience with her husband for raising this difficulty. Then, in a flash of shrewdness, she looked directly at Supaya and said warningly, "He intends to speak to Gerald Toomis about it."

Supaya was incensed. Why did they all badger her! And about what was none of their concern! Impatiently she stood up and walked aimlessly about the room, feeling, as always when irritated, the need for physical action. And why was Kineu so stubborn! Such a simple matter! So easily resolved! Realizing that Amy was watching her unhappily, Supaya tried to explain.

"According to our custom, we are already married. You should tell him that," knowing as she spoke that Amy would not be able to tell Reverend Crowell anything. "We were . . ." she hesitated, searching for the right word, "bound to each other years ago, before I came here."

"Before . . ." Amy's small, faded eyes opened wide. "But then . . . you and Eli Red Sky . . . !" That was more than she wanted to know, and she averted her head, murmuring, "Reverend Crowell would never approve of that! Never! I couldn't tell him that!"

Exasperated with Amy's weakness, yet sorry for her, Supaya made an effort at kindness. "Don't worry. I will speak to Kineu."

At once Amy brightened. "Oh do so! Please speak to him!" Shyly, "He is such a handsome young man. He reminds me of . . ." She trailed off, then brought herself back, "I'm sure he will understand. Tell him . . ." she cast about, ". . . tell him it would make Reverend Crowell so happy!" At that Supaya had to laugh, and Amy, misunderstanding, was encouraged, and exclaimed "It would make us all so happy! Why . . . we could even have a party! I haven't had a party since . . . we could have a wedding breakfast!" Amy took Supaya's hand, held it a moment in both of hers and said earnestly, "It will work out perfectly! I am sure it will!"

When Kineu came home, Supaya said, "Kineu, Reverend Crowell is going to speak to the agent about our not being married in the church."

"Let him speak. We have done nothing wrong."

"But the preacher thinks we have. He won't let his wife speak to me any more. Lizzie and Miss Harris think so too. And so will the agent."

Kineu shrugged impatiently. He had no sympathy for Supaya's friendships with these white women. He would rather she kept away from them as he had always done. The agent could cause trouble, he knew, but because it was his own bent, he persisted in believing that if they kept quietly to themselves, their private lives might go unnoticed.

Supaya was vexed, both with her friends and Kineu; but she said nothing more, keeping her irritation to herself and, for the time being, her worry about what the agent might do.

A few days later, Gerald Toomis came to see them. He knew his wife was fond of Supaya, and he himself was sympathetic with her. She was a fine, hard-working young woman, and he felt an innate reluctance to enter her home and tell her what she must do. Reverend Crowell said Indians didn't know any better; like children, they must be told what to do. But that, Gerald knew, was mistaken. They understood all right, he was certain, and they knew very well when they were being coerced. But as agent, he had to consider the peaceful, orderly operation of the reserve, where everyone had to conform, live Christian lives, as the government expected them to do. Gerald had observed Kineu at council meetings. He was quiet and thoughtful, much respected by the old Indians as well as by the young ones. If Kineu were to set an example in opposition to the government's policy, he could create trouble. And that sort of trouble it was Gerald's obligation to prevent.

Holding his hat on his knees and accepting what he felt was an obligatory cup of tea, Gerald faced them, Kineu opposite him smoking his pipe, Supaya stirring a pot on the stove, her pregnancy quite visible in profile. Now that he was on the point of speaking, Gerald found himself embarrassed. Gratefully, he accepted Kineu's offer of tobacco, it giving him something to do with his hands. As he puffed, squinting down at the pipe, he said, "I've meant to stop by

249

and see you folks before. But fall is always a busy time for every-body." He paused, but Kineu merely nodded once, politely, his eyes watchful. Seeing he would get no help from Kineu and finding no graceful approach, Gerald stroked back his unruly red hair and said bluntly, "I think it's time you let Reverend Crowell marry you and come by the office to register as man and wife. We have to keep the records straight, you know."

"We are *already* man and wife," said Kineu calmly. "You can write that in your record book."

"Well, no, I can't," said Gerald diffidently. "Not until Rev-erend Crowell marries you and gives you a certificate stating that you are married."

"I do not belong to Reverend Crowell's church," said Kineu. "I permit my wife to go to his church because she wishes to. It is not necessary that he marry us. As I have said, we are married. That *we* know it is enough." Having made his position clear, Kineu expected Gerald to leave.

Instead, Gerald persisted, as Supaya had known he would. "But it is not legal. Proper records must be kept for the government. You are a fine young couple. You should set an example for your people."

At his unconsciously patronizing tone, Kineu stiffened. His eyes glazed over, became impenetrable. "My people know how to live. They are not children who need to be taught. Each chooses his way, as we have chosen."

Gerald stirred uneasily. He looked at Supaya, hoping for her support. But Supaya watched them sidelong and remained silent, waiting.

"But your child," pursued Gerald, "what about him?" He paused, but Kineu said nothing, only looked at him suspiciously. Supaya, however, was suddenly very still. Realizing he had her full attention, Gerald pressed his point. "He must be brought up in the church, just as he must go to school."

"I do not see that he need do either," said Kineu coldly.

"But the government says he must. He must be a Christian and educated for his own good. Besides, you must want him to be legitimate, to have your name."

Kineu stared angrily at Gerald. He slapped one hand flat down on the table, warningly. "My child will have his own name!" he declared, hard-voiced.

"If you are not legally married," said Gerald, rising, "the

child's name will be Red Sky." His bland, calm manner indicated he had given them the facts. No further discussion was necessary, he being powerless before the dictates of the government. "Bye, Mrs. Red Sky, Mr. Bruley," he said clearly, deliberately. Nodding to them both, he departed, more confident of the eventual outcome than he had been. Gerald couldn't explain why, but because of the coming child, he felt Supaya would bring her husband round.

As soon as the door closed behind Gerald, Supaya came swiftly to Kineu, who stood by the fireplace, his mouth set and angry. Laying her hand on his arm, Supaya said, "Kineu, we must do as he says." Kineu looked at her in astonishment."Yes, we must," she insisted.

Kineu frowned. "Why must we?"

"Don't you see? If our child doesn't have your name, they might take him away from us!" Kineu's frown deepened as he saw her earnestness, her alarm. She shook his arm impatiently. "Don't you remember? My father *had* to send me to school and to church! I had no mother. If he hadn't, they threatened to take me away! As they did Eli! If our child has no father, they could take him away!"

Kineu considered. "But your mother was dead. Eli's mother was dead. I am alive!"

"But Kineu! If you aren't *recorded* as the father, to them our child will *have* no father!"

Still Kineu studied her, weighing her words. Filled with impatience at his reluctance to understand, she exclaimed angrily, "It would be their way of forcing us to do what they want!"

Before Kineu could reply, there was a knock on the door. Supaya opened it to a small, breathless boy who begged her to come at once. Staring with fright, he said his mother was worse and needed Supaya's help.

Supaya hurried to get her bag and was putting on her wraps when Kineu, still standing by the fireplace, suddenly said, "But I would not let them!"

"Let them!" Supaya laughed scornfully over her shoulder as she went out the door. "How would you stop them!?"

The boy's home was at the far side of the reserve, and Supaya was gone for most of the day, as she stopped off to treat several of her other patients on her way back. Walking home she was preoccupied with thoughts of the agent's visit. She had misinterpreted his glance at her, had seen it as threatening, as implying more than he said: that they would take her child away to a government school. She remembered vividly her own fears of being taken from her family, and they were bad enough, but the grief and waste of Eli's life were overwhelming. She determined to be patient with Kineu, to help him realize the danger.

Kineu greeted her gravely. Her parting remark had shocked him, questioning as it did his ability to defend his own family, questioning, it seemed, his very manhood. As he carefully, soberly cleaned his gun, he glanced at her defensively, knowing the matter had yet to be settled.

Supaya put more wood in the stove and heated up the pot of soup she had brought home as payment from her last patient. She regretted her anger. As she served Kineu his food, she stood close behind him. Lovingly, she smoothed back his hair. He put an arm around her, and she leaned her heavy body against him and rested her cheek on his head. She understood his hurt, he her regret. After a moment, she drew away and sat opposite him while he ate.

"Kineu, please let us marry in the white way. I lost one child. I cannot live with the dread of losing another."

"But you do not know they would take it."

"They can take any child who has one parent. The agent is friendly to us; he might not, left to himself. But the preacher is angry! His wife is forbidden to speak to me!"

"That does not matter. He does not frighten me!"

"*He* does not frighten me either, Kineu! It is his power that is frightening. If he is displeased with us, who knows what he might persuade the agent to do? Oh, Kineu!" Supaya reached her hands across and grasped his. "It will mean nothing to us, but it will satisfy them. Then we can live in peace!"

"Peace!" Kineu said the word with contempt. "What kind of peace, bought with our independence, our pride!"

"But we will live as a family! And we can take pride in doing so in spite of these things imposed on us!"

Kineu smiled at the thought of their family. "For your sake, Suppy, and for our child, I will try to do so." His smile faded. He gazed at her sadly and said quietly, "Let the preacher marry us."

The wedding was held in the church on a morning in early spring. Amy, untroubled by Supaya's advanced pregnancy and delighted that she was being married, had seized the occasion and to the amazement of her husband had organized the wedding and arranged a wedding breakfast. With an extraordinary display of energy and initiative, she had walked to the homes of those she wanted to invite to extend a personal invitation, never doubting their eagerness to come. Eyes bright with memories of wedding parties she had attended as a young girl, Amy polished silver, prepared food, and laid the table, moving about her husband as oblivious to his efforts at restraint as a rushing stream to a half-submerged rock. She had decorated the church as best she could, for the season was early for flowers, by bringing in budding branches and a few of her potted plants.

Now, as Supaya and Kineu entered the church, she played the piano with an enthusiasm, an ebullience, that threatened the proper seriousness of the occasion. Reverend Crowell frowned slightly and cleared his throat several times, looking sternly over the heads of the couple before him, a man determined, despite his deep embarrassment at the condition of the bride, to bring this wayward couple into the bosom of the church, to bless their union and legitimize their child.

When the brief, simple service was over, Amy led the way to the house, through the gate and onto the porch, where the waiting guests had taken shelter from a light spring rain. There was a moment's confusion over the order of their entering.

"The bride! The bride must go first! Then the groom!" exclaimed Amy, guiding Supaya inside and then Kineu, who walked erect, his eyes straight ahead. Reverend Crowell stood back, holding the door, and gravely nodded the other guests inside.

Herded into the dining room, everyone stood in awe at sight of the table until Amy, with unusual authority, directed each to his chair.

"How charming!" said Agatha Harris, quite at home.

"Pretty!" exclaimed Sarah, excited over eating breakfast at the preacher's house.

The table, laid with a white cloth, sparkled with cut glass and old silver. At either end were silver candlesticks, each holding three white candles. The china was scalloped and gold-edged, with violets around the border. And in the middle of the table was a majestic white cake on a china pedestal cake-server with a ruffled edge.

Amy beamed, delighted by their stunned admiration. These were her treasures from home. Unwrapping and setting them out had given her boundless pleasure, like meeting old friends. She bustled around the table, pouring hot tea, urging everyone to please help himself.

But only Agatha Harris, Lizzie, and Sarah were at ease. Reverend Crowell was still embarrassed, not only by the bride, but by his wife's irrepressible animation, which he in no way comprehended. Gerald, feeling awkward and out of place at such a formal table, kept silent. The Indians—Supaya and Kineu, Soos and George, Uncle John and his wife, Hattie—sat stiff as boards, hands in their laps, faces impassive. Only their eyes moved, alert to Amy's every move, as amazed to find themselves sitting down for a meal with whites at such a table as if they had been transported there by magic. Excepting Supaya and Kineu, they had come only because Amy had invited them. They had found her on their doorsteps, a slight, frail woman, strangely touched by the Great Spirit. They had listened gravely to her excited, almost incoherent invitation and had solemnly agreed to come out of their desire to humor her. Now they watched her studiously for cues, wanting to perform correctly.

Agatha and Lizzie passed around the cold meats, cabbage salad, and buttered bread. There was no conversation. Sarah, after one word, had been quieted by a severe glance from Soos. Only thank-you's were murmured as the food passed from hand to hand. All concentrated on eating with dignity. Even so, the sounds of their eating seemed unnaturally loud. As the silence stretched on, the general tension increased. All were relieved when Amy, completely absorbed in the progress of the breakfast and unaware of her guests unease, suddenly decided it was time for the cake. Whisking their plates away, she exclaimed, "Now the bride must cut the cake!"

Leaning over between Kineu and Hattie, she lifted pedestal and cake and set them down triumphantly in front of Supaya. In a dead silence, with all eyes focused on her, Supaya self-consciously cut the cake, and Amy handed round the small, flowered plates. Sarah, relishing the yellow cake and butter icing, finished her piece first. Immediately Amy offered her a second helping. Conscious of her mother's silent admonition, Sarah hesitated, but she rolled her large, dark eyes so longingly at the half-demolished cake that for the first time everyone smiled. Attention veered from the newlyweds to Sarah, Indian and white finding common ground in amused understanding. After the cake and many cups of tea, the end of the breakfast was in view, and the atmosphere lightened.

When Reverend Crowell rose from the table, everyone rose.

Amy hurried to wrap up a piece of cake for Supaya to take home. As the guests departed, expressing their thanks, Amy pressed each one's hand and gazed with such intensity into their eyes that each felt he had, willy-nilly, played a part in a special rite that in Amy's eyes had bound them all happily together. Beside her, Reverend Crowell, slightly stunned at his wife's having somehow taken the whole affair out of his rightful jurisdiction, gravely shook each hand, trying to restore a properly serious tone to their leave-taking.

Outside the misty rain was still falling. No one lingered. With smiles and nods, they all parted. Supaya glanced sideways at Kineu, who had not spoken a word. He faced straight ahead, his unsmiling profile shadowed by his hat brim. Now that it was all over, Supaya felt inclined to giggle, and she slipped her arm through his, hoping he would respond. But Kineu, feeling diminished and robbed of dignity, did not turn his head. His arm hung unresponsively at his side, and they walked home in silence.

Rain washed away the last of the winter's snow, and in the woods, leek blades, tender and green, thrust up through the damp earth and soggy leaf mold. Hungering for the bulbs' fresh, pungent flavor, Supaya took a basket and went into the woods.

This morning, as soon as she left the open field, she again had the uneasy sense of being watched. She had experienced this a number of times during the winter when she had entered the woods alone or had been in remote, lonely sections of the reserve, visiting a patient. Always she had left the woods for the road and had sought company on the long walk home. And always she had carried an axe. Now, taking a firmer grip on the helve, she looked sharply round. Seeing nothing, hearing nothing, she went on. Her time was very near, and she moved clumsily, leaning slightly backward to balance the weight of her body. She stepped slowly, careful of her footing, and cautiously, alert for any sound because more strongly than ever she felt a watchful, unseen presence.

Pausing frequently for breath, she climbed up a steep slope. Every spring at the top of this hill she had found patches of leeks growing in the shelter of larch and cedar. Reaching the summit, she stopped to rest on a fallen log. Sitting there, she heard a faint sound, a furtive rustle that ceased the instant she heard it. Her back prickled. With an effort, she got up to her feet and turned, axe ready. Nothing moved. No breeze stirred. An almost breathless hush filled the woods; only a watery sun shone through still branches, casting a pale tracery of shadows on the ground. Thinking she had been foolish to come so far alone, Supaya hurried toward the cedar grove. She found the leeks and saw at once that some creature had already been feeding on them. The ground was disturbed where leeks had been uprooted or broken half off. Then, to one side, she saw in the mud a huge print of a bear's foot. It was early for a bear to be out. Still, perhaps what she had heard was a hungry bear foraging on leeks. A nearby birch had been raked and gnawed, and black fur was snagged in its rough bark. As quickly as she could, Supaya stooped to pull some leeks, thinking to get a few and go before the bear returned. As her hand closed around the shoots, she heard, behind her, a low growl. For a second she froze. Then in one swift motion, she dropped the leeks, grasped the axe, and raising her unwieldy body, turned, expecting to face a hungry, irritable bear. Instead she faced the white dog.

It stood quite still, in no hurry to attack, a deep growl rumbling in its chest. Its thick, luminous fur bristled. Its gleaming, deadly eyes stared at her with hate. Now she understood her uneasiness of past months: the dog had been stalking her, biding its time until it caught her at a disadvantage, alone, awkward, unable to properly defend herself.

An unreasoning, blind anger burst in her. Let the dog attack! Let them fight it out! She was sick to death of living in fear of it! Forgetting her clumsiness and with intent as implacable as its own, Supaya stepped forward, axe raised, ready to strike, eager in her rage to sink its sharp edge into the dog's flesh, to feel it bite into the bone, to see the blood gush out that would mark the end of this struggle between them.

Responding to her move, the dog jerked its head back and snarled. Then, running in at an angle, it dashed to her right, then to her left, snapping at her, causing her to turn from one side to the other, dodging her blows, driving her back toward the trees, hemming her in.

Each time the dog came at her, Supaya lunged at it with a vicious swipe of her axe. Maddened by her attempted blows, the dog suddenly rushed straight at her. Again Supaya swung the axe, but the dog's headlong attack threw her off balance and the size of her belly hindered her aim. As the dog swerved past her, Supaya pitched sideways as she strove to drive the axe into its back. With the impetus of her thrust, the axe flew from her grasp, landing with a thud beyond the dog.

Stumbling, Supaya managed to catch her balance, but now she stood defenseless. Breathing hard, she faced the dog. Bracing herself against the attack she knew would come, she crossed her arms to protect her face and throat.

The dog swung round and paused, legs splayed out, huge jaws gaping. Its eyes shone with triumphant malevolence. It hunched its shoulders and with a crackling, spitting snarl, sprang at her.

Under the impact of its great body, Supaya was thrown to the ground, the dog upon her. With its hind feet braced on her body, nails pressing into her flesh, it ripped and tore at her arms. Panicking, Supaya kicked out and strove to roll from under the massive animal, whose hot, fetid breath sickened her. Seeing her death and that of her child, Supaya's agonized spirit cried out piercingly for her Grandfather. Desperately she grasped her shoulders with either hand to keep her arms crossed and tried to keep her head pressed against them. But the enraged dog dragged at her arms with its teeth and thrust under them with its bloodied snout, reaching for her throat.

Her strength failing, Supaya cried out again. Suddenly, above the dog's gnashing and snarling, sounded a deep, reverberating roar. The dog screamed. Its weight lifted abruptly from her. A different odor, strong and rank, filled Supaya's nostrils. Cautiously raising her head, she saw looming beside her a huge black bear, stooping forward toward the white dog, which, with one powerful sweep of its paw, it had lifted off Supaya and hurled to the ground. Terror-stricken, Supaya inched herself back under the cedars and watched as the dog, blood staining its shoulder, scrambled to its feet and whipped about. Its left leg buckled under, but the dog regained its balance and, in a snarling frenzy of hate and pain, faced the bear. The bear stood upright, paws raised, its coarse, scraggly spring pelt hanging loosely on its gaunt frame. Its small eyes were bright with anger, its muzzle wrinkled with distaste at the dog's scent. Baring its teeth, the bear lunged forward, paws flashing out. The dog swerved aside, but too slowly to avoid the bear's claws, which caught the side of the dog's head, ripping its ear. Crazed, the dog rushed again at the bear, daring another swipe of those powerful paws, and seized the bear's leg with his teeth. The bear roared and swung itself about in a wild, ungainly dance, dashing the dog's outflung body against a tree.

Its grip broken by the thudding impact, the dog fell to the ground and rolled over. Crouching low, it heaved for breath, blood running down its head and mixing with threads of saliva hanging from its open jaws. It stared with glazed eyes at the bear, who loomed over it, snorting and growling. Then the dog, in one desperate, powerful leap, sprang headlong at the bear, fastening its jaws on the loose skin of the bear's throat. The bear roared with pain, but it clasped the dog's body in close embrace. Tighter and tighter the bear pressed the straining, struggling dog to its chest until the dog, finally loosening its grip, threw back its head and screamed.

Grunting, the bear threw the dog to the ground and stood waiting, its head weaving. But the white dog lay where it fell, gasping for breath, eyes staring blindly. Supaya thought it was dying, but after a few moments the dog raised its bloody head and rolled onto its haunches. Several times it opened its jaws in soundless grimaces of pain, nervously licking its chops. Heaving forward, it attempted to rise and failed. Trying again, with a mighty strain of its powerful shoulders, it succeeded in getting to its feet. Head hanging, indifferent to the bear's threatening presence, the dog swayed, almost fell, steadied itself, and turning, staggered slowly away into the woods.

Mouthing the air and grumbling to itself, the bear pawed irritably at its neck where the dog's teeth had pierced the skin. Dropping to all fours, it sniffed at Supaya's axe, then at her basket of leeks. Reaching in, it scooped up some and stuffed them into its mouth. Rearing up again, its bright, round eyes looked directly at Supaya, crouching back under the cedars. It cocked its ears and lifted its head in a series of little sniffs, testing her scent. Supaya held rigidly still. Then the bear dropped down again and loped off through the brush at a rapid, rolling gait, its head stretched forward intently on the path it pursued.

Both dog and bear were gone. Trampled leeks, an overturned basket, and some dark, already-drying patches of blood were the only traces of their encounter. Realizing she was alone and alive, Supaya was overcome with dizziness. Trees and earth blurred, tilted sideways, and faded away. Eyes closed, she leaned her head against a branch. When her vision cleared and she felt steadier, Supaya crawled from under the tree and got carefully to her feet, her immediate concern not her lacerated arms but her unborn child, so near to term. Her attention focused inward, she rested her hands on her belly. She felt no pain there, only a stirring under her hands that caused her abdomen to bulge oddly. Satisfied, Supaya picked up her basket and stubbornly paused long enough to pull some leeks. Then, retrieving her axe, she started down the hill toward home.

Four days later Supaya's baby was born. Alma had come the night before, Soos in the morning as Kineu was leaving to go fishing. When he returned in late afternoon with a basket of fish, he heard as he entered, the hungry, squalling cries of his firstborn. Alma had already gone, having taken the afterbirth, wrapped in a cloth, and buried it in the field near the woods on her way home.

Supaya sat in her rocker by the fireplace, cradling the baby in her arms. She turned back the blanket so Kineu could see his son. The baby curled and uncurled tiny fingers that trembled with the intensity of his cries; his eyes squeezed into slits, his crimson face all open, hungry mouth. When Supaya turned him to her breast, there was sudden silence as he worked away, pulling strongly on the nipple. The angry red faded from his face, and his thick, soft hair looked sooty black where it lay in wisps against his cheek and neck.

Supaya and Kineu smiled down at him. "Little Waboose," said Kineu, touching him gently.

And so he was named, Little Waboose, Little Rabbit, although when Supaya had him christened, his name was set down as Walter Bruley, and as Walter he was entered into the band registry.

Supaya's badly mauled arms were healing well. She had told only Kineu of the white dog's attack and its fight with the bear, and she was careful to keep her arms covered. Even Soos and Alma, when they helped her with the birth, had not seen them. The wounds were sore and painful for days, but Supaya doctored them very carefully with an infusion of cow parsnip and poultices of dried and powdered wild geranium root and spikenard.

Sarah, who took a proprietary interest in Waboose, came every day after school to help. One afternoon in early summer, Sarah arrived breathless. "Aunt Suppy! Guess who I just saw coming through the woods!"

Supaya smiled. "I don't know, Sarah, but sit down and catch your breath. I saved some bannock for you."

Sarah sat and poured syrup on her bread. "But Aunt Suppy! I was so scared! He was coming toward me, limping. He had a cane!"

"Who, Sarah?"

"Wenonga! He had a black bag and a cane! He could hardly walk! But I was scared because he looked awful! The side of his face was all red and twisted! You know, like this!" And Sarah pulled the skin around her eye. "And he was all bent over and I ran as soon as I saw him!"

Supaya rested her hand on Sarah's shoulder. "I know you must have been frightened, Sarah, but he is an old man and not well. When you go home, go by the road."

Wenonga was not well. Moving or still, his whole body pained. Each breath cut his chest. When he coughed, a choking, spasmodic cough, it hurt so sharply that black spots blurred his vision and sweat beaded his forehead. Often he spat out blood. Friendless, he sat alone, not bothering to light the lamp, watching the darkness fill his empty house. Since news of his being disabled had spread rapidly through the reserve, no one had come to ask for his services as a doctor. At first he had sneered, filled with contempt for those who thought that because he leaned on a cane and his face was disfigured his powers as a doctor were impaired.

Then he ceased thinking about them as he faced a deeper misery. Night after night, dragging his left foot, he had hobbled into his bedroom and, grimacing with pain, had let himself awkwardly down on the floor, sitting with one leg bent, the other out straight like a useless stick. He had unwrapped his wild goose whistle, had blown it and prayed, summoning his spirits to aid him. The piercing notes of the whistle carried far; their melancholy, atonal sound reached many ears, yet Wenonga's spirits did not respond. Humbling himself, Wenonga besought their help, but the deep silence of night was his only answer, though he sat on until the early light of morning touched his pain-wracked face. Then he seemed to hear a distant drumming, and a rustling like the autumn wind in dead reeds. Finally he knew himself abandoned.

One day he took off his amulet and put it, together with his ceremonial pipe and the whistle in its fur wrapping, into a plain black velvet bag in which he kept his doctoring gear. Then, using a twisted branch as a cane and dragging his lame foot, he made his way haltingly across the field into the woods. Pain sealed his lips. Sweat stung his eyes and soaked his shirt. But he clung to his intention, his strength of purpose lending strength to his broken body. Near a grove of cedar trees he went down on one knee. Prizing up a stone with his stick, he dug the earth from under it, making a deep hole. He laid the bag in the hole, filled in the earth, and pressed it down. He replaced the stone in its same position, carefully arranging dirt and leaves about it so it appeared undisturbed.

He could not eat. He had swallowed nothing in days. But when he returned home, he made up a small fire in the stove and brewed a pot of tea, stirring into it a powder that he had put aside. Then he opened wide the front door and sat down facing it in his rocker. He leaned back against the chair, despite the pain it caused the suppurating flesh of his back. Slowly he drank the tea, then lit his hawthorne wood pipe and rested his head back, his weary, reddened eyes fixed on the open doorway through which he could see the evening sky.

The top of his pipe gleamed red when he drew on it. Smoke hung in a thin bluish haze about his head. As the sunset faded, the room grew dim; its bareness softened, and the quiet figure in the chair grew vague and indistinct and was finally swallowed up by the tide of a moonless night, a night as profoundly dark inside the house as out—darker, for outside the eternal stars were shining.

Gerald Toomis found Wenonga, an experience, he told Lizzie, the like of which he hoped never to have again. Several Indians had dropped by the office for one vague reason or another, and each mentioned quite casually that he had not seen any smoke from Wenonga's house in a week, or he had not seen Wenonga preparing his garden, or Wenonga had not been seen at the store in some time. Not until one gray-haired man, squinting at him impatiently from under his hat brim, said with arresting directness, "Wenonga's front door has been standing open since before the last rain," did Gerald make a point of going to Wenonga's house.

The front door was indeed standing open. There was a puddle on the floor inside the threshold. Gerald had knocked, had called out, "Mr. Red Sky!" and getting no answer, had stepped inside, avoiding the puddle. For a moment, coming in out of the sunlight, he had not realized anyone was there. Then he saw Wenonga, sitting in the rocker, staring defiantly straight at him, his lips drawn back against his clenched teeth in a ghastly grimace. Startled, Gerald jumped back, seeing Wenonga, as in a nightmare, ready to leap forward, axe in hand. Recovering, Gerald approached the body. Wenonga's pipe lay on his lap; his hands grasped the chair arms. It seemed plain to Gerald that his teeth were clenched not in anger or threat but in an effort not to cry out. Beside him on the table was a nearly empty cup of tea. Sadly, gently, Gerald reached out and closed Wenonga's eyes.

Gerald wrote a letter to Cyrus at Stone Island, telling him of his brother's death and notifying him that he had inherited the house and land, but he came to Supaya, as the nearest relative on the reserve, to care for the body.

Supaya asked Alma to help, and together they washed the body and laid Wenonga out. Then they heated cedar branches to purify themselves and the house of the stench and contamination of death. Daniel, the boat builder, made a coffin and brought it to the house. Before he fastened down the lid, Supaya, saddened by the loneliness of the corpse, by the absence of any mourner, laid inside Wenonga's pipe and his pouch of tobacco.

Reverend Crowell had announced the service, but only Gerald, Supaya, and Alma came. Daniel brought the coffin to the church in his wagon and stood by to help move it into the cemetery. The service was brief; Amy played the piano, and they sang and prayed, their too few voices sounding thin in the empty church.

Wenonga was buried next to his wife, whose grave had settled and was overgrown with weeds. As Reverend Crowell prayed at the head of the grave, a surprising number of Indian men, elderly and in pairs, passed by on the road, drawn there by a grudging respect for Wenonga's curing of their children, their wives, themselves and by a secret satisfaction that a dangerous man who frightened them and seduced their wives and daughters was now gone. Though they didn't turn their heads, they observed the little group under the trees: the preacher and his wife—of course; Daniel— necessary; Supaya—daughter-in-law; Alma—probably an old witch herself. And they walked on, understanding everything except their own diminution.

Seeing them pass, Supaya resented their curiosity and lack of respect. Her father, like Wenonga, was a shaman, a doctor—would he also be so shunned? Perhaps these old men had not yet realized there was no one to take Wenonga's place. He had had no son, no grandson, not even an apprentice whom he could have trained and to whom he could have bequeathed his knowledge. Sarah had seen Wenonga carrying a bag. Supaya knew now what it was and what he had done with it.

Wenonga would have sneered at Reverend Crowell's ceremony, but like all his people, he had enjoyed a good sing. When the preacher ended his prayer and Amy in her reedy voice began the closing hymn, Supaya raised her voice vibrantly, finding in the strong, simple melody an expression of her sorrow for the loss, not of a frightening wickedness, but of a hemmed-in, lonely, defiant, and aging man whose strengths and skills were those of an Indian born free and whose like would never come again.

Later that summer Cyrus' son Angus moved from Stone Island to Two Bluffs. He transferred his band membership and that of his wife, Pearline. He took over Wenonga's land and built a new house, on the far side of a grove of trees, out of sight of Wenonga's house.

No one would live in Wenonga's house. No one would go near it. Squirrels and chipmunks, quick to sense a deserted house, ran busily in and out, pausing only to flick their tails on the doorstep. They cached food in the loft and built nests in Wenonga's mattress, undisturbed by his clothes left hanging on the pegs. Both doors stood gaping. A gritty dust gradually settled on the shelves and the table, where the tea cup, a dried sediment staining its inside, still sat, untouched. Wind blew through the house, lifting the dust and swirling the dead leaves that collected in corners. It stirred the curtains hanging at the doors and set Wenonga's chair to rocking, back and forth. The smokestack was blown down, and shakes were blown off the roof, exposing the beams and letting in rain and snow. Grass sprouted in the dooryard, and the lane where no one walked disappeared as if it had never been. But passers-by sometimes heard strange sounds, the wistful calling of distant voices or a low, forlorn muttering, and sometimes, in the dark, they saw a faint yellowish light flickering inside the empty, desolate house.

PART FOUR
1916–1936

CHAPTER TWENTY-ONE

Kineu was one of the first men on the reserve to enlist in the war. From the moment he told Supaya of his decision, she saw there was no use asking him to stay, to wait until he was called. He and George were going off together, sure of their strength, eager to prove their manhood, and already he had put her and the children behind him.

She, her half-brother Wagash, and the children, Waboose, Shooskonee, and little Taw, had stood and watched him go. Bitterly, Supaya saw how easily, without a backward look, he left them to go and fight a white man's war. Taw, too young to understand how long the father he doted on would be gone, waved. At bedtime he cried. All their efforts to console him were useless, and he cried himself to sleep as he was to do many times. Supaya's resentment at being left alone so readily to make a living for herself and four children was deepened by Taw's grief. But she kept her resentment to herself, for all the men had gone; even many of the old men, looking younger than they were, lied about their ages and enlisted, proud of their skill as warriors. For two long years now there had been only boys and very old men left on the reserve.

All the women, supporting their families alone, were underfed and overworked. Some, with children old enough to work the garden, were free to fish. But since 1915 meat had been scarce on the reserve. Stockpiles of wood were small and houses were cold. There were many cases of exposure and pneumonia. Supaya spent hours preparing medicines and walking long distances to visit pa-

266

tients, sometimes finding old people dead, sitting by their cold stoves. Sarah came after school to tend the children and usually had some food warm when Supaya returned, but frequently she was too tired to eat.

And too restless to sleep. As soon as she closed her eyes, worries and painful memories filled her mind, repeating themselves in endless patterns. For Supaya, the war was a culminating sorrow, preceded by two more personal losses. Though she wished for sleep, she also dreaded it, fearing a dream that might tell her Kineu was injured or dead. For she had dreamed of her father.

Rather, her father had come to her in a dream, five years before, when Shooskonee was only a baby. Snow had been falling for days and was blown into high, curved drifts at the corners of the house and shed. In her dream also snow was falling. From a distance she heard her father's voice, calling her. Gradually he had come closer until she could see his shadowy figure. She had tried to go toward him, but could not lift her feet or move through the thin but impenetrable veil of snow that separated them and obscured his face. She saw only the outline of his head and one arm extended toward her, but his voice was as distinct as if he spoke into her ear.

"Supaya, when you hear the wolf howl, be comforted, for that will be me, speaking to you. Know that I will always be near you." Her dream had filled her with foreboding. Several days later on her way back from visiting a patient, she heard the mournful cry of a wolf. Wolves were rare at Two Bluffs. Never in her years there had she heard one. She stopped instantly to listen. Again, much closer, it uttered a series of short barks, then a long, ululating cry that when it ended left a gap in the still air. Supaya waited, longing to hear it again. But the woods were still and silent. No bird called, no wind stirred in the branches. Then she knew. Pulling her shawl forward over her face, she stood in the snow and wept.

Weeks later, when the first boat brought the mail, there was a letter from Jacques. Jules had died of pneumonia. Rhea was caring for Quayo. Everyone else was well. Supaya never spoke of her dream or of hearing the wolf. But always, when in the woods, she listened for it, and when lying awake at night, she could still feel the utter emptiness that had followed its cry.

Two years later, as spring was warming into summer, Supaya was working in the garden and paused to watch a flock of birds that rose from the trees and soared out over the meadow. Moving as with one spirit, they curved and swooped, stretched apart, drew together in fluid motion. As they streamed across the field above her head, Supaya was startled to see in their midst one pure white bird. As it passed, wings outspread, it dipped below the others, then soared up to rejoin its fellows and was lost to sight as the whole flock swept away over the trees. Supaya looked after the bird of death, so swift and unexpected in its flight. She wished she had not seen it, and her heart filled with dread. Instead of another letter, Rhea and Wagash had appeared on her doorstep.

Rhea had cried endless tears, tears of grief, frustration, and tension that ran unheeded down her face. As she talked she stared at Supaya, her mouth trembling over her words, her hands twisting in her lap. Wagash stood close by her, his head hanging, until Kineu quietly drew him over to the table to sit with Waboose and Shooskonee.

"I didn't know what to do! I'm not strong like you! He wouldn't listen to me! Or Quayo! He wouldn't stay inside, not until the very end! Jacques brought a doctor but he just laughed! And then . . . he was gone! Just like that!" Her voice rose, cracked; then, exasperation showing through her tears, "He never did marry me with a paper! I wish . . ." she swallowed and bit her lip, unable to say what she wished. "None of my family came to the funeral! And Reverend Harris . . . he didn't come to the wake! He's a mean man! But everybody else came!" Rhea almost smiled. "It was a good wake! All his friends spoke and sang songs, and there was lots of food." Her smile faded and fresh tears came. "He's buried beside his . . . beside your mother. After that there were just the three of us . . . but Wagash was too little to help and Quayo was too old! I tried, Supaya, I tried hard! Jacques and Maud helped. They helped me with the garden and gave us fish and meat. I tried to get a job. I asked Mr. Jackson, but he . . ." She pressed her lips together, glanced over at the children, then down at her lap. ". . .and I spoke to Mr. Bonnet. . . ." Her face crumpled and she sobbed, "Oh, if only Jules had married me!" Through her tears she saw the pain in Supaya's face and hastened to add, "But Quayo was good to me! She talked to me and taught me how to do lots of things. Here," she fumbled in her bag, "she gave me this to give to you. She said to tell you your grandfather gave it to your father, and Jules gave it to Quayo to give to you." Rhea held out a delicate necklace made of tiny dark blue beads with a flat, ovate skin amulet, a little bag with a small wooden frame fitted inside, stretching it taut. On one side, several inches above the amulet, the beads had been looped into a knot.

Slowly Supaya reached out and took it. She remembered seeing the beads around Jules' neck. Often she had caught herself thinking of Jules as if he were still alive. His amulet, filled with the accumulated power of generations of healing, was like a hand stretched out to her, and she held it gently, finding no words.

But Rhea, obsessed with her own experience, went on speaking. "Quayo . . ." Rhea shrugged helplessly, ". . . just went to sleep! Wagash woke me, said his grandmother wouldn't answer him. . . . She's buried on the other side of your mother. Then Jacques and Maud, they wanted the house. They've three children now. Their old house was too small. I . . . I didn't know what to do! Jacques said maybe I could get a job in Wellston, that if I came to you . . . you might . . . might keep Wagash for me . . . just until I find a job!"

Wagash turned to look at his mother, his eyes wide, his face sober. Rhea, avoiding looking at him, appealed to Supaya. "Just until I can find a job! He'll start school this year anyway, and . . ." she bit her lip in a vain effort to control a fresh flood of tears. ". . . he's a big help, now, he . . ." Her voice thinned and choked off. Bending forward, she covered her face with her hands and cried.

Rhea had stayed for a week. She regained her composure and even found it possible, finally, to speak of her future without tears. Supaya took her to see Reverend Crowell and Amy, then Gerald and Lizzie Toomis, introducing her as Jules' widow. They gave Rhea names and addresses of people in Wellston where she might stay and who might help her find work. When she left, wearing her best clothes and carrying a carpetbag, she was excited and hopeful. Stepping up eagerly into Gerald Toomis' buggy, she arranged her skirts and smiled down at them all, her eyes large and bright under the wide brim of her hat. She promised to visit often.

She had returned once, almost a year later, riding out with a farmer she had met in Wellston, where she worked as a waitress. She stayed only one day, saying she couldn't take more time off or she would lose her job. Wagash, who had lost all hope of her returning, rushed to her, his face glowing. But Rhea was cool and withdrawn. Whenever Wagash came close to her, she moved about restlessly and responded absentmindedly to his excited questions about his going with her. Rebuffed, he went to sit halfway up the stairs. Arms across his knees, forehead leaning against the rail, he watched her and listened, knowing he was to be left behind.

With Supaya, Rhea was evasive and petulant. She had changed jobs several times, wasn't sure how long she could keep the one she had. She had a room, but it was small and her landlady didn't want children. Since it was clear that Rhea had not come to take Wagash with her, Supaya tried to discover why she had come. She was too ill at ease to have come simply for the pleasure of a visit. Thinking Rhea had something else to tell her, Supaya gave her opportunities to speak, but Rhea, increasingly nervous and constrained, let the pauses in their conversation lengthen and turned to the door in relief when the farmer returned for her. She had no special word for Wagash, who hung behind the others when she said her brief good-bye. As the wagon rolled away, she looked straight ahead, dry-eyed and unsmiling.

Shortly after Rhea's visit, Supaya received a letter from her, two lines only. She was leaving Wellston for Toronto and would send an address when she got one. Supaya knew then what Rhea had not had the courage to tell her.

After Kineu left, Supaya worried about Wagash. He was, as Rhea had said, a big help. Six years old when Rhea brought him, he was now eight. He worked in the garden, fed the pig and chickens, ran errands, and Supaya was grateful. But with Kineu away, there was no man to teach Wagash the skills of hunting and trapping. Or to send him out in search of a vision, as Jules certainly would have done. Supaya was teaching him how to fish, but she hesitated to send him out to fast. Two Bluffs in 1915 was not the same as Stone Island in 1897, when she had had her vision. Even then her family had faced much opposition. Now opposition would be much stronger, from both church and school, and, Supaya knew, from Wagash himself.

For Wagash found comfort in adopting white ways. Unaware that as Jules' son he had a special appeal for Miss Harris, Wagash nevertheless felt the warmth of her favor, the subtle unconscious softening of her manner whenever her eye fell on him. With a child's unerring guile, he confided in her, elicited her interest and her sympathy. Her approval gave him security, even a sense of superiority. When Supaya had taken him with her to gather bark and herbs for medicines, he protested because Miss Harris said they were worthless, that Indians should look to a white doctor when they needed treatment. His smugness as he put down his family's customs made Supaya uneasy. She saw Wagash, his young life disrupted, turning away from his people, and she hesitated to try to turn him back. She could imagine his saying to her: "Miss Harris says that fasting and visions are pagan. We must go to church, read the Bible, and learn to be good Christians." She knew that if he ever said that to her, she would be angry, and she did not want to be angry with Wagash, or widen the distance that already existed between them. She reassured herself by thinking that Soos and George had not sent their children out fasting, nor had any other family that she knew of at Two Bluffs. Studying Wagash covertly as he bent over his school books, Supaya thought how strongly he resembled Rhea. His mouth was petulant like hers, and his brows curved downwards, giving his face a faintly wry, humorous expression. Supaya thought that Wagash—William, as Miss Harris called him—would grow up to calculate his chances, perhaps with more success than his mother. But that spring something happened which took Supaya's attention away from Wagash.

It was at the women's weekly meeting at Amy Crowell's that Supaya first heard of Louis Hagerstrom. Annie Jones had just scandalized Amy by saying that Hagerstrom had stolen a cow off the reserve.

"Oh my, no! Surely Mr. Hagerstrom wouldn't steal a cow! Not right off the reserve!" Amy paused in pouring the tea. Annie prodded her by holding up her cup.

"He did. He says it's his cow that strayed into Jake's field."

"Maybe Mr. Hagerstrom made a mistake," said Lizzie. "I hope Jake told my husband. Gerald will get Jake's cow back."

Annie would not flatly contradict Lizzie, but implied that Jake's cow was gone for good by saying, "There's no fence, and Jake has no paper for the cow."

Supaya had been in Annie's home many times, treating her children, and knew her as a gossip but also as a strong, shrewd woman, who would speak out when others were silent. Clearly she had something further to say, as all the Indian women in Amy's parlor knew. Sitting on extra chairs and cross-legged on the floor, the women were busy knitting socks, scarfs, and mittens to be sent to the soldiers overseas, and they waited to hear what else Annie would say. They understood she wanted to take full advantage of Lizzie's attention since informing Lizzie often proved a most effective way of reaching Gerald's ear.

"Stealing a cow is easy. Stealing land is harder. He tried to steal Harry Black's land before Harry enlisted."

"What! Steal Harry's land!"

"Sure," said Annie, pleased at having shocked Lizzie. "He came with a bottle. Got Harry drunk. Then wanted him to sign papers giving his land away."

Lizzie said, "I can't believe he'd do such a thing! He has a farm! And he must know a white man can't buy land on a reserve!"

"Sure he'd try. His land is poor, full of rocks. But Harry couldn't sign. He was *too* drunk." Annie smiled ironically, as did some of the other women; then she added, "He got Harry's wife, Edna, drunk too." At that their smiles faded. Lizzie and Amy missed the significance of Annie's comment, but Annie let that pass out of consideration for Amy, as the others understood.

Annie said no more; the conversation shifted. But she had alerted the other women, and Lizzie, she knew, would speak to her husband.

That night for the first time in years Supaya locked the doors and thought as she did so of the cow in the shed, the cow she and Kineu had bought just before the war began. Had she known she would be left alone to make a living, she would not have agreed to buy a cow. Winter feed was expensive. She had barely managed to keep the cow through last winter. If she couldn't feed it through the next, she could at least sell it. But if it were stolen!

In late spring, Edna Black came to Supaya for medicine. Supaya suspected Edna, sullen and unresponsive, was pregnant. Knowing she was a stranger who, like herself, had come from another reserve, Supaya was sympathetic. Since Harry had gone to war, Edna had been living alone. Supaya thought she understood Edna's plight after hearing Annie's gossip, and she took to stopping in at Edna's on her way to or from other patients. Edna's house was small and bare, almost empty of furniture. Often the fire was out, and Edna, always startled by Supaya's visits and very defensive, would hasten to make one in the small stove. Plainly, she was short of food and fuel. Supaya asked Lizzie and Uncle John to help.

Lizzie had called on Edna when she first arrived, but Edna had not been friendly and Lizzie had not returned. But when she heard of Edna's illness, poverty, and loneliness, Lizzie brought her food, rummaged in her trunks and through bundles sent to the reserve from Wellston for clothes, curtains, old rugs, anything she could find to warm and brighten Edna's life. She urged her to join the weekly meetings at Amy's and to attend Sunday service.

Uncle John, in exchange for some of Supaya's dried berries and apples, took Edna cut firewood. One day, as he sat by Supaya's fireplace, smoking his pipe and holding Taw on his lap, he said, "I will not take her any more wood. I will not go to her house again."

Supaya was surprised. "Why not, Uncle John?"

John's eyebrows lifted haughtily. "She must be a bad woman. She keeps bad company."

"She lives alone."

He glanced shrewdly at Supaya. "She is not alone. A white man opened the door when I brought the wood. He had a gun. When he saw the wood, he laughed and slammed the door. I stacked the wood and came away. I will not go again."

Then one Sunday Edna did come to Sunday service. She entered the church shyly, her face almost hidden by her shawl. The women greeted her and made room for her. After the service, Reverend Crowell shook her hand and said he hoped she would come again.

Seeing her there, Supaya was encouraged, but when she stopped by Edna's house, Edna flung open the door and, seeing Supaya, turned quickly away. Her pregnancy was now quite evident. She stood with her arms pressed tight across herself, and Supaya thought she was sick.

"No!" exclaimed Edna, suddenly facing her. "No! I am well! You see that I am well!"

Supaya gasped. Edna's left eye was almost shut, the skin around it an ugly green-black. "Edna! Let me help you! I can put something . . ."

But Edna backed stiffly away. "No! Go away! I don't want you!" Her right eye was wide and staring in her thin face. Her mouth twisted with resentment and anger. "Leave me alone! All of you! Go away!"

Supaya had gone only a short distance from Edna's house when she saw a man off to her right, headed toward Edna's. Seeing Supaya, he stopped and stared. He was a tall white man, shabbily dressed. His hair stuck out from under a knitted stocking cap that hung on one side of his long, bony head. In one hand he carried a rifle, in the other a jug. He squinted at Supaya and grinned.

Supaya did not stop nor did she hurry. She took a fresh grip on her axe and swung it at her side so he would be certain to see it. When she crossed the field and looked back, he was still staring after her. Looking back from the shelter of the woods, she saw him entering Edna's house.

Edna did not come again to Sunday service.

Some weeks later, Supaya, with Wagash, went to the store to sell baskets. Several old Indian men were sitting on the porch, enjoying the warm spring sun. Inside, two white farmers stood near the stove, discussing the latest war news in the Wellston paper. Mrs. Fallon was showing cotton prints to a white woman, whose little boy pulled at her skirts and pointed to the candy jars; Jess was waiting on an old, gray-haired Indian woman.

When the door banged open and Hagerstrom clomped in, carrying his rifle, the men by the stove glanced up. One nodded, but Hagerstrom gave him a sour, suspicious look.

Recognizing him as the man who had gone into Edna's house, Supaya quietly moved back, drawing Wagash with her.

Aggressively, Hagerstrom banged his fist on the counter for attention.

Jess, bagging the old woman's groceries, said, "That's one dollar, fifty-two cents, Mrs. Johnston."

Hagerstrom banged the counter again. "Hell with her! I want three boxes of 22 shells!"

The men by the stove turned their heads to stare; Mrs. Fallon and the white woman glanced up.

"I'll get to you in your turn," said Jess shortly.

"Turn hell!" exclaimed Hagerstrom. With a backhanded sweep of his hand, he hit the old woman's arm, knocking her sideways and scattering coins over the counter and floor. "Since when do you wait on a squaw before a white man! Old bitch! Not even worth a good . . ." He stopped, suddenly aware of everyone's eye on him.

"Get out," said Jess quietly.

Hagerstrom gaped. "Like hell I'll get out!" He slammed his rifle down on the counter. "I come for shells! A man's gotta have shells! Or don't a fancy vest man like you understand that?" he sneered.

"I said get out, Hagerstrom!" said Jess, reaching under the counter.

"Hell with what you say! My rifle says somethin' diff . . ." His voice died as he saw Jess' revolver leveled at him.

The white woman gasped and pulled her small son behind her.

"Say now! This here's a public place and . . ."

"This is *my* store," said Fallon, coming from behind the counter, "and I'm telling you to go."

Jaw sagging, Hagerstrom backed up. He looked to the men for help, but they only watched him, their eyes scornful and disapproving.

Jess nodded toward the door. "Get out now and don't ever come in here with a gun again!" Then, as Hagerstrom didn't move, he cocked the hammer.

Hagerstrom jerked into motion and backed toward the door, his staring, washed-out eyes on Jess' gun. Fumbling behind him, he got the door open, turned, and rushed out. The old men on the porch paid no attention to him as he stumbled down the steps and stood irresolutely in the road, looking in one direction, then in the other before finally going off.

Later, walking home, Wagash said, "I like Mr. Fallon. He's brave! I'd like to have a store and be like him when I grow up!"

Jess had brought a newspaper for Supaya, and she read it carefully. The headlines shouted of the Battle of Ypres, of the Germans launching the first gas attack, of thousands of casualties. The Canadians, true to their fighting reputation, had held on with a "magnificent display of tenacity and courage." Supaya was horrified by what she read. She burned the paper in the stove and resolved to read no more newspapers.

Instead, she looked determinedly to the day of Kineu's return. In a composition book she kept exact figures of the sums she made by selling baskets, vegetables, fruit, and fish. Kineu *would* return, and when he did, she would have the accounts to show him. Everything would be in order, his family and his home.

Supaya sold the cow. Working the garden and treating patients left little time for milking. Besides, she had several times observed Hagerstrom standing at the edge of the woods, looking in their direction, the cow in full view in the pasture. He had made no move to come closer, but when she was away and the children were inside with Sarah, it would be easy for him to walk off with the cow. She spoke to Fallon, and he found a farmer who paid her a fair price.

A pig, however, was no extra work and furnished a fine supply of meat for winter. Soos had gotten two to fatten, one for

275

herself and one for Supaya. One day when Sarah came to stay with the children, she said, "Aunt Suppy, Mother said you can come and get your pig. She didn't trust me to bring it." Sarah giggled. "Mother forgets I'm as big as you!"

Supaya laughed too, but as she left to visit her patients, she realized that Sarah was now seventeen, a year older than she herself had been when she came to Two Bluffs to marry Eli! Sarah was old enough to marry! Remembering her own girlhood, Supaya felt certain Sarah must favor some young man. But George and Soos had been very protective. And now, all the young men had gone to war.

When Supaya returned, it was dusk. Sarah had fed the children and put Taw to bed. Wearily, Supaya sat down in her rocker. Waboose and Shooskonee leaned against her knees. Wagash stayed where he was at the table, a book and paper in front of him.

"There's some warm soup if you want it, Aunt Suppy. And I mixed up the medicines you needed."

"She let us watch," said Shooskonee.

"I handed her the herbs," said Waboose.

Supaya laughed. "And what did you do, Wagash?"

"Arithmetic problems. Miss Harris said if I got them all right, I could put them on the blackboard."

"I'm going home now, Aunt Suppy." Sarah drew her shawl over her head, and Supaya thought how lovely she was, with her dark oval face and almond eyes.

"Thank you, Sarah. Tell your mother I'll come for the pig tomorrow morning."

Dawn came with a great wind that thudded and beat against the house. The windows and doors shuddered in their frames. In the fireplace, ashes stirred and blew about.

"Stay on the field side of the road," Supaya cautioned Wagash when he left for school. "And don't take the shortcut through the woods."

Walking to Soos', she and the children, with Taw in the middle, clung together, leaning into the rushing, buffeting wind that pushed against them and blew grit into their faces. Supaya and Shooskonee covered their mouths with their shawls, and Taw, gasping, turned his face against his mother's side. Waboose threw his head back, laughed, and spun around, walking backward into the wind, excited by this force that whipped his hair and carried away his voice. Trees bent almost double, their newly leaved branches streaming. Broken limbs and shredded leaves littered the road. From within the woods they could hear the splitting, falling crash of dead branches.

Soos let them in and pressed the door shut behind them. For a moment they stood like refugees, blinking away wind tears and catching their breath.

"Bad wind this morning," said Soos, setting the kettle on the stove. She had been boiling clothes and hanging them in the lean-to to dry. "I have a bag you can carry the pig in, but you better sit for a while. Maybe the wind will die. Where is Sarah? Didn't she come with you?"

Supaya, hanging their wraps on pegs, said, "She must have come after we left. What did she want? I told her I would come this morning."

"No, no," said Soos. "Not this morning. She stayed over-night with you, didn't she? Where did she go this morning?"

Supaya turned and looked at Soos. "She didn't stay over-night with us. I got back just after sundown, and she left then to come home."

The two women stared at each other. "But . . . she didn't come home. Where," asked Soos, her attention arrested, "where could she have been all night? Suppy," her voice suddenly fearful, "what could have happened to her?"

"Where else might she have gone? Would she have stopped to see Josie and then stayed?"

"No! She couldn't have stayed overnight with Josie! There's no room. Suppy, where could she . . ."

"Soos, think a minute! Is there a boy that she might have . . ."

"No!" exclaimed Soos indignantly. "Sarah wouldn't. . . ."

"Soos," chided Supaya gently, "Sarah's seventeen! You're sure there's no one she might have gone to meet?"

Soos sat down abruptly; her plump body suddenly collapsed. Her eyes looked inward. "She . . . I think she liked Caleb . . . Caleb Sims. But he joined the army last fall." Soos pressed her hand to her mouth and stared at the floor.

"Soos . . . listen to me." Soos glanced up and nodded. "I am going out to look for her. I'll go along the shortcut through the

277

woods. She might have fallen and hurt herself and not be able to walk. Then I'll come back here. You wait for me. Will you? Don't go anywhere until I come back."

Soos nodded again.

Hurriedly, Supaya put on her jacket. She spoke firmly to the children, who were subdued and silent. "You stay here with Auntie Soos, and be very good." She left by the back door, cutting across the field into the woods.

Overhead, the great pallid disk of the sun hung in a strangely empty, translucent sky, its wan, hazy light casting no shadow. As she half ran along, clutching her shawl, Supaya was oppressed by a sense of calamity, of a malicious force sweeping down upon them all. The day Eli had fallen over the bluff had been such a day as this. As now, she had gone running through the woods and had been too late. Struggling against the wind that leveled the meadow grasses and whipped her clothes, Supaya searched along the path, looking to either side, hoping to see Sarah, propped against a tree and waiting for help, hoping for anything, a footprint, a torn scrap of clothing. But the ground was dry, the path windswept. Old dead leaves were lifted and whirled about. Supaya called Sarah's name, screaming against the wind, but her voice was carried away. Supaya knew that if Sarah were calling, she could not hear her.

Supaya came out of the woods and raced across the meadow to her own house, grasping at the possibility that Sarah may have returned. Slamming the door behind her, she leaned against it and called out, but there was only the stillness of empty rooms.

Snatching up her medicine bag and her axe, Supaya started back. She must reassure Soos, help her to be calm. But she was filled with foreboding. Something dreadful had happened. She sensed it. The fierce indifference of earth and air confirmed it. A branch cracked off and hurtled down, hitting Supaya a sharp blow on the shoulder. She stumbled and nearly fell. Regaining her balance, she ran on, all hope of finding Sarah in the woods now gone. Where the path emerged into the meadow, a large tree had blown down and lay across the path, its split branches like broken arms, its huge mass of tangled roots stretching outward, earth still clinging to them. Supaya climbed over the tree, hacking at its trunk and branches in blind fear and anger.

In one glance Soos saw that Supaya had found no trace of Sarah. She moaned softly and turned away, her hands clasped together. "Where can she be? Oh, if only George were here!"

Supaya touched her shoulder. "I'm going to the school now

and speak to Miss Harris. Sarah sometimes stays to help her. Then I'll speak to the agent."

Soos gave a little cry and covered her face.

"Soos," said Supaya, forcing herself to speak firmly, "while I'm gone, finish your work and make some soup. The children will be home soon, and they'll be hungry. You don't want to alarm them."

Miss Harris came to speak with Supaya at the back of the schoolroom, seeing by Supaya's expression the seriousness of her questions. But Agatha had not seen Sarah for several days. As Supaya hurried away, she begged to be given any news.

Supaya arrived at Lizzie's disheveled and out of breath. Lizzie made her sit down and called Gerald at once. They both listened attentively, then asked Supaya the same questions she had asked Soos.

Gerald, making no comment and wasting no time, left at once to organize a search party. He enlisted the aid of Indian men left on the reserve, and for days they methodically searched every section of the reserve, along its remotest back roads and through the woods, walking abreast, thrashing through the underbrush, down into gullies and through swampy areas. They searched along the cliffs and the shorelines of the long narrow bays. They asked in every home. Soon everyone on the reserve knew Sarah was missing. No one who had ridden into Wellston had seen her or given her a ride.

Everyone came to visit Soos, to offer her comfort and encouragement. Reverend Crowell and Amy prayed with her. Miss Harris came after school every day, walking back with James and Ruby, Soos' younger children. But as the search continued and no trace of Sarah was found, there was little anyone could say to Soos, who went about her work mechanically, her lips pressed tight, her eyes filled with grief. Neighbor women dropped in and sat with her, coming and going in silent sympathy.

Supaya and the children came every day. She brought food and they all ate together. She kept a sharp eye on Soos, and gave her a medicine to help her sleep. At night in her own room, Supaya prayed to her Grandfather for Sarah's safe return, as she did for Kineu's. But soon a week had passed, and there was no sign.

Then it was that Gerald, after consulting with Reverend Crowell and Jess Fallon, widened his search to the white farms adjoining the reserve. Reverend Crowell rode with him in the wagon, and Gerald's gun was on the seat between them.

CHAPTER
TWENTY-TWO

The farmhouse, narrow and steep-roofed, stood well back from the road. Once it had been painted, its roof whole and tight. Ornate molding and shining windows had proclaimed industry and confidence in the future. But as generations had lived out their lives under its roof, birthing and dying in the small, slope-ceilinged bedrooms, each had aged sooner, worn out sooner in their struggle against the unyielding land than the one before until they seemed to be born old, with hopeless, angry eyes. Their bright hopes long buried in the rocky soil, they fought their dismal poverty with a blind, dogged endurance, sitting together for lamp-lit meals in the dull silence of those who had little to express save their smothered violence.

Without the softening presence of tree or bush, the house was as drained of color and life as an old piece of driftwood. Light shone harshly on tin patches nailed to the roof. The narrow outlook of two front windows was obscured by grime and stringy, lifeless curtains. The front door was left naked to face the west, with only a peaked outline above it of the once protective roof. The door itself, had it not been boarded over, would have opened to a three-foot drop into knee-high weeds, the steps having long since been used for patching. The lane ran alongside the house past a side entrance. The stoop pitched away from the side of the house and the worn steps seemed to have shrunk, exposing rusty nail heads. Beside the stoop a load of split wood had been carelessly dumped. Beyond, where the lane widened into a turnaround, stood the barn, its roof swaybacked, with ragged holes that exposed its dark beams, where swallows flitted in and out. Near the barn was an open shed, designed to shelter buggies and wagons. Now old boards were piled there, a barrel or two, and rusted, broken-handled tools. A few scrawny chickens, shifting for themselves, roosted on the boards and laid an occasional egg in the dirty straw behind the barrels. Drawn up behind the shed was a long-abandoned wagon with a bone-dry seat and one broken wheel. It sat crookedly, hubs deep in weeds, its cracked shafts empty, the gray horse that once pulled it long dead.

A girl came out of the side door, picked up an armload of kindling, and went back inside, kicking the door shut behind her. One broken pane, broken from just such a kick, was stuffed with a rag. Unceremoniously she dropped the wood on the bare floor beside the stove. At sixteen, there was nothing youthful or rounded about Louisa. Her old print dress hung straight from her bony shoulders. Her sallow skin was never touched with color; her straight, stubborn mouth never smiled. She had been born early and badly born as well, coming a girl when she should have been a boy to help work the farm. When Louisa was eight, her mother, worn out by failure—her own, her husband's, the farm's—had gone to bed and died, the most welcome task she had ever faced. Louisa had gazed at her mother's dead, wasted face with silent resentment: she had deserted and left her burdens to her daughter. Sometimes Louisa studied an old framed photograph of her mother that hung on an otherwise bare wall in the cold front room, no longer with resentment but with mixed wonder and envy that she had so escaped.

"Louisa!"

The girl went on thrusting wood into the old iron stove.

"Git up here and empty this slop!"

When she had finished building the fire, Louisa went up the steep, enclosed stairs, leaving the long butcher knife she always kept near her on the kitchen table.

Her father was waiting for her, stooped forward in the low doorway of the bedroom opposite hers. His thinning, uncombed hair stood out like dirty straw; a week's stubble darkened his bony face. His neck, above a worn, gray undershirt, was reddened and wrinkled like the neck of a plucked chicken.

Always watchful for signs of age and decay, estimating when her father too might lie down and die, Louisa noted with satisfaction the wrinkles and the scalp showing through the thin hair.

"Took your time! Think you can do as you damn please, don't you! It's time I give you a good hiding!" He squinted at her and thrust out his lip, but made no move, remembering the knife.

Louisa didn't answer. She picked up the chamber pot, her glance sliding past her father into the room beyond. She could see the girl's head, turned away, and her arms outspread, her wrists tied to the bedposts. The fetid odor of vomit fouled the air.

"And I want breakfast ready when I come down!" he shouted after her.

There were leftover potatoes, sliced and fried in grease, stale bread and tea. Louisa sat at the far end of the bare wooden table, the knife beside her cup, while her father ate, grumbling about the food.

"Always potatoes! God-damned potatoes! Where's the meat! A man's gotta have meat!"

"There ain't no meat," said Louisa, chewing bread and watching him steadily. "Ain't been any since you stopped bringing home stew."

"Them stews were good," he nodded, remembering. "Too damned good for a squaw. Why don't you cook like that! You're no proper daughter! You're wasteful! Like your ma! Everything I got, she wasted! That's why this here farm's no good!" He shoved his plate away in disgust. "Hell, I'm gonna see to the cows."

Louisa stood up as soon as he stood up, and moved so she was facing him. At the door he paused, glanced at the ceiling, then shook his head. "Needn't save anythin' for her. Food's too hard come by. 'Sides," grinning, "she's nice and plump, not skinny like you. Comin' out to help me?"

"No."

He stared at her, at the knife near her hand, then sneered, "A man works to make somethin' and that's the help he gets. I oughta turn you out!"

After he left, Louisa went upstairs and stood outside the door, listening. There was no sound. There had been no sound since the screams that first night. When her father had pushed the girl through the back door into the kitchen ahead of him, she hadn't screamed. He had held her long black braids in one hand, like reins, and with the other had twisted one of her arms behind her. Whenever she struggled or tried to pull away, he had yanked on the braids, pulling her head sideways and back until the tendons of her neck stood out. She had been almost too frightened to speak, her eyes wild, her mouth shaking. In a whisper she had begged him to let her go. But her father had grinned and dragged her head back until the girl had stumbled backwards, her back arched, her chin pointing sharply toward the ceiling.

"Hell no! You're goin' to pay! Pay for those houses and land and cows! Given you, by God, given you! Bitch! All of you should be kept in barns! Louisa! Git me that bottle! Then git upstairs! Time you was in bed!"

She had watched from behind the stair door and seen him drink, then hold the girl's head in the vise of his arm to pour the liquor down her throat. When he hauled her toward the stairs, Louisa had hurried up and into her own room. She had jammed the chair under the doorknob as she always did and laid the knife beside her bed. She heard his heavy, stumbling footsteps, the slamming door, a thud, and the screech of the old bedsprings. Then the girl had screamed and screamed and Louisa, shaking, had pulled the ragged quilt over her head and curled herself up tight, her tears dampening the bed under her cheek.

Since then the girl had not spoken. Louisa had seen her only through the partially opened door. Twice, after her father had forced the girl to drink, Louisa had heard her retching.

Louisa's hand was on the doorknob when she heard the back door burst open. Quickly she went downstairs in time to see her father grab his rifle and rush outside. She went and stood in the doorway.

A wagon was coming up their lane, with two men riding on it. The driver pulled up beside her father, who stood with his rifle raised.

"Good morning, Mr. Hagerstrom. I'm Gerald Toomis, Indian agent, and this is Reverend Crowell."

Hagerstrom scowled. "What business you have, comin' on my land!"

"Please, sir," said Reverend Crowell, "lower your gun. There is no need for that."

"'Til I hear anythin' to change my mind, you're trespassers!"

"Not at all! We've come to ask for your help in finding a young Indian woman who disappeared from the reserve last week. We're asking all the farmers to join in our search."

"Hell! I wouldn't waste my time searchin' for no squaw!"

"Maybe," said Gerald, looking at Louisa, who watched from the doorway, "your daughter might have seen her?"

Her father jerked around, his gun still raised and squinted at her. "Her? Hell, no! She never sees nothin', do you, Louisa?"

They all three stared at her. Slowly she shook her head. "I ain't seen nobody."

Her father grunted. "Told you. She's stupid. Now I got work to do. Can't spend my time like some, chasin' after . . ."

Reverend Crowell's stern, disapproving eye bore into him. "You had better spend some time on your knees before your Lord and beg that He teach you not only industry but charity as well!"

Gerald turned the horses and, as the wagon rolled down the lane, Hagerstrom strode after it, waving his rifle and yelling.

"Charity hell! Ain't nobody ever showed me none! Now get off my land and stay off!"

Three days later when her father came in from plowing and sat at the table to eat, there were boiled potatoes, turnips, and a pitcher of milk. He gasped at Louisa, his small eyes bright with anger. "What's this? Food for pigs?"

"That's all there is. I would've kilt a chicken but I couldn't catch it. They's gone wild."

"All!" He hit the table in a fury of disbelief.

Despite her own hunger, she took pleasure in taunting him. "Tea's gone. Flour's gone. You ain't been to the store in a long time."

Like a man finally gone mad, he jerked his head, glaring about the room as if expecting it to explode from around him. Louisa could hear his breath like a moan in his chest, and she quietly backed off, holding her knife hidden in a fold of her skirt.

His eyes came round to her. "You! There was plenty of food! Plenty! But you wasted it! Quick as I bring it home, you use it up!" He rose, saw her hand hidden in her skirt and sneered. "To hell with you! I know where I can get food . . . good food . . . plenty of food!" Grabbing his rifle, he slammed out of the house.

Louisa went to the door, then out into the lane, where she stood and watched him cross the field beyond the barn and disappear into the woods. Months before she had followed him, and she knew where he was going, where he'd begun going ever since she'd started carrying the knife. She smiled to herself. It had been so easy to scare him with the knife. He was really afraid of the knife. That

284

first time, when he'd come into her room and gotten into her bed, she had been afraid, too afraid even to scream as the girl upstairs had done. Then, after that time in the barn . . . she could still see the spilled pail of milk, spreading out, white and foamy on the dirty straw and manure, and the sky blue between the beams where the shingles were blown off . . . she squeezed her eyes tight shut against the memory. But after that time she'd found the courage to pick up the knife.

Going inside, she picked it up again and went upstairs.

CHAPTER
TWENTY-THREE

At first, because the children were talking and laughing, Supaya was not sure she had heard anything. But when she heard again, a bit louder, a kind of scratching, she went to the back door and asked, "Who is it?"

A voice, low and faint, said, "It's me, Aunt Suppy." Quickly, with a rush of hope, Supaya undid the lock and opened the door. Dusk was deepening into night. Above the trees stars glittered in a dark blue sky. To one side, out of the light that fell through the doorway, a figure huddled on the ground.

"Sarah!" exclaimed Supaya in a whisper, bending over, "Is that you?!"

"Are the children in bed?"

"Sarah! It *is* you! Oh, Sarah! Where have you been! Come in! Come in! Here, let me help you!" But Sarah shrank away.

"No! Not till they're in bed!"

As she spoke, Shooskonee came running into the lean-to. "Mama, what are you doing? Who are you talking to?"

Supaya straightened abruptly and stepped inside, pulling the door to behind her. Leading Shooskonee into the other room, she said quietly and firmly, "Children, you must go to bed now. Sarah has come back, but she is tired and hungry and needs rest."

"Did a witch take her away?" asked Waboose, remembering the fairy tales Miss Harris had read to him.

"I want to see her!" exclaimed Shooskonee, who was strongly attached to Sarah.

"You can see her tomorrow. Now go."

The children went upstairs, and Supaya opened the door again. "Sarah, they've gone to bed. Come in now." She put out her hands, cautiously this time, to help her up.

"No!" exclaimed Sarah, jerking back. "Don't touch me! I am filthy!" Her voice was low and rasping, as though her throat were raw or parched. Supaya stepped back and watched as Sarah, holding to the door jamb, shakily pulled herself up and stepped inside, where she leaned against the wall, her head hanging, too weak to go further and shrinking from the light in the next room.

Quickly Supaya brought a chair and Sarah sank down on it, her head drooping sideways. Supaya had many questions, but Sarah had said she was filthy and certainly there was a sour, rank odor about her. "You'd like a bath, wouldn't you?" Sarah nodded. Supaya put two large kettles of water on the stove, stirred up the fire, and put on more wood. She pulled the tub into the middle of the lean-to and said, "Now let's take off your clothes."

But all Sarah had on was a man's shirt. She fumbled at the buttons. Supaya undid them for her, biting her lips to keep from crying out, for even in the half-light she could see welts across Sarah's breasts, abdomen, and thighs where the skin had been split. Blood had smeared and dried along the ridges of skin and between her thighs. Her braids, half undone, were tousled and matted with filth. Supaya turned away, speechless, her hand over her mouth. Behind her, Sarah spoke.

"Scissors."

Supaya turned. "What?"

Sarah raised her head slightly. "Scissors." When Supaya brought them, Sarah said, "Cut it off."

Supaya hesitated. Then Sarah lifted her head and spoke with loathing and anger. "Cut it off!" And Supaya took the long braids in her hand and sawed through them. "Shorter!" said Sarah and was not satisfied until her hair barely reached the lobes of her ears. She sat a long time in the tub. Too weak to wash herself, she allowed Supaya to do so, and to treat with salves and poultices the welts and abrasions. Supaya brought her clean clothes and moccasins and helped her dress. Then she heated a pot of soup.

Sitting in Supaya's rocker, a blanket wrapped around her, Sarah ate the soup. "I had a boiled potato," she said, glancing up. "The girl Louisa gave it to me. She cut me loose. And gave me that shirt. He . . . he tore . . . ."

Supaya saw her eyes widen with horror. "Don't speak of it now Sarah. Just tell me who."

Sarah stared into the bowl of soup she held in her lap. With lips and chin trembling, she managed to say, "That white farmer . . . who stole the cow . . . Oh Aunt Suppy! Will you get . . . my mother tomorrow? I . . . I couldn't go back to her like . . . like I was!" Sarah's voice shook, her hands began to tremble. "I'm so dirty! I'm still so dirty!" she cried, rocking back and forth. Supaya took the bowl away, and Sarah bent her head to her knees, her body shaken by long, shuddering sobs.

"Sarah, Sarah!" Supaya knelt beside her and cradled her against her breast, stroking her short, spiky, wet hair. "Tomorrow Uncle John and I will make you a sweat lodge. We will line it with boughs from grandmother cedar and you will sit in the hot steam that rises from the stones of the earth. You will rub your body with the boughs, and you will be purified! Then when your mother comes, you will greet her."

The next morning Supaya rose very early. She rolled up the shirt and buried it in the field beyond the garden. She made up a fire under the drying frame and rolled stones into it. Then, taking her axe, she went into the woods and lopped off cedar branches. She was putting out some food for the children when they came rushing downstairs, eager to see Sarah.

"You must wait until she has had her sweat bath," said Supaya. "You must not wake her before it is ready. Wagash, you go to Uncle John and ask him to come."

Not until Uncle John had made the sweat lodge and the cedar boughs and hot stones had been placed inside did Supaya wake Sarah and, putting a blanket around her shoulders, lead her out to the lodge.

Then Supaya went to see Gerald Toomis. He had saddled his horse and was starting out to continue the search with three white farmers who had volunteered to help. Lizzie was standing on the back step. They both listened, horrified, to what Supaya had to tell them.

"Oh dear God!" exclaimed Lizzie, both hands pressed against her mouth.

Gerald, sickened, turned his face away. Without a word he nudged his horse and rode off, his rifle across the saddle bow.

On her way home, Supaya stopped to see Soos. James and Ruby had left for school and Soos was sitting in her chair, hands folded in her lap. Told that Sarah had returned, Soos started up excitedly and grabbed Supaya's arms. "Where is she? Where? Why isn't she here with you?! I must see her! Where has she been?!"

Gently Supaya quieted her, told her how Sarah had returned and what she was doing before facing her mother and brother and sister. Soos listened intently, as still as if paralyzed. But as she listened, her eyes grew fierce, her face hardened, and her lips tightened to a thin, vengeful line. When Supaya finished, Soos, like Gerald, said nothing, but went into the lean-to and took up the knife George used for butchering pigs.

"Soos! What are you doing?!"

"I will kill him," said Soos flatly.

"Soos! No!"

Soos shook off Supaya's hand. "Let go!"

"But the agent has gone for him! He'll put him in jail!"

Soos, her face rigid, ignored Supaya and went out, heading across the field.

"All right!" called Supaya angrily from the doorway. "Go and kill him! Then *you'll* be in jail! That will leave Sarah, James, and Ruby without father *or* mother!"

Soos stopped. Her head tilted back as if in her anguish she appealed to the sky above her; then her shoulders went slack and her head fell forward. Supaya went to her and took the knife. Soos turned, and leaning her head against Supaya's shoulder, wept softly.

Gerald and the three white farmers rode up the lane to the Hagerstrom house. Louisa came out of the barn carrying a pail in one hand, a knife in the other. Seeing the men, she came straight toward them, stopping in front of the man she knew to be the agent. She wore a pair of her father's old split shoes, absurdly large and clumsy around her thin ankles. Her dress, once her mother's, hung loosely on her thin body, the shoulders too wide, the waistline too low, the bottom edge frayed where the hem had been cut off. Her hair, unwashed and uncombed, hung in a limp tangle. There were dark smudges under her eyes. She stared at the men, waiting for them to speak.

"Your father inside?" asked Gerald.

"He's gone." The men glanced at each other, and Louisa added, "He went out yesterday and ain't come back."

"Do you know where he went?"

Louisa nodded once.

"Where?"

Louisa thought about that question, pondering their faces and their guns. Gerald waited, thinking she wouldn't answer. Then, "You goin' after him if I tell?"

Gerald hesitated. The others stirred restlessly, pulling up on the reins as their horses arched their necks and stepped sideways. "Yes," he said finally, "we will."

A spark of animation flickered in Louisa's eyes, and she answered at once. "He went to that Indian woman's house, the one on t'other side of them woods." Pointing with the knife, she indicated the woods beyond the barn and the field.

At once the men moved their horses forward. As they passed, Louisa turned and called out, "If you get him, I hope you kill him!"

Shocked by her words, Gerald glanced back. Thin as a lath and as if weighted down by the overlarge shoes, the full pail, and the knife, she stood looking after him. He had wondered about that knife. Now, in an instant, he understood.

The men emerged from the woods and rode up the slope behind Harry Black's house. As they approached, the lean-to door opened and Hagerstrom stumbled out, heading for the backhouse. He stopped short at sight of them, startled, half awake. In undershirt, baggy pants, and suspenders, he stared at them groggily, then suddenly ducked back inside and slammed the door.

"You two stay here," said Gerald. "Jim and I'll go round the front."

Inside, Hagerstrom, half drunk, staggered crazily about, kicking a chair out of his way, waving his arms and yelling. "Where's my gun! I know it's here! What'd you do with it, you bitch!" Edna had seen the men pass by the window and was cowering against the wall. Hagerstrom paused and squinted at her. "You told 'em I was here! You sneaked out and told 'em! Didn't you!"

Edna, her eyes wide with fright, shook her head. "No, no . . . !"

"You stinkin' vermin!" Swinging his arm like a scythe, he threw her to the floor. "You wait 'til I find my gun! I'll show you!" Turning, he stumbled into the table, grunted, backed off, saw his rifle leaning in the corner. "There it is!"

Edna, on hands and knees, saw him lunging for the gun. Panicked, she got to her feet and threw the door open.

"Har' there!" yelled Hagerstrom, turning in time to see her run out. "I'll fix you!" From the doorway, as the men yelled at him

290

to stop and raised their own guns, he fired at Edna, who was running toward one of the horsemen. His third shot hit her and she fell, back arched, hands outstretched.

"Hagerstrom! Stop! Put up your gun!"

But Hagerstrom, in a blind rage, rushed at the men, firing wildly, as the frightened horses bucked and reared.

Hearing gunshots, the two men at the back rode quickly around the house. Seeing Hagerstrom shooting at Gerald and Jim, who were trying to control their plunging horses, they raised their guns and fired. Struck, Hagerstrom stumbled and spun sideways, mouth gaping. After a long, breathless moment, his legs buckled and he fell on his back, his rifle across his chest.

Dismounting, the men gathered around Edna. She lay face down, her fingers dug into the earth. Gently the men turned her over, carried her inside and put her down on her bed. Hagerstrom they carried in and laid on the floor. Shaken, they stood silent, undecided what to do next, until Gerald told them quietly to go on home.

"I'll send someone to lay them out. And write a report."

They nodded to each other and rode off, going their separate ways.

Gerald was thankful that none of the men with him—all family men—had been hit, and he was able to put Hagerstrom out of his mind. But he couldn't forget Edna, her bruised face, her unborn child. Nor could he forget Louisa, holding her knife and wishing her father dead. After he had spoken to Daniel about the coffins and to Reverend Crowell about the funeral and had made out his report, he sat in his own kitchen, hunched over the table, his hands cupping a mug of tea. He told Lizzie what had happened, briefly, not wanting to linger over Edna, whom he felt he had failed. But he described Louisa, vivid in his memory, as she had stood there, looking after him.

"You don't mean you left her there!"

Gerald, taken aback, looked indignantly at his wife. "I couldn't have taken her with us!"

"But we must go and get her! Poor child! Left there all alone!"

"We? What will we do with her?"

"We'll keep her, of course! Now don't stare at me like that, Gerald Toomis! She's an orphan, isn't she? And we have an empty room upstairs. Are you a Christian or aren't you?"

They went together in the wagon, Gerald's depression dispelled by Lizzie's immediate decision to take Louisa into their home. Edna was beyond his help, but Louisa was not. He slapped the reins over the horses to hurry them on and smiled sideways at his wife.

When they pulled up alongside the house, Louisa was sitting hunched over on the back stoop where she had a full view of the field and the woods beyond, her chin resting on her crossed arms, the knife ready beside her. She raised her head at the approach of the horses and wagon, her eyes watchful as Lizzie got down and came toward her.

Lizzie thought she had never seen such a sorry sight, but she liked the girl's attentive, steady eye. Here, she thought, was something to build on. "I'm Mrs. Toomis," said Lizzie, and nodding at Gerald, "that is Mr. Toomis, the Indian agent. We live on the reserve."

"Yes ma'm," said Louisa.

"What is your name?" asked Lizzie, seeing nothing would be volunteered.

"Louisa Hagerstrom."

"Well, Louisa," said Lizzie, her voice gentle though her words were blunt, "your father is dead. He shot an Indian woman and then was shot himself."

Louisa reflected a moment. "Did he do it?" nodding at Gerald.

"No. One of the men with him."

"I wouldn't have minded if he had."

"Louisa," said Lizzie, "Mr. Toomis and I, we want you to come with us, to come and live with us. That's why we're here—to take you home with us."

Louisa's guard slipped. Her eyes widened. "Why?" she asked, puzzled.

"Why?" repeated Lizzie, smiling and restraining an impulse to reach out to her, "why because we want you. Will you come?"

Louisa pondered this awesome stroke of fortune. Glancing at Gerald, watching from the wagon seat, she asked doubtfully, "You sure he does?"

"I'm sure."

"You mean it?"

"We mean it."

Louisa sighed. "Then I guess I'll come." She looked down at the knife and swallowed hard.

"You won't need that," said Lizzie gently.

"I'll just put it inside," said Louisa.

Lizzie followed her into the kitchen. "Can I help you get your things together?"

"Ain't got no things," said Louisa, putting the knife down on the kitchen table. She hesitated a moment, thinking of the photograph of her mother, then shook her head. "Ain't got nothin' to take."

Outside, she addressed herself to Gerald. "There's cattle in the barn. You won't leave them, will you? They're sorry-lookin' 'cause they ain't been fed much, but they're good cows. Two is ours. Th' other he stole a time ago."

Gerald tied the cows to the back of the wagon. He paced the horses carefully on the way home because the starved cows could only plod along, necks stretched out, dull eyes vaguely surprised, every swinging step accenting the sharp bones under their sagging hides.

Louisa, sitting between Gerald and Lizzie, looked straight ahead, her hands folded in her lap. Not until they were nearly home did she speak. Then she remarked, to no one in particular, "I sure am glad them cows'll be fed."

CHAPTER TWENTY-FOUR

The boat rocked gently, water slapping rhythmically against its sides. The air was still and unusually warm—a midsummer's day in spring. Kineu faced outward, eyes dreamy, his back to the land. Since returning from the war and months spent in a hospital, he was at ease only here, away from everyone but his young son, where the only sounds were the gulls' mewing and the lap of water. Lulled by the motion of the boat, he gazed deep into the sun-shot water, wondering if the lights he saw there were the huge, shining eyes of Nzagima, the water serpent. And sometimes a vision of Stone Island rose in the distance, floating mirage-like on placid blue water. Contemplating its peak and woods, he was at peace and forgot his son.

Opposite him, Taw waited patiently, squinting into the dazzling sunlight that sparkled on the water and cast patterns of light over his father's blemished face. But being forgotten frightened Taw, made the lake too vast, the shore too remote. "Father," said Taw, wanting to recall him, "Father, let's go back and pull in the net. Let's go now."

When their catch was good, they stopped on their way home to give some to Uncle John, who had lost heart for fishing and hunting alike since his wife, Hattie, had died of influenza three weeks before.

Many, both in Wellston and on the reserve, had died from influenza. Angus Red Sky, so recently returned from the war, had died as Supaya and his wife Pearline, sat by him. All Supaya's efforts to save him had failed. Now, three days later on her way home from treating his small son, Supaya was oppressed by the fear that the son, too, would die. Needing encouragement, she stopped by to see Soos and George.

Soos welcomed her, made her sit and rest, and gave her hot tea but no reassurance. She merely shrugged and remarked, "When a man does evil as Wenonga did, the whole family suffers."

"But Angus . . . !" Supaya protested, tears coming to her eyes. "I remember my father curing him!" As she spoke, Beedaubun's shrewd old face came to her mind, and Supaya again heard her saying, "To be a good healer, you must be a good fighter."

Soos broke into Supaya's thought. "Miss Harris is better. Sarah went to see her today, took her a bowl of soup."

"How is Kineu?" asked George. "He didn't come to the council meeting."

"He . . . he's well. He and Taw went fishing. He doesn't like going to the meetings. He says they make him feel . . . closed in." Supaya looked directly at George, and he saw the question in her eye.

George, a square, stocky man of cheerful disposition, was able to joke about the leg he had lost in the war and even, in play, show the children the wooden leg he had made for himself and pretend to chase them with it. But he never spoke of his war experience. Now he tapped his pipe against his palm and said evasively, "The war did that to him," adding, "He'll get over it." But his tone was unconvincing.

And Supaya, increasingly troubled by Kineu's withdrawal, was not convinced. Kineu had returned just before New Year's, 1918, startling them all by appearing in the doorway late one afternoon. After a stunned moment, they all had rushed to greet him, excitedly embraced him, laughing and asking questions too fast for him to answer. Only later, lying side by side, constrained as strangers, did she recall that he had said almost nothing, had been stiff and unresponsive when she kissed him. His faint, uncertain smile was that of a man not sure he had come to the right place. He had even been reluctant to remove his hat and expose to them the purplish-red blotch staining part of his brow and the side of his face, the outward mark of the gas that had seared his throat, burned his lungs, and nearly killed him.

In bed she had gently turned his head toward her and kissed his brow and cheek to show him that it didn't matter. She had leaned against him and kissed his mouth, longing for him to embrace her. But he had pulled away, raised his arm to ward her off, and protested in his changed, harsh voice that he couldn't breathe.

Every night for a week they had lain together, both staring into the dark, each aware of the other's tenseness. Once she had reached out and touched his shoulder. He said nothing but shrugged her off. Finally, one night, she had taken his hand, cradled it against her breast, and in a whisper begged him to speak to her, to tell her what was wrong. But he had pulled away and gotten up, saying he needed to walk about. From then on and with no explanation, he slept by himself in the downstairs bedroom and kept the door curtain pulled, shutting her out.

One morning, shortly after his return, Kineu had said, "I'm going fishing, Wagash, you and Waboose come with me."

The children, eating bannock and the last of the maple syrup, looked up in surprise.

"You forget," said Supaya, reminding him gently, "they go to school."

"I did not forget," said Kineu. "It is time they learned what an Indian needs to know."

"But Kineu, they *must* go to school."

"Why must they?" Kineu's harsh voice easily turned aggressive. "What good has it ever done you or me? Aren't we penned in, confined like animals to a little space? Has your reading and writing given you back the freedom our grandfathers lost?" His flaring anger intensified his facial burns. He felt his face redden, heard his loud, rasping voice, and saw the children's startled faces. But he could not stop himself. Angrily, he asked them, "And has Miss Harris," sneering the name, "taught you as she did us that your grandfathers and great-grandfathers were savages! Pagans, with no religion! That you must go to her church and become Christians?!"

Frightened by his outburst, by this man so unlike the father they remembered, the children bent their heads and sat very still.

"Is *that* what you would have them learn?" he demanded of Supaya. "Then you should tell them that Miss Harris and her people also are savages! Worse! Their god of love approves killing! Tell them that they destroy life without reason, even the very earth itself! Tell them! Tell . . ." Suddenly he doubled over, gasping and coughing as if the words had clogged his throat. He grasped the edge of the table and breathed in long, shuddering gasps.

Alarmed, Supaya came to him, but he waved her away. Taw

came and stood beside him, staring up into his face. "I am . . . all right," said Kineu hoarsely. He laid his hand on Taw's head, but would not look at the others. At a nod from Supaya, they slid off their chairs and quietly left for school.

Kineu had tried once more. He told Wagash he wanted his help in mending the net and would teach him how to fish with it through the ice.

Wagash answered boldly. "I don't want to be a fisherman. I'm going to school so I can be a storekeeper like Mr. Fallon. He promised me I could work in his store afternoons and weekends. He'll pay me too!" Seeing Kineu's face tighten with displeasure, Wagash hung his head and said sullenly, "You can't tell me what to do! You're not my father!"

Supaya tried to explain, to soften Wagash's impertinence. "Please, Kineu, let him go. This is his chance for the freedom we lost, don't you see? The freedom you spoke of. To get off the reserve he must get an education! They all must! Miss Harris teaches them many good things!" Kineu had stared at her, saying nothing, and Supaya, baffled, had exclaimed, "Even with an education, they will still be Indians!" At that he had smiled faintly and walked out, Taw running after him.

On the morning of Angus' burial, his son died. Supaya had stayed by him through the night, using all her knowledge and exerting all her will to keep him breathing. Pearline was numbed by grief, her eyes empty and dull. "He's gone. I knew it would happen. We should never have come here. We should have gone far away. Ah! that evil old man! He has brought death to us all!" She pulled her shawl forward over her face and rocked back and forth, lamenting.

Alma came to stay with Pearline and lay out the fever-worn young body. Supaya, exhausted and depressed, was walking home when a horse and buggy came rapidly down the road, its wheels throwing up muddy water. Supaya stepped to one side, but the driver, Jess Fallon, reined in sharply at sight of her.

Supaya! I've been looking everywhere . . . could you come and treat my wife?"

Supaya was so amazed by his request that she didn't reflect until later on his use of her name. Treat Mrs. Fallon! To whom all Indians were as one, faceless!

Seeing her surprise, Jess said, "I called the doctor in Wellston, but he can't come until tomorrow. She's burning up with fever! Please come!"

She wanted to refuse, but the urgency and fear in his face touched her. Without further words, she stepped up into the buggy. Instantly Jess cracked the whip. Staring ahead, he said, as if to explain his haste, "She's all alone. I had no one to leave with her."

"Mrs. Crowell or Mrs. Toomis, they'd be . . ."

He glanced at her sharply. "She needs help! You can help her!"

"But will she," asked Supaya, too tired to be polite, "want *me* to help her?"

Fallon frowned and answered shortly, "Of course she will." He pulled off the road onto the lane that ran alongside the store, past the small loading platform to the back.

Supaya had never been behind the store and was surprised to see that the end of the building was like the front of a house, with a roofed porch facing the wooded slope beyond. There was a rocker on one side of the front door, a parson's bench on the other. The door and the windows had ruffled white curtains and at the threshold lay an old braided rug, its colors faded from many washings. Supaya, still hesitant, paused by the bench. "I'll wait here until you speak to her."

"No!" Jess thrust the door open and swung out his arm to hasten her inside. "Just up these stairs." He indicated a flight of steps at one side of a center hall.

The bedroom was small, with a slanted, papered ceiling and one curtained dormer window that admitted little light. A massive bedstead dominated the room. Dwarfed by its high, deeply carved headboard, Kirsten Fallon lay, her delicately veined eyelids closed in a restless half-sleep, her long blonde hair spread on the pillow and about her shoulders like pale silk. Dark smudges shadowed her eyes, but her normally delicate complexion was flushed with fever. Her body trembled spasmodically as she gasped for breath. Supaya, bending over her, was moved to compassion by her desperate struggle, her worn face and quivering lips. Quickly, Supaya opened her bag.

"I'll rub this ointment on her chest," she whispered to Fallon, who stood at the foot of the bed, his hands gripping the footboard. As Supaya began unbuttoning the high, confining collar of Kirsten's nightgown, Kirsten murmured and moved her head. Her eyes opened slightly, and her heavy-lidded gaze fell first on her husband, then, realizing someone was leaning over her, she raised her eyes and with difficulty focused on Supaya's face.

Supaya smiled at her and said softly, "This will help the tightness in your chest," and began gently rubbing on the ointment.

But as recognition came, Kirsten's eyes and mouth widened with horror. Her arm jerked up in an effort to push Supaya away. "Don't touch me! Get . . . away from me!" She labored for breath, her eyes startlingly wild and bright.

Instantly Supaya backed away. Alarmed, Jess bent over her. "Please, Kirsten, It's Mrs. Bruley! She has come to help you! Please, let her help!"

"No! No!" Frantically her fingers pulled at the neck of her gown. "What was she doing to me! Take it off!"

"It will ease your breathing, Kirsten!" pleaded Jess, then, seeing Supaya close her bag and turn to go, "Please stay! In a moment she'll . . ."

But Kirsten, in a frenzy heightened by her fever, tossed and twisted, crying, "Clean it off! Clean it off! It smells! I won't be touched by an Indian! Dirty! All of them! She wants to kill me! Make her go!" In her weakness tears rolled down her hot cheeks into her tangled hair. "Make her go!"

"All right, Kirsten, all right." Jess spoke softly, reassuringly, and stroked her hair. "She's gone now, she's gone. You mustn't cry. Close your eyes. You need to rest." Exhausted, Kirsten closed her eyes and drifted off. Seeing she slept, Jess rushed down the stairs. "Wait! Please wait!"

Supaya, stiffly erect, stood with her hand on the doorknob. She would not deign to look at him.

"Mrs. Bruley, I apologize for her. She would want me to! She has never . . . never spoken like that before. Please believe me! If she had, I would not have asked you to come. It is her sickness, her fever talking."

Then Supaya looked at him, her eyes hard and opaque. "I do not believe that," she said flatly.

"Could you . . . would you . . . give me something for her fever, something I could give her?"

Supaya smiled with contempt. "I am a doctor and the daughter of a doctor, but for her I have nothing!" She opened the door and went out.

"And for me? Have you no help for me?"

Supaya stopped, caught by his question, and turned to face him, this man who presumed to lay a claim on her. His appeal, personal and direct, still more, his tone of voice, cut through her anger, striking a chord he had never sounded before. For the first time she regarded him without reticence or confusion. Steadily he met her gaze and waited as she considered him. In swift flashes she saw him laughing over a bowl of soup, bringing her splints and cotton print, pigs, mail and newspapers, driving her father, helping, advising, whenever he could. She recalled how his face had frozen in polite unconcern when he'd seen her after Eli's beating. Remembering all this, she frowned in astonishment as she recognized the strength of the bond between them. Commitments, assumptions unspoken but acted on, had, over many years, subtly woven their two lives together in a pattern she had not, until now, perceived. Her anger gone, she looked at him almost accusingly, so surprised was she by the extent of their involvement.

Jess saw her anger fade, saw her frown, as if puzzled. But he saw too a subtle change in her expression, in the almost black depths of her eyes, a new awareness of the ties between them.

Inclining her head in acknowledgment, Supaya sat down on the bench and opened her bag. "Here," she held up a small packet. "Make a tea with this. It will ease the congestion in her throat. And this. She will not taste it in soup and it will give her strength. Here is the ointment. You could smooth it on when she's asleep. Most of all, you must bathe her with cool water to bring down the fever." She closed her bag and stood up to go.

Jess, seeing her weariness, said, "If she's asleep, I'll drive you home."

"No. You should begin at once to bring down her fever."

"Then take the buggy. I'll pick it up later."

Supaya shook her head. "No. I would rather walk." She went down the steps, then paused to look back. "I'll speak to Mrs. Toomis. Maybe Louisa can come and help in the store with William."

Lizzie eyed Supaya critically. "You're working too hard," she said brusquely. "You can't nurse the sick all day and all night too. I'll bet you haven't eaten a thing! Sit down here."

Realizing she was hungry as well as tired, Supaya ate what Lizzie set before her. When she asked if Louisa could help in the store, Lizzie said proudly, "Of course, Louisa can tend the store. She and your William will manage very well while Mr. Fallon takes care of his wife. Did you know, Sophia, that Louisa keeps all Gerald's ledgers? She even does the figuring. Agatha says she's excellent at figures. Mr. Fallon needn't worry, need he, Louisa?"

Louisa, at nineteen, was still spare of figure but she fairly shone with cleanliness. The gentle curve of her face now had a touch of color, her fair hair was combed smoothly back and coiled into a knot from which no ends escaped, and her dress was as starched as her speech. Buttoning her jacket, she briefly considered Lizzie's question. "No," she said, "he needn't."

When Supaya reached home, the house was empty and quiet, and she fell asleep in her rocker. Then, through layers of consciousness, she heard her name urgently spoken in a raspy voice like Joe Crow's, and thought she was dreaming until she felt her hands being shaken. Startled awake, she saw Kineu bending over her, speaking excitedly.

"Suppy! Suppy! I know what we must do!"

"Do?" Wakened so, she was befuddled. "Do? What must we do?"

"Go back to Stone Island! I've thought about it for many days! We must go back!"

"Kineu!" Dumbfounded, Supaya stared at him, trying to understand.

"Yes," he said purposefully, "we will go tomorrow."

"Tomorrow! But Kineu . . . ! I don't . . . what do you mean? Go back! This is our home!"

"It is not! Stone Island is our home! We should never have left! If we go back, everything will be as it was!"

"But, Kineu, I had to leave! And you came because you wanted to! This is our farm now, our house, our children's home! There is nothing for us on Stone Island! It could never be as it was! We wouldn't even have a house to live in!"

Kineu turned away, his face stubbornly set. "We could do without a house! We could live in a tent."

"A tent! Kineu! Look at me! Please! He faced her, scowling, his lips pulled tight. "Kineu, I . . . I don't *want* to live in a tent! We *never* lived in a tent! Kineu, we can make everything all right again, here . . . at Two Bluffs. We can be just as we were before you left!"

"We can never be as we were here," he said grimly. "Never!"

"Why not, Kineu? I don't understand!"

"You don't *want* to understand!" he exclaimed, going to the door. "You want to live like a white woman!" He was gone before she could answer.

That night Supaya dreamed of Kineu, dreamed she was following him, trying to catch up with him. The nearer she got, the smaller he became, until, as she finally reached him and held him, like a doll in her hand, he dissolved completely, only to reappear in the distance, again receding from her. She started awake, frightened and disoriented. She sat up and gradually the room took shape. A bar of moonlight angled through the window and across the bed, draining her hands, clenched before her on the quilt, of all color. She stared at her own fists, ghostly and disembodied, like bloodless symbols of the growing discontent and anger steadily driving her and Kineu apart. Somehow she must reach him, must break down the barrier that had existed between them ever since his return. Swiftly, determinedly, she rose and went downstairs.

Kineu was sleeping on his side. Lifting the covers, she lay down beside him. She slid her arms around him, holding him close against her, fitting the curve of her body to his. Aching with tenderness for him, yearning for the love they had once shared, she kissed his neck and shoulder, caressed him, murmuring his name. Gently she pulled him over onto his back, pressed herself against his breast, her arms around his shoulders, her legs against his.

Kineu, rousing to the pressure of a body against his, to constraining arms and legs, was terror-stricken, feeling again the horror of leaden bodies falling on him, of the heavy, polluting limbs of the dead lying across his chest, stifling him as he lay at the bottom of a shell hole. Explosions boomed and flared in the night and everywhere about him were the dangerous spirits of the dead. Panicked, he cried out and lunged forward. His elbow hit sharply into Supaya's breast as he thrust her off, freeing himself. Gasping with pain, she doubled over.

Coming fully awake, Kineu found himself standing by the bed, trembling from shock, and realized he was not in the nightmare of a battlefield, that the heavy, rasping breath he heard was his own. In the dark he saw Supaya's face, a pale, indistinct blur, and her hands, reaching out toward him.

"Kineu," she whispered, "what's wrong?! Please, you must tell me!"

But he could not put into words the awful defilement of death, or his terror at having been unable to purify himself or pacify the spirits of the dead, more frightening than bombs or tanks or even the invisible gas that had scorched his lungs and throat. Unable to stop shaking or to steady his voice, he forced himself to speak. "I . . . I can't . . ." then, his voice harsh and accusing, "you smother me!"

Supaya drew back, too stunned to speak or cry. After a moment's stillness, she got up and left the room where she now knew herself to be an intruder. Moving silently through the shadowy, moonlit house, she went upstairs to her own room. Taking from its bag the stone bear, she knelt on the floor by her bed. Despairing, she prayed to her Grandfather.

The bar of moonlight had shifted, slanting now across a corner of the room, leaving the bed in darkness. Outside, the roof and side of the house shone as if powdered with crystalline snow. The declining moon reflected glassily in the windows and washed over the shallow garden furrows. In the meadow, past the gray mound of boulders, a fox, pale as his own ghost, flashed by, pursuing a field mouse. Then both fox and mouse, whose tiny eye shot fire in the moonlight, were gone, leaving only the brilliant, empty night.

Kirsten Fallon died. Lizzie's opinion was that had she lived elsewhere than in the backwoods on the edge of an Indian reserve, she might have tried harder to live, but as God and Fallon had brought her where she was, she'd sooner go than stay. Lizzie, Gerald, and Supaya went together to the wake.

Jess stood in the hall at the foot of the stairs, one hand gripping the newel post. He took little notice of those who arrived or departed or of Louisa and Sarah, carrying trays of food and tea cups, going past him between kitchen and parlor. He answered quietly enough when spoken to but stood like a man forcing himself to remain where he was.

The parlor was full of people, white farmers and their wives, people Supaya had often seen in the store, and Indians who liked and respected Fallon. There was also a small group who sat apart, exclusive in their pride of grief, whom Supaya took to be relatives because of the man's resemblance to Jess. He was older but tall, with the same curly black hair, though his was streaked with gray, the same strong though more fleshy features, and the same brilliant blue eyes. He stood by his wife, who was sitting on the sofa, a plump woman who fanned herself from time to time and refused to speak, only nodding and closing her eyes to indicate her wishes, her mouth primly shut as though she disapproved of the company around her. Beside her, a young woman, Jess' sister, held a little boy by the arm. Her black, wavy hair was swept up in an intricate arrangement difficult to maintain, for the escaping strands curled forward against her cheeks and about her ears and neck. She wore an elegant dress with little tassels that hung from the collar and sleeves. Now and again the boy, leaning against her with one arm across her lap, made an effort to move, but was firmly held and given a sharp, disciplinary glance.

At the graveside, Jess stood apart from everyone. His brother chose to ignore him but his sister-in-law and sister silently rebuked him, then gave their dignified attention exclusively to Reverend Crowell. The little boy, held by his shoulders against his mother's skirts, stared curiously at the strange faces and at the hole in the ground into which the coffin had been lowered. When the service was over, the Fallons moved sedately toward their buggy. Jess, without a glance at anyone, walked rapidly off in the opposite direction.

As the days of summer passed, Supaya watched for an indication that her prayer had been answered, that the breach between Kineu and herself and the children would be healed. Instead it widened until she saw her family split apart. Kineu took no interest in the three older children, who were silent in his presence. Whenever she tried to involve him in family matters, he turned away. Even her providence during the war years was of little interest to him. She showed him her carefully kept records, suggesting he could now have Daniel build him a boat, paying partly in money, partly in fish and meat. Kineu said there was no need to buy a boat. Uncle John had given him his in return for a steady supply of fish. Supaya suggested they buy a cow, but Kineu only shrugged. He refused to plan beyond the storing of some food for winter, and even in that he showed less urgency than he once had, preferring to dream away much of the day on the lake or in the woods. Sometimes she caught him looking at her sadly, wistfully, and she held her breath, hoping he would come to her, but the moment Kineu encountered her eye, he turned away, leaving her more disheartened than before. Often he and Taw went hunting and didn't return for two or three days, staying instead in the little shack at the end of the bay.

Supaya, uneasy because of Kineu's absentmindedness and Taw's youth, gradually grew accustomed to their absence, comforting herself that they would remain at home when colder weather came and Taw began school.

304

But when school began, Taw was not there to go with the other children. Nor did Kineu return with him. The next day Miss Harris walked home with the children after school.

"Where," she asked as Supaya poured her a cup of tea, "is Tom? Wasn't he to start school this year?" She knew very well that he was, as she had been looking forward to having another of Supaya's children.

Not wanting to speak of Kineu's wish to keep him out of school, Supaya assured her that Tom would come to school. "I'm sorry he was absent. He and his father went out hunting and haven't returned. Kenneth does not realize school has begun."

Unconvinced, Agatha said forthrightly, "I've noticed that since Kenneth's return Tom has not come to Sunday service with you and the other children."

Supaya smiled. Miss Harris, older and slightly heavier, had not changed. "Tom missed his father more, I think, than the other children did. Now he wants to be with him and goes everywhere with him. Kenneth has been teaching him many things."

"But not," said Agatha, gently chiding, "what he most needs to know. William and Walter and Sally are all good students. I'm sure Tom would be too. William especially works very hard. And did you know, Sophia, that Sally has an aptitude for music? I really think she should have piano lessons. Mrs. Crowell would be happy to teach her."

They spoke then of the other children, but as Agatha left, she said, "Tell Kenneth the best thing he can do for his son is send him to school." As Supaya only smiled, she added shrewdly, "Remind him he is required by law to do so."

Supaya was glad to shut the door on Miss Harris. She had not been surprised at her coming to ask about Taw, and knew that if he did not come to school, Miss Harris would surely speak to the agent. She thought she would have to go out and look for them, but that evening they returned.

"Mother! Look!" exclaimed Taw. "I snared a rabbit! I made the snare myself!"

"That is good, Taw. Kineu, I'm glad you returned. Miss Harris was here asking about Taw. He should have been in school. Tomorrow he must go."

"Tomorrow we're going hunting!" cried Taw.

"Taw, come here," said Supaya. She sat down and took his hands in hers. "Now listen carefully. You are old enough now to go to school. All the children your age go. You won't be alone. You'll be going with Wagash, Waboose, and Shooskonee. And you'll learn to read and write and do arithmetic the way Wagash does. Then, when you grow up . . ."

"He can live on a reserve," interrupted Kineu, his hoarse voice shaking with anger, "selling baskets and potatoes for a living! Or he can go to the city and be a drunk because nobody will hire a dumb Indian! Or maybe there'll be another war and he can go and see how the white man fights!"

"Please, Kineu!" pleaded Supaya. That she understood so well Kineu's charges made it all the more difficult for her to oppose him, to make clear to him the necessity for their children to get along in a white world. "It doesn't have to be like that! You only make it harder for them! You know he should go to school! He has to go or they will take him away from us!"

"Father!" Taw laid his hand on Kineu's arm and gazed up imploringly. "I don't want to go! I want to stay with you!"

"You *will* be with your father, Taw! You live here together! You'll see him every day! And in the summer you can . . ."

"Taw," said Kineu, "go outside and wait." Taw went quickly, and until the door closed behind him, Kineu regarded Supaya silently, his eyes hard. Then he said, "He is not going to school. He is *my* son and he is coming with me!"

Supaya stood up. With a calmness she did not feel, she returned his look and asked, her voice dangerously quiet, "What do you mean, coming with you? This is our home, his home. He is *my* son also. Or do you forget that?"

In that moment, Kineu's frustrations, his overwhelming sense of loss, burst inside him. Outraged, he turned on Supaya, his wife, whom he wanted and thought of as his. That he shrank from her, that he shrank from all others except the unquestioning child, confused and frightened him. Unable to confront himself, he confronted her; wanting to strike at himself, he struck at her. "You have given up your right to him! He is an Indian still, and I will teach him how to live as one! For the others it is too late! You have turned them from the old ways and made them into white children! You can keep them! You and your white friends! More and more you live as a white woman! Your father would turn from you, sick at heart! You shame your people!"

Stunned by his words, Supaya forgot her patience and concern. "You dare speak so to me!" she exclaimed in a furious whisper. "You, whose life I saved when you were helpless! You, who to prove yourself a man," her voice full of contempt, "left us by ourselves for three years! How do you think we lived then? All of us, here, on this reserve! We *must* get along with the whites to survive! It's a white world! And my father would be *proud* that we survived! He would say we have done well!"

They stared at each other, their faces hard and bitter, neither able to yield. Then Kineu stepped past her. The door opened and closed. Supaya heard him go, too proud to call him back. As her anger drained away, she covered her face with her hands and wept bitter tears, wretched that she had lost her temper, that she had not been able to hold her family together. Neither her efforts nor her prayers had been of any help. Now, though her loyalty to Kineu rebelled against doing so, she knew she would have to speak to the agent about Taw.

Supaya waited several days, hoping Kineu would relent and bring Taw back. When he did not, she went to Gerald and informed him, in an official way, that her husband, Kenneth Bruley, had left her and had taken their youngest child, Tom, with him. "My husband is free to live as he likes," she said, to forestall any criticism of Kineu, "but my son should be in school, and I want him returned."

Gerald was saddened by this trouble that had come to Kenneth and Sophia. Several times since Kenneth's return Gerald had tried to speak with him, had urged him to attend the council meetings, where he had always been a good and stable influence. But Kenneth had not responded. Gerald had hoped he'd recover from his war experience, from having been shell-shocked and gassed. Now he doubted it. Respecting Supaya's restrained, dignified statement and seeing the pain it caused her, Gerald promised to look for Kenneth and return her son to her. As Sophia kept her feelings to herself, he followed her example and shared his only with Lizzie.

Gerald searched for Kenneth and Tom and occasionally found traces where they had been, but, although he often felt himself observed, he never caught sight of them. As winter came on, searching became more difficult and Gerald had less time to spend tramping through the woods.

When the temperature dropped and heavy frost coated buildings and fields, Supaya, concerned for Kineu's and Taw's health, took warm clothing to Kineu's little house at the end of the bay. Returning a few days later, she was relieved to find the clothing gone. After that, without telling anyone and all through the winter, especially in bad weather, she made countless trips through the snow to leave supplies of food there. Sometimes it was untouched for days, and she knew they were in a distant part of the reserve. Then one day it would be gone, and she'd know they were near.

Supaya thought herself unobserved, but Gerald, seeing tracks in the snow, waited and watched and soon understood what she was doing. He even thought he might catch Kenneth entering or leaving the house, but he never did. Nor, out of respect for her feelings, did he let Supaya know he had seen her.

Whenever Waboose and Shooskonee asked about their father and brother, Supaya reassured them, suggesting that perhaps in the spring they would come back home. But she had no faith in her own words. Or in her prayers. One day she took the stone bear from its bag and dropped it out of sight in the bottom of her trunk.

Spring came, and the lake ice cracked and boomed and split apart. The fields were soggy with melting snow, and the woods hazy with the delicate pink of swelling buds. But Gerald still had not found Kenneth and Tom, and they did not return.

CHAPTER
TWENTY-FIVE

For Kineu the winter passed like a dream, one day blending into the next. He and Taw might have been gone a week, a year, or several years. They hunted and fished through the ice, and easily eluded the Indian agent, occasionally watching him as he passed by within yards of where they hid. Kineu spent hours reliving his past, not his life at Two Bluffs, which had become for him the existence of a strange, unwanted part of himself which he had sloughed off, but the past of his boyhood and youth. Huddled in temporary shelters of pine boughs and a blanket, warmed by small fires or sitting by the stove in his little shack, Kineu spoke often to Taw of those days on Stone Island when he had stalked deer through the woods and laid cunning traps along streams and in the meadows for muskrat and beaver and had never returned home without meat. He spoke of the spring deep in the woods and the streams, and how he had understood the winds and the hidden lake currents, and how he netted many fish. His eyes glowed and his hoarse voice softened as he told how he had gone into the woods and fasted and how early on one never-forgotten morning when the world was just awakening, he had been granted a vision, and how thereafter, because his guardian, the Great Eagle, had blessed him with a keen eye and a fleet foot, he could outrun everyone and had won all the races. He felt himself flying over the fields, glorying in the strength and swiftness of his legs, his feet scarcely touching the ground, leaping rocks and streams, the rushing air cooling his face. Then, seeing that Taw, curled up beside him, had fallen asleep, Kineu would silently turn over his memories until his head sagged against his chest and he fell asleep.

The food Supaya left for them, Kineu took without question. He thought of Supaya often, but never as wife and mother. He saw her always as she had been on Stone Island, his deeply loved companion whose loss he mourned. Sometimes in the stillness of the spring mornings he would hear a bird singing, and its song would fill his heart with an ineffable sadness, as if there were no one left in the world save the bird and himself. In his loneliness, he would waken Taw, and as the ground fog slowly dissolved, they would walk through the woods and look down from the cliff edge at the rippled water far below them and at the gulls that soared and tipped their wings in the pale morning sunlight.

On one such morning in early summer, as they pushed their boat over the stones into the clear, cold water, Kineu saw an eagle, soaring high. Powerful wings outspread against the blue-white dome of sky, it floated above him in wide circles, riding the air currents above the cliffs. As he watched, it swung far out over the water, then glided back over the land, and with one slow beat of its great wings disappeared to the west.

Kineu and Taw set their net and, as the sun rose high, oared lazily out into the lake. The land fell away behind them, the cliffs seeming to sink below the water swells. As they drifted, Kineu lost himself in a daydream. A long wrack of cloud appeared, rising from the west. Stretching far out across the sky, it obscured the sun, dulling its light to an eerie sulfurous yellow. The swells deepened and above the distant strip of land the clouds now towered up in great dark, churning masses that glowed with an inner fire. The water, turned to gray metal, rolled with an ominous smoothness.

"Father!" exclaimed Taw, pointing at the sky. "Look!"

As he spoke a sudden wind roughened the water, and the boat jerked and swung about as the first white-tipped wave slapped against its side.

CHAPTER
TWENTY-SIX

It was Gerald who found the boat, partly grounded on the rocks, and pulled it up onto the beach. Further along, near the mouth of an inlet, he found Taw, face down in the shallows, the now calm water gently lifting his black hair and outstretched arms as it washed about him.

Gerald sent Lizzie on ahead to be with Supaya when he brought Taw home. The moment Lizzie entered, Supaya knew from her troubled face that something was wrong. Blunt, direct Lizzie had difficulty speaking, and Supaya, who had been washing clothes, dried her hands and waited, struck with a growing fear.

"Sophia, I . . . that is . . . let's sit down, Sophia!"

Supaya didn't move. "What *is* it, Lizzie?"

"Well . . . Gerald was out this morning looking for . . . for Kenneth and . . . Tom, and he . . . well . . . oh, Sophia!" Her chin trembled and she caught her underlip between her teeth.

Supaya, with the angry impatience of fear, came close to her and demanded, "And he what?"

"He found their boat, and . . . and he found Tom!"

Supaya stared at her. "*Found* Tom!"

"Yes! Oh, Sophia, he's bringing him home in the wagon."

Supaya winced. Her mouth opened, her lips moved, but no sound came. She stared at Lizzie, not wanting to believe but reading the truth in her tear-filled eyes. Lizzie reached out to her but Supaya, her face agonized, turned away. Sinking down in her rocker, she covered her head and began to wail, her high, drawn-out cries filling the house.

When Gerald carried Taw inside, Supaya raised her head and, running to him, took her child's soaked body in her arms. Holding him close, she bent over him, lamenting. Suddenly she stopped and stared at Gerald. "Kineu?" she asked fiercely.

Gerald shook his head. "I haven't . . . found him. I . . . I'll look again."

Supaya turned quickly away. She carried Taw into the bedroom, laid him on Kineu's bed, and pulled the curtain.

"You'd better get Susannah," Gerald told Lizzie. "I'm going back out again. I'll get old John Bruley to help me."

Soos came at once and sent Sarah to fetch Alma. When they entered the bedroom, they found Supaya kneeling on the floor beside the bed, her arms around Taw's body, her head bowed against his arm. She had cut off her hair. It lay in dark clumps on the floor where it had fallen. Gently but firmly they urged her to her feet and guided her like a sleepwalker to the outer room. Oblivious of those around her, she mourned with each breath, her voice wrung from her in thin cries and agonized moans.

George brought cedar boughs, and when Alma finished laying out the body, she and Soos purified the house, themselves, and Supaya, who submitted as though unaware of what they were doing. Late in the afternoon Gerald stopped to say that he and John Bruley had found no trace of Kenneth.

Both Alma and Sarah stayed with Supaya, who ignored the food they brought her and refused to leave her chair. That night Alma left the lamp burning, and whenever she roused from her fitful sleep, she saw Supaya sitting quietly in her chair, her eyes dry and staring.

The day of the funeral Soos, George and their children, Alma, and Uncle John gathered at Supaya's and received the people who came not to the wake that would have been held for an adult but to express their condolences. Reverend Crowell and Amy, Gerald and Lizzie and Louisa, Agatha, Jess, all came, and many of Supaya's patients, but for Supaya, enclosed in grief, though she saw them speak and stretch out their hands, they were too remote for her to hear or answer.

For the church service and burial, people came from all over the reserve, whole families whom Supaya had treated and who wished to show their respect and sympathy for her. The earth in the

cemetery was still damp, but the weather, chastened after the violent storm, was mild and still. To Supaya the bland, sun-filled day
was painful. She drew her shawl close about herself, hiding her face,
trying to shut out the bright, green, living world. She wanted only to
sit alone in the dark. She stood by the graveside dry-eyed and silent
as Reverend Crowell led the prayer and everyone joined in singing
a hymn. When the burial was over, she turned away and walked
home by herself.

Sarah walked with the children, Soos and George with Alma,
to whom they expressed their worry about Supaya. "She hasn't
eaten or spoken since that first day," said Soos.

Alma, her shrewd old eyes on Supaya's distant back, nodded. She knew Supaya well. "She is lost. I will speak to her and try
to help her find her way."

That evening Alma knocked on Supaya's door. Sarah let her
in. Supaya sat in her rocker, staring fixedly into the blackened fireplace.

A fire burned in the stove and the house was not cold, but
Alma said, "Here, let me make up a fire. It will warm your soul."
Alma was a small, wiry woman, her thin, ropy arms surprisingly
strong for her age. Her wrinkled skin was delicate as paper, but her
bony hands, ridged with veins, had all the skill of her years. When
the fire blazed up, she settled down in Nonen's rocker opposite
Supaya. Sarah and the children, watchful and subdued, sat at the
table, their hands in their laps. Alma glanced over at them, her eyes
bright and lively in her lined face.

"Make us all a cup of tea, Sarah, and if you look, there might
be a bit of leftover bread." She smiled at the children's immediate
interest, and leaning forward, tapped Supaya's knee. "You are fortunate. You have two rockers. You also have three fine children to
raise and a life to live. But I see you have forgotten them in following
after the dead. You have strayed off the path and are lost."

Supaya turned her head slightly and looked at her.

"Ahhh," nodded Alma, "I see your misery, but you have
forgotten something else. You have forgotten the four hills of life. I
will remind you. Then you will find your own way back." She
rocked and smiled again at the children, who were listening attentively. She waited until Sarah had given them all a cup of tea, except
for Supaya, who shook her head.

"Keep the pot warm," said Alma. When she had sipped of
her tea, she began to speak. She raised her head, her eyes looking

far off. The pitch of her voice altered so it seemed to come from a distance, and as she spoke, she slowly raised one hand and described the jagged shape of a hill.

"The first hill is very steep and hard to climb. Many have not the strength to begin and perish before they start. Many young ones fall on the sharp rocks and never reach the top. For those who do, even coming down the far side is dangerous, for they are not yet strong, and the obstacles are great. Taw was just starting down when he fell." Her hand dropped. For a moment she was silent, her gaze now holding Supaya's. Then she spoke again, expressing her own remembered sorrow seen anew in Supaya's eyes. "It is hard for those climbing the third hill to look back and see their children fall, to see their frail bodies bruised and not be able to save them. But though they groan with sadness and ache with the loss of their young, so beautiful, so full of a promise that will never be, they must go on climbing. As they struggle on, burdened with grief, they can hope their loved child will live again, that his spirit will find a home in another being, and they can take comfort in knowing he will never suffer the hardships and sorrows that come to all who are driven to climb on."

Alma paused. She leaned forward and poked the fire, sending a flurry of sparks up the dark maw of the chimney. Sarah and the children watched her, forgetting their bread and tea. Supaya too watched, her eyes glistening, anxious for her to continue.

Alma sat back. Head raised, her sharp eyes half closed, she gazed far off over their heads. Solemnly she stretched out her arm as if to touch what she saw.

"Kineu had climbed the first hill and the second, for he was strong and had a great heart. He had reached the third hill, not as steep as the first or second, but strewn with rocks so sharp they cut a man's feet, and rocks so smooth he can find no handhold. There are deep gorges, dangerous to cross. He had acquired many burdens, but burdened as he was, he had climbed well. He had followed his vision. But his burdens grew heavier. They pressed hard on him, weighing him down until he stumbled and fell. His body was almost crushed to death." Alma's voice deepened. In the firelight her face shone with compassion. "Still his spirit drove him on. He pulled himself up and started to climb once more. Only now he was bent. He could not see his way. He lost his vision and turned off onto a side path. There he wandered, lost and confused. Those who loved him called to him, but he couldn't hear them. Those who

314

would help him had to climb on, and though they stretched out their hands to him, they couldn't reach him, for life drives each one on, and each must find his own way. Exhausted by the struggle, his heart failed him. He fell again. This time he could not rise."

Alma closed her eyes, her weathered old face rapt by her inner vision. "Now he is free of the struggle. No more does he turn in circles like a wounded animal, his soul crying out in pain. Now his spirit is at last free. He can enter the land of souls and be united with those who have gone before him. There he will rest and find tranquility."

Slowly Alma opened her eyes. There was no sound in the room except for the soft breath of the fire and Supaya quietly weeping as she had not been able to weep since she'd held Taw's dead body in her arms. Alma rested her hand on Supaya's shoulder.

"She'll be able to drink her tea now," she said to Sarah, and to Supaya, "You must leave the dead now and turn to the living, for the climb still before you is a long one, full of much joy as well as sorrow. Life is a gift of the great Kitchi Manito, and you must accept it with a full spirit and a grateful heart."

CHAPTER
TWENTY-SEVEN

On two successive Sundays Frank Jones fell in with Supaya as she walked home from church with Soos and George, the children, free to follow their own pursuits, running on ahead. The first time Supaya thought nothing of it, and only nodded briefly at Frank when she turned in at her own lane. The second time she noticed a quick exchange of glances between Soos and George and felt vaguely uncomfortable when they turned off and she and Frank went on together. She knew Frank slightly; that is, she knew who he was. He was Annie Jones' brother-in-law. She had encountered him once or twice when calling at Annie's to treat her children. But that had been before the war. Since then she had not seen him, but she had heard the women speak of him admiringly as an attractive, hard-working man whom none of the young women had been able to entice into marriage. Still, Supaya paid little attention to him, being preoccupied with thoughts of spring planting.

"Your garden will have to be plowed soon," remarked Frank, watching her sideways.

"Yes," agreed Supaya absently, wondering if she should enlarge it this spring.

"I'll plow it for you," said Frank.

"George always does it," said Supaya.

"George has enough to do. I'll do it. Tomorrow."

Surprised, Supaya turned and looked at him inquiringly.

Frank was pleased. Finally he had her attention. "I'm plowing my own tomorrow. I'll do yours first. In the morning. Early." He found it hard to speak of plowing when she gazed at him like that. He wanted to stay, but he made himself nod politely and walk off before she could find an answer. He had made a good beginning. She was not flirtatious or coy like the other, younger girls he had known. With her he could be direct. He could hardly wait for tomorrow.

Before the children left for school she heard him.

"Mama," said Waboose, "there's a man plowing our garden."

"Yes," said Supaya, not sure if she was pleased, "I know. That's Mr. Jones."

Frank waved at the children as they went down the lane. Shortly after, he knocked at the back door. "Wouldn't you like it a little larger this year?" he asked.

Supaya stared at him. Had he read her thoughts? "Yes," she admitted, "I would. Would you like a cup of tea?"

"When I'm finished," he said, and went back to his plowing.

Frank would have been gratified to know that Supaya had given him some thought. She knew now that his walking home with her had been no accident. She needed no reminder that a year had passed since she'd cut her hair. It seemed a shorter time. But she had not expected that anyone else had marked the time. Frank had surprised her. When he came to the door again, she invited him in and offered him fresh cooked bannock and tea. As he washed, splashing the water over his face, he reminded her of her father, a strong, compact man with large, deep eyes and a strong jaw, possessed of an easy self-confidence. Watching him comb his hair—still cut short as in the army—and sit down comfortably at the table, she realized that here was a man who, like Jules, was at home within himself wherever he was.

He ate the bread with relish. "You're a good cook," he said, glancing up at her, and before she could thank him, he added, "as good a cook as you are a dancer."

"A what!" exclaimed Supaya, taken aback.

"I've seen you at dances before the war," he assured her mischievously, as though he knew more of her than she guessed. "Will you come with me to the Pay Day party?"

"I'm going with Soos and George," said Supaya quickly.

He smiled at her haste to answer. "Then I will see you there," he said and left.

Supaya had not intended to go to the party, though her

children had begged to go and Soos had urged her to come. Now she was committed.

A wind blew on the day of the party, a soft siren of a breeze. Birds wheeled across the sky, fanning out, then swirling together to land with much fluttering and clattering in the treetops. Cloud shadows slid over the fields, rippling smoothly over rocks and roads and buildings. Everyone was exhilarated with the coming of spring. The men playing soccer ran and leaped and kicked their legs with exaggerated vigor. Older men, watching, puffed their pipes and slapped their hands over a good play. Children raced about, put their heads together in deep conference, then at a common signal scattered as if chased by demons. When the first round of food was served, the older people gathered around the long table, eager to eat their fill of dishes some of them had not had since the New Year's dance. Supaya and Soos helped serve. Lizzie, who had helped with the preparations, stayed in the kitchen, chatting with the women and watching with fond pride as Louisa, a sharp-eyed self-appointed monitor, instantly whisked away empty platters and brought them to be refilled.

By evening everyone had eaten and gone upstairs except for a few children who had played until dusk and still lingered at the table. The dancing had begun, and the old people sat along the sides of the room, watching the dancers, their feet and hands keeping time with the fiddler. The drinking had also begun. Men went outside in twos and threes and stood about in the dark by their wagons, then returned with noticeable swaggers. On these occasions Gerald pretended not to notice. He stood talking with a group of men including Jess Fallon, whom he and Lizzie had persuaded to come along.

Fallon had come with one intention: to see Supaya. He had seen her arrive with George and Soos when he and Gerald were watching the game. He had tried to catch her eye at the table, but it had been Sarah who served him. Now, past the heads of the dancers, he caught sight of her across the room.

Supaya, with Soos and George, who could not dance, and Sarah, was standing talking to old John Bruley and Alma, who were sitting down. Supaya stood with her back to the room, hoping to avoid Frank Jones' notice. He had caught her eye when she'd been serving, and the purpose in his eyes as he held her glance had been as clear as if he had spoken. She had instinctively drawn back. She did not want to be involved; she was not ready to disturb the emotional balance she had only just achieved.

Sarah too was hoping to pass unnoticed by Caleb Sims. He had tried to speak to her several times, but she had evaded him. Now, fearing he would approach her again, she was thinking of a reason to go home when he appeared at her elbow and asked her to be his partner in the next dance, the fiddler having gone outside to refresh himself.

Soos smiled at him and nodded, but Sarah said hastily, "Oh no, I . . . I can't."

Seeing Caleb's disappointment, Soos exclaimed, "Why not! Go on and dance."

Sarah appealed to her mother and Supaya. "I should see where the children are. They may . . ."

"The children are downstairs stuffing themselves," said Soos. "Go on!" and she gave her daughter a little push.

Caleb touched Sarah's arm gently. "It's just a dance. Please come."

Not wanting to make a scene, Sarah moved stiffly out onto the floor with him, but her face, tense and unsmiling, was averted from him.

There was painful silence as they all looked after her, all hoping that she could somehow rid herself of the horror they knew she felt. In that moment Frank spoke into Supaya's ear.

"Come, let's dance. The fiddler's about to start."

Supaya drew back, much as Sarah had done. "Thank you, but I don't want to dance."

"Why not? You're here, aren't you?"

"Yes, I came only . . ."

Alma, who had been watching and listening, tugged at Supaya's arm and pulled her down close, her shiny dark eyes staring hard into Supaya's. "He is right," she whispered. "Remember, life will not wait!"

The fiddler tuned up and called for the dancers to take their places.

"Come on!" said Frank, not waiting for excuses. "They need another couple!" Catching her hand, he turned quickly, almost colliding with Fallon, who had just made his way across the room.

"Sorry," said Fallon. The men regarded each other briefly; then, with a slight smile, Fallon stepped aside.

Up on the platform the fiddler stomped his foot and flourished his bow, and Frank pulled her into position in the square. Before the dancers all swung into motion, she had a glimpse of Fallon, leaning against the wall watching her, his arms folded across his fancy vest. Not since she was fifteen had Supaya felt so absurdly girlish, being dragged out onto the floor, but she had no time to feel embarrassed. Not having danced since before the war, she had to pay close attention or be even further embarrassed. As she remembered the patterns, she relaxed and began to enjoy herself, responding with enthusiasm to the rhythm of the music and the swift motion of the dance. Weaving in and out and around about, skirts flaring, she was glad she had come and grateful to Frank for his insistence. As she linked elbows and whirled about, her spirit lightened and she felt an exuberance she had not felt in years.

When the fiddler took his break and the dancers scattered, Frank, firmly grasping her hand, said they would go outside until the next dance. But Supaya, flushed and slightly breathless, gently pulled her hand away.

"You go," she said, smiling. "I must see where my children are."

Frank hesitated. He knew she had enjoyed their dancing, and though her smile was only polite, still she had not smiled at him before at all. "I will be back soon," he said, as if to pin her to the spot until he returned.

Supaya found Shooskonee asleep with her head in Alma's lap and Wagash and Waboose downstairs playing a game with some other children. Wanting to continue their game and thinking Supaya had come to take them home, they dodged in and around people still gathered at the table in an attempt to hide. Satisfied, Supaya pretended not to see them and went back upstairs. Like the children, she did not want to go home after all. She felt buoyantly alive, as if revived from a long numbness, full of energy that for a change could be expended just for the joy of it. She wished for the fiddler to return so she could dance again. Entering the upstairs hall, she came face to face with Fallon, who smiled with pleasure at seeing her and said, "Ah, I was looking for you. Would you," he asked, making her a mock-serious little bow, "be my partner in the next set?"

Amused by his manner, Supaya inclined her head, and they took up their positions just as Frank returned. Hiding his chagrin, he entered the dance with another partner. Frank danced with much vigor, but Fallon, to Supaya's surprise, danced with smooth, effort-less grace. They danced until the fiddler tired, and a second fiddler took his place, a younger man who played at a faster tempo. Supaya felt she was flying through the steps, but Fallon easily kept the pace, his arm and hand always ready, his eye always on her as if in that hall they were the only dancers.

When the second fiddler finally took a break, Supaya saw that many people had gone home. Soos and George were gone. And Sarah. Alma was still there with several of her friends, but Shooskonee was no longer asleep on her lap.

"Alma, where is Shooskonee?"

Alma's old face wrinkled into a grin. "Don't worry. Soos took her home. The boys too." Her bright eyes looked appreciatively at Jess, standing close beside Supaya. Seeing her shrewd eye, Jess smiled back at her, and her wicked grin deepened.

"I must go," said Supaya.

Fallon, who saw Frank coming toward them, took her arm. "I'll take you home," he said.

As they left, the dancing continued, though it was nearly three in the morning. The night was very dark, having grown over-cast, and a light spring mist was falling. Frank, standing silhouetted in the hall's lighted doorway, saw them go. As the buggy turned onto the road, he stepped out into the night.

Supaya didn't see him. Pleasantly tired, she pulled her shawl around her shoulders and leaned back against the seat, enjoying the ride.

Fallon shook out the reins lightly, and, being in no hurry, let the horse go at his own sleepy pace. They said very little. The night air cooled Supaya's face and made her drowsy. She was too con-tent to give much thought to her companion, and would have been surprised to know the tenor of his thoughts. For Fallon was resisting an impulse to go past her house to his own where he would carry her inside and up to his own room, across the hall from what had been Kirsten's. He smiled to himself picturing her shock and indig-nation. Glancing at her drowsing in the corner, he wondered that she could be so seemingly unaware of what he felt for her. He had observed Frank Jones and his proprietary manner with Supaya. He, Fallon, recognized serious purpose in a man when he saw it, and he had seen Frank eyeing him coldly when he and Supaya were danc-ing. He could not afford to go too slowly. He knew Frank would not. He would have to startle Supaya, but gently.

He pulled the horse up near her front door. When the buggy stopped, Supaya sat up. "Thank you," she said, and got out. But when she reached her door, she found Fallon right behind her.

"Supaya," he whispered, putting one arm around her shoulders and turning her toward him. Surprised, she looked up, and he took her face gently in his hand. Bending his head, he kissed her softly on the mouth. "Good night, Supaya." Even in the dark he saw her eyes open wide in shock. Unable to resist and before she could move or speak, he kissed her again, more firmly, then let her go and stepped back. "Good night," he said, smothering an impulse to laugh at her astonishment. She stood for a moment, stunned, and watched him drive off before she opened the door and went inside.

Sarah and Shooskonee were asleep downstairs, the boys upstairs. Supaya touched their heads and adjusted their quilts in a kind of daze. In her own bed, she stared into the dark and tried, at first, to tell herself that Fallon's action was entirely surprising, that whatever ties existed between them were those of friends and merely practical, a matter of mutual help and understanding. But she knew that was not so, had known since Kirsten's illness. She had never allowed herself to think of it. Now . . . but she could not think beyond tonight. She pressed the back of her hand lightly against her mouth and fell asleep still feeling his kiss.

The next day she was working out in the garden when Frank came down the lane. He stopped by the house and gestured for her. He had a bundle in the crook of his arm.

"Give me a cup of tea and I'll show you what I've brought," he said. His deep-set eyes studied her as if he suspected her of mischief.

Puzzled by his manner, she warmed up the tea and set out the cups. Then he unwrapped his bundle. It contained a packet of pumpkin seeds and a large number of porcupine quills, neatly tied together.

"Frank! These are beautiful!" exclaimed Supaya, examining the quills. He smiled slightly, somewhat mollified by her enthusiasm. "You must have gotten these last fall!"

"Yes, I did," he said flatly, his tone and hard, direct look telling her she had been in his thoughts even then.

She felt herself flush. "That was kind of you, Frank."

"It was not kind of you not to wait for me last night. I said I'd be back."

He put it as an accusation. Supaya considered a moment, then said carefully, "I did not go to the party with you, Frank. I was free to dance with anyone I chose. I made no promises."

"You danced all night with a white man!"

"He is my friend," said Supaya coolly, trying not to lose her temper.

Suddenly Frank reached out and grasped both her arms. Holding her firmly so she couldn't move, he leaned close and said, "And if I'm a friend do I get to kiss you too?"

Startled by his action, she made no attempt to pull away, but stared directly into his eyes, her own flashing with anger. "So, you are a spy! I had thought better of you than that! You should go now."

He gave her a little shake. "I am no spy! I have told you what I did. I watched to see no harm came to you."

"When I need protection, I will say so," said Supaya scornfully.

Reluctantly, Frank let her go, but he said insistently, "White men are not to be trusted."

"I have known this man since . . . !" Supaya flared out, then stopped, exasperated. "But I need explain nothing to you! Or to anyone! Now go and take your quills with you!"

"No! They are yours! You must keep them to show we are still friends."

Supaya stared at him. "I will not be spied on!"

"No more," he said, adding stubbornly, "unless I tell you." At that Supaya had to smile. Her anger dissolved and she shook her head at his obstinacy. Encouraged, he moved closer. "You are alone. You need a man to look after you." Supaya's expression of amused tolerance faded. She said nothing but looked at him haughtily. He remembered stories he had heard of her power and quickly amended his words. "You need a friend."

Supaya's expression softened, but she looked him in the eye as she said, "It is always good to have friends. As a friend you will always be welcome."

Frank went away almost satisfied. He understood that she would not be easily won and that a woman with her pride would not explain what he had seen the night before. But she had accepted him as a friend. He was confident he could soon turn their friendship into a permanent, warm alliance.

That, however, was before the incident of the two pigs.

For several days Supaya saw neither Jess nor Frank. Then one sunny, breezy afternoon she was in the backyard hanging out the wash when she heard a wagon coming up the lane. She expected it was George, who was to bring her some chickens. Instead it was Jess. He waved his hat, and pulling up the horses, jumped down and strode toward her. To hide her agitation, Supaya went on taking clothes from the basket and hanging them up. When he reached her side and spoke to her, she glanced at him sideways, uncertain what she would read in his face. But she saw no hint of presumption or smugness, only an open, eager smile that made him look almost boyish, standing there in the sunlight, his hair ruffled. His vivid eyes met hers candidly, and her constraint disappeared. It seemed only natural that he should ask her to come with him to deliver supplies to a farm some distance away, a farm, moreover, that had pigs for sale.

Simply being together filled them both with exuberance and sharpened their perception. Everything about them, the blue sky streaked with wind-swept clouds, the stretches of deep green woods, the treetops bending, the plowed fields and grazing cattle, all delighted their eyes, but particularly they delighted each other. He spoke of ordinary matters of general interest, and she politely responded, but the true dialogue lay in their sidelong glances. He had never known such a strong, beautiful woman with such natural pride and grace, nor she such a strong, handsome man with such humor and gentleness. He admired the gleam of her blue-black hair in the sunlight and she the crisp wave in his. He remembered the softness of her lips, the feel of her within the curve of his arm. She remembered the firm touch of his hands, the pressure of his mouth on hers. They smiled a great deal and laughed sometimes at nothing unless it was at each one's awareness of the glances of the other.

The farmer's sow had a fine litter. While the farmer and Fallon unloaded the wagon, Supaya leaned on the pigsty fence and chose the pig she wanted. Fallon insisted on buying it for her; she insisted he must then stay for dinner and he immediately agreed to do so.

When they got back, the children were home, and they crowded around to see the new pig, who squealed and snuffed and trotted about, mystified at finding himself alone. While Supaya, with Shooskonee's help, prepared the meal, Waboose made up a fire in the fireplace and Wagash sat on the floor beside Fallon and asked him questions about storekeeping. Supaya had just served him fish, potatoes, and scone when there was a knock at the back door.

Supaya opened it to find Frank standing there with a burlap bag slung over his shoulder.

"Come out," he said, "I've brought you something."

Surprised, Supaya stepped outside and followed him as he walked toward the pigsty. "A pig," he said proudly, opening the bag, and then paused, nonplused, at seeing a pig already in the pen.

"I'm sorry, Frank," said Supaya, seeing his disappointment. "It was kind of you to bring it. Maybe Annie would like it."

"No," said Frank. "I got it for you. It's yours." He tumbled the pig into the pen with the other, who came trotting to greet it. "You will have two pigs to raise," he said, and when she protested, he declared, almost angrily, "You will have twice the amount of meat next fall." Then he stood, facing her squarely, waiting to be invited in.

"Well, come in then, Frank. You must have dinner with us."

He came willingly until he reached the table, when he stopped abruptly. Jess, equally surprised, greeted him, but Frank, for once, had no answer and only nodded.

Supaya turned to the stove. "Please sit down, Frank." As she served him a full plate, she said, not looking at anyone, "Frank just brought us a fine pig."

There was a moment of deep silence.

"Does it look like the other one?" asked Shooskonee.

Fallon bent his head over his plate.

"Very much the same," said Supaya carefully. As she spoke there was another knock at the back door. Welcoming any interruption, Supaya opened it to George.

"I've brought you those chickens I promised," said George.

Supaya stepped outside and shut the door behind her. They put the hens and cock in the roost on the far side of the shed.

"I see you've got two pigs," remarked George, mildly surprised.

"Yes," said Supaya and giggled. George raised his eyebrows at her and then she laughed outright. "Oh George, come in and have some fish! Please come in!"

It was unusual for Supaya to be distraught. His curiosity piqued, George came. He stopped short at seeing both Jess and Frank seated at the table, and pursed his mouth thoughtfully.

"Please sit down, George," said Supaya.

George did so. Eyes wide as saucers, he solemnly greeted the other two, "Mr. Fallon, Frank," nodding gravely at each in turn. Then, studying the fish Supaya placed before him, he said, "I just stopped by with five chickens."

"Gee!" exclaimed Waboose. "Two pigs and five chickens!"

Fallon choked. Supaya hurried into the lean-to. Frank stared at George as if he suspected a trick, but George, his face blandly innocent, serenely ate his fish and potatoes.

They all drank their tea in a heavy silence. George left first, sharing a sly amused glance with Supaya as he went. Frank and Jess left together, going in opposite directions.

That evening, after the children were in bed, Frank returned. When Supaya opened the front door, he gazed at her crestfallen. "I want to talk to you."

"Not tonight, Frank, please."

"Just for a few minutes."

"Tomorrow."

"I'm going to the logging camp tomorrow."

"Come before you leave then."

He walked away, but at the curve in the road, he sat down on a stump and took out his pipe. He'd almost finished his smoke when he saw a man on foot come down the road and turn in at Supaya's lane. Pale light shone out as the door opened. The man stepped inside and the door shut.

Supaya had been on the point of going to bed, but when she opened the door a second time, Jess stood there. He took off his hat and smiled at her, and then, remembering the two pigs, they both laughed.

"May I come in?" he asked.

Supaya stepped back, holding the door open, then closed it behind him. "Would you like some tea?"

"No thanks," he said, laying his hat on the table.

Needing to busy herself with something, she stirred up the fire. As she did so, Jess turned out the lamp. Supaya looked up, startled.

"It's nicer with just the firelight," he said. "Besides, you can't expect a man to propose in a glare of light." His tone was light, but he wasn't smiling. Almost panicked, Supaya turned back toward the fire. "You know that's why I've come, don't you?" He put his hands on her shoulders, leaned his face against her hair. "Please, Supaya, don't turn away. Look at me, won't you?" Gently he turned her around, but her eyes were on his tie. "Look at me." He tilted her chin back and she raised her eyes, so deep a brown they were almost black, and looked directly at him. His hand slid around her throat, and as if he were mesmerized by her glance, he whispered, "I love you, Supaya! I love you! So long I've waited to tell you! Now . . ." Drawn irresistibly, he kissed her gently; then, as he felt her yield, his arms tightened and he kissed her with all the passion he felt for her. Holding her close, his head against hers, he spoke softly into her ear. "Will you marry me, Supaya? Please, be my wife!"

At that she braced her arms against his chest, holding him off so she stood in a loose embrace. He tried to see her face, but she kept her head bent, her eyes on his watch chain. "You are a white man. I am an Indian. And have, besides, three children."

He almost laughed. "I don't care what we are! Or how many children you have! What difference does that make! I love you. I've loved you for years. I want to live the rest of my life with you. If you could love me . . ." He paused then, his voice suddenly tight. "*Could* you, Supaya?"

She raised her head and looked at him a long moment, her eyes lingering over his face, the hint of a smile at the corners of her mouth. Then she put her arms around his neck and pulling his head toward her, kissed him with a passion that equalled his own.

For some time they sat by the fire, he in the rocker, she on his lap, his arms around her, their heads close together. "When we're married," he said, his lips against her forehead, "we can live in my house or in yours or both, whatever you wish. You've been living in my house anyway, for a long time now." He laughed at her puzzled look and kissed her lightly. "You've been there constantly, sitting in my chairs, eating at my table . . . sleeping in my bed." His arms tightened. "But whenever I reached for you, you disappeared."

Smiling, she laid her hand against his face and promised, "I won't ever disappear again."

When the fire sank down to a handful of embers and the room was almost dark, Jess rose to go. Holding both her hands against his chest, he asked, "When shall we be married, Supaya? You say when it shall be."

Surprised that he would now leave her, Supaya's eyes widened, but she said nothing, marveling at the ways of this white man.

"There's no reason to wait, is there?" he asked, not understanding.

"No," she agreed, her eyes inscrutable.

At the door he embraced her once more and asked again, "You'll say when soon?"

"Yes," she promised and waited to close the door until he disappeared in the dark.

Walking home, Jess pondered what seemed to him her reluctance to say when they would marry, but only briefly, for he was a happy man, walking under a moonless, starry sky. There was no one at the curve of the road to see him go.

After he left, Supaya paced about restlessly, and had Jess seen her thoughtfulness, he might have been more troubled. She trailed her hand along the mantlepiece, over the backs of Nonen's and Jules' rockers, across the end of the table Eli had built. She wandered into the lean-to and touched Aunt Hettie's little mirror, its surface a dark glimmer. She went upstairs and opened her trunk. Sitting on the floor, she took out the bear claw necklace and placed it around her neck. She touched the smooth claws and held the cold blue stone tight in her hand. When, much later, she took the necklace off and laid it carefully back in the trunk, she knew what she would do.

Frank came very early, but Supaya was up and had tea and scone ready. She insisted he sit down.

He looked at her with hurt, troubled eyes. "I saw him come back last night," he said accusingly, "and you let him in."

"Frank! I told you . . ."

Frank held up one hand, palm out. "I wasn't spying. I've told you what I saw. I speak honestly to you. I will tell you now what I wanted to say when you would not let me in. It is that I want you for my wife." Supaya started to speak, but he raised his hand again. "Wait. I have not finished. I have a job at the logging camp. I will come back when I can. But I know he wants you too. It would be bad for you, a powerful woman, to marry a white. Still, being a woman, you might. I want you to promise to do nothing until I return." Having said what he wanted to say, he gazed solemnly at her, waiting for her answer.

Supaya was amused by the seriousness with which he took himself; still, she respected his forthrightness. "Frank, I cannot promise you that."

He stood up instantly, clattering the cups, and leaned toward her, his face tense. "Promise at least you will not marry until I return!"

"Frank," said Supaya gently, "you have done me a great honor in choosing me to be your wife. You are a fine man. You would be a fine husband. I know that. But I will not promise you anything. I will not be bound."

He stared at her dumbfounded. He was pleased by her praise, but astonished by her independence. After a moment's silent contemplation, he saw that she was adamant.

"Thank you for the tea and scone."

"You are welcome, Frank."

"We are still friends? We will be friends when I come back?"

"We will *always* be friends, Frank."

All that day Supaya was busy. She cooked and cleaned and washed her hair. At sundown, she took a basket with a pot of stew and some scone and started down the road. She had taken special pains with her appearance, dressing her hair carefully and wearing what she considered her prettiest skirt and blouse. Sarah was staying with the children and though she wondered where Supaya was going, she did not ask, nor did Supaya tell her.

Supaya avoided the storefront and approached from the side, through the trees, going to the verandah at the back. She knocked at the door with the ruffled curtain and waited, holding her basket.

Jess, in vest and rolled-up shirt sleeves, was working in the kitchen. Answering the knock, he saw with delight Supaya come as if in answer to his thoughts. He threw wide the door. With a roguish smile and complete self-possession, she stepped past him, avoiding his arms, saying, "I've brought some stew for our supper."

She went into the kitchen and made herself entirely at home, setting the basket on the table, folding her shawl over a chairback. She glanced at Jess, who was watching her closely, trying to sense her intention. His expression, a mixture of curiosity and anticipation, made her laugh.

"There," she said, sitting down, spreading out her skirt, and folding her hands in her lap as if posing for a picture, "you see me sitting at your table!" She gave him a moment, then jumped up and crossed the hall into the living room. He followed, smiling as he caught her pattern, and watched as she surveyed the chairs, deliberating over which one to choose. "This one will do." She sat down and leaned back with regal aplomb, her arms resting on the chair arms, her chin raised haughtily. "Now," she said pertly, "you see me sitting in your living room," and after a brief pause added in a lower, softer tone, "and I am not going to disappear." It was a challenge, one Jess was quick to seize.

He stared down at her, a purposeful glint in his eye, then grasped her arms and pulled her up close. "And what," he asked, "about seeing you in my bed?"

She tilted her head, eyed him narrowly, and said, "The stew will get cold."

"Let it," he said and kissed her hard.

His room was sparsely furnished—an unimposing bedstead, a chest of drawers, one straight chair, and an oval braided rug. The uncurtained dormer window was shaded by a grove of fir trees. The angles of the low, slanted ceiling were already deeply shadowed.

Supaya glanced around the dim room as if to acquaint herself with it, then turned to Jess and laid her hands flat against his chest. "You asked when we would marry, and I say . . . now. Do you understand? This is our marriage. I give myself to you now, as wife, and take you as my husband."

Jess understood Indian tradition. He knew also that before she had been married in the church. He didn't know her reasons for not doing so now, nor did he care. Laying his hands over hers, he clasped them tight. "Then from now on," he said softly, "I am your husband, and you are my wife."

Supaya took off her blouse and unfastened her skirt, leaving it on the floor where it fell. Standing before the chest, she began taking the pins out of her hair when Jess gently put her hands aside. Caressing her bare arms, he kissed her shoulders and the nape of her neck, then carefully removed her hairpins until her long hair uncoiled and fell down over his hands. She moved away from him to the bed and, pulling off her underclothes, stood for a moment, her naked body gleaming softly in the dark room before she slid under the quilt. Lying back, her eyes shadowy, her hair dark against the pillow, she said, with a slight tremor, "Now you see me in your bed."

Their coming together was swift and certain, the rhythm of their love as sure as if they had been moving toward this completion since they'd first flashed onto each other's consciousness. Clasped together, they slowly, like spent runners, regained their breath. He separated from her reluctantly, and they lay close, split apart, until aching with separateness, they embraced again and were once more lost in each other.

The morning sun had filtered through the firs and was shining in patches on the braided rug before they roused. Jess raised himself on one elbow and gazed down at Supaya, the strands of her hair spread out like a bedded mermaid's. She gazed back at him languidly, but under her drooping lids, her eyes were roguish. Smiling, she reached up and pulled him down against her.

They had the stew for breakfast. And the store didn't open until noon, to the mild surprise of the Indians who had gathered on the front porch and were patiently waiting.

CHAPTER
TWENTY-EIGHT

The following winter was a bad one, unusually damp and bitter. There was much illness. Supaya was constantly busy preparing medicines and visiting patients, among them, Caleb Sims. He was a strong young man, but Supaya worried because he lived alone.

"Look!" She pointed to the smokestack of Caleb's house. "There's no fire." She quickened her pace so that Sarah found it difficult to keep up with her. They made a new path to the back door through the heavy, wet snow that had fallen during the night.

"Bring in some wood, please, Sarah." The day before, Supaya had dragged Caleb's bed out of the bedroom and placed it near the stove. She had left a good fire burning. Now it was out. Caleb lay shivering under an old quilt. He moved restlessly, muttering unintelligible phrases, his eyes glassy with fever.

Sarah, working as Supaya's apprentice, had not wanted to come when Supaya visited Caleb, had been reluctant even to enter his house.

Supaya had given her a hard, impatient look. "He is ill," she had said tersely. "We do not choose patients."

Not wanting to anger her, Sarah had come without further protest. Foolishly, considering Supaya's concern, Sarah had not expected Caleb to be so ill. She was shocked by his flushed face and labored breathing. When he failed to recognize her or Supaya or even be aware of their presence, Sarah turned in sudden fear to Supaya.

"He needs more covers," said Supaya. "Get his coat and spread it over him. He needs nursing, but there are others I must . . ."

"I'll stay, I'll nurse him," interrupted Sarah. "I'll get some quilts and be right back. I will, really, Aunt Suppy! Leave the medicine here. I'll do just as you've taught me."

With other patients to visit, Supaya wasted no time. She set out medicines on the table, gave directions, and, wrapped up in her coat and shawl, hurried off, saying she'd be back in the morning.

That evening, as Supaya stirred a pot of soup and waited for Jess, she thought about Sarah and Caleb. She heard the jingle of Jess' horse and buggy passing the house, the horse now as familiar with Supaya's shed as with his own. Left to himself, he invariably turned down her lane and cut sharply around the corner of the house, heading for feed and shelter.

Jess stamped in, scattering snow about the lean-to, flung off his coat, dashed his hat against his thigh, caught Supaya about the waist and kissed her. After nearly a year, it still seemed to him miraculous that he could lock up the store and come home to Supaya.

Usually, unless she were late returning from a patient, Supaya was waiting for him, secretly amused by his dramatic entrances, delighted by the way his presence filled her house with life and vigor. Now there were only four of them at the table. Wagash was going to the high school in Wellston and living with a family recommended by Reverend Crowell. Several times during the winter Jess had brought Wagash home for short visits. His name, Wagash informed them, had been shortened from William to Bill, and he regaled them with how well he was doing, how much he had learned, and how many friends he had made. Waboose and Shooskonee listened awestruck, but Supaya, less impressed, noticed he spoke only of white boys and how he ingratiated himself with them.

When they were alone, Supaya spoke to Jess about Sarah. "She begged to stay with him. Maybe his illness will be a good thing for them both."

"What Caleb should do," said Jess, "is wait until she comes near and then grab her. Some women, you know, are stubborn."

Supaya laughed. "I don't know *any* stubborn women! Besides, Caleb is very sick. He didn't even know we were there."

Jess put his arms around her and pulled her head down

against his shoulder. "I could never be so sick I wouldn't know you," he said softly. "I would have to be dead not to know your touch."

Sarah slept not at all that night. She bathed Caleb's head and arms, lowering his temperature so that he slept less fitfully. Whenever he roused, she patiently got him to swallow the medicine Supaya had prepared. She brought in more wood and kept the fire going. She made herself a cup of tea and as she drank it, sitting close to Caleb should he start in his sleep, she looked about the room. He had built his house himself, but whenever he had tried to tell her about it or his plans for the future, she had turned coldly away as though none of it had anything to do with her. Now, sitting in Caleb's house with her shawl around her, in a room lit only by the lamp flickering on the table, with the fire breathing softly in the stove and the black night shutting them in, she experienced the loosening of a tension she had thought would never leave her. Everything she saw was familiar to her, for now she remembered all he had told her in his quiet steady voice, persisting in the belief that one day she would listen. The rocker she sat in had been made for her comfort, the cupboards for her convenience, the table for her use. Though she had stepped inside only that morning, she already felt part of his home.

Caleb, dreaming, started forward as though to sit up. Quickly Sarah eased him back down and held the medicine to his lips. His temperature had risen again. For five years any physical contact had filled her with revulsion. Now, smoothing back his hair and bathing his burning face, she touched him as naturally in his need and her anxiety for him as if her repulsion had never existed. She remembered how he had looked as a boy, how handsome she'd thought him, stronger and kinder than any of the others. When he'd gone to war, she had longed for his safe return, for though neither had spoken, both had understood their future lay together. Now the fear of losing him was unbearable. Her eyes filled with tears and her lips barely moved as she whispered, "Get well, Caleb! Please, please get well!" When he muttered and she, listening intently, thought she heard her own name, she clasped his hand and whispered to his closed eyes and drawn face, "I'm here, Caleb, I'm here."

Over the next few days Caleb slowly improved until Supaya no longer doubted his recovery. Then she suggested that Sarah, who had not left the house, should go home and refresh herself.

"Oh no!" exclaimed Sarah. "I couldn't leave him! I mean..."

Supaya smiled. "I know what you mean. But look at yourself. You haven't bathed, changed your clothes, combed your hair for three days. He'll be all right. I'll stay with him. Go. You can come back later and bring him some food."

Sarah went. When she returned she brought a bowl of soup, bread, and a pot of stew. Supaya offered to feed him, but Sarah said at once, "I can do it." Supaya, pleased, left them alone.

Not feeling free to put her arm under his head now that Caleb was awake, Sarah elevated his head with folded blankets. He ate slowly, his tired eyes fixed on her face. Unable to hide her happiness at his recovery, Sarah smiled and said, "You're much better today. You must eat. Soon you'll be well." He appeared to listen, but after another mouthfull or two his eyes closed of their own accord and he fell into a deep sleep. The next day he was brighter and even struggled to sit up when Sarah brought him food. She chided him, saying he should not exert himself, and he settled back, content to obey.

When Caleb slept, Sarah cooked or sewed or napped. Once she woke to find him awake, watching her. She blushed, and he raised his hand. Not understanding his gesture, she bent forward and he laid his hand lightly on her head, making an effort to stroke her hair, which she, out of a deep, abiding disgust, had continued to cut short.

"Your hair . . . you should let it grow long," he said.

"I will," said Sarah, feeling that she too had recovered from a long illness. "I will now."

To everyone's delight, Sarah and Caleb were married at the end of the winter. But no one, not even Lizzie or Agatha, urged Supaya to marry as they once had done. Her confident, independent manner allowed them no opportunity, was even, in a way, intimidating, and they did not presume. Having once decided how she wished to live, Supaya went about it serenely and openly. Sometimes she stayed in Jess' house, more often he came to hers. Often she appeared in the store in the mornings, greeting customers as though her being behind the counter were perfectly natural. Jess' buggy and later the Model T became a familiar sight in Supaya's yard. And her friends, dropping by, grew accustomed to having Jess open the door. Once, in Lizzie's kitchen, Lizzie had raised the question of marriage in general. Gerald, who knew the direction of his wife's thoughts and who had come to understand Supaya, answered shrewdly, saving Supaya the trouble of replying. "In Supaya's case, she would have to give up her house and land, Lizzie, if she were to marry a white man."

And that Lizzie had accepted. She and Supaya had been good friends for a long time. A breach was unthinkable. Besides, Lizzie had seen enough in her years on the reserve to be no longer certain that her way was the only right way.

George and Soos, pleased to see Supaya and Jess happy together, made no comment whatever, nor did old John Bruley, who often came to smoke his pipe by Supaya's fire and eat a bit of soup; he accepted Jess as he accepted the weather. Alma, eyeing Jess, grinned at Supaya and said, "You've done well."

Frank had not grinned. At the logging camp he had news of Supaya from various friends and had stayed weeks longer than he'd intended, working off his anger and disappointment. He encountered Supaya on the road one morning when she was going fishing. He gave her no greeting, but looked at her so accusingly that Supaya had to laugh.

"Frank! You can at least speak to me!"

"Why should I. You didn't wait for me to come back."

"Remember! I promised only that we would be friends. We are still friends, aren't we, Frank?"

"You know I must say yes," he said glumly.

"Come on, Frank, you don't really mind. You have lots of girls."

"But no wife!"

"Well choose one! I'm sure there are many who would be glad . . ."

"I know that!" he said. Then, looking at her sideways, "You remember, white men are not to be trusted. I'll be watching him. When you need me, I'll be here."

"Oh Frank!" laughed Supaya. "I'm going fishing. Come along! You can take some fish and give Annie some too."

"Why doesn't *he* do the fishing?"

"He runs the store. Besides," she added, looking him in the eye, "I like to fish, and as you know, I do what I want to do."

He studied her a moment, then said, "I won't go fishing with you. But maybe some day you'll *want* to marry me."

Amused, Supaya smiled and shrugged. "Maybe. Some day."

Supaya used Kineu's boat, the one Uncle John had given him and later purified after the drowning. Supaya, wrapped in her shawl, had stood on the beach and watched. The day had been overcast and the water, lapping quietly against the rocks, was like gray, rippled metal. Uncle John had turned the boat upside down, hauled it onto supports, then lit a fire in a pit underneath it. When the fire was burning well, he had dampened it down with green cedar boughs and made a thick smudge that billowed up into and around the boat, and through this smoke he had passed the oars. The scene remained in Supaya's memory as infinitely sad: damp, chill, and lonely, the black smoke rising into a gray sky as an old man performed his ritual on a narrow, rocky shore. It was a memory she tried to put aside as she did the memory of Kineu's and Taw's deaths. Kineu's anger and rejection of her had come to seem unreal, like a bad dream in which an evil spirit had inhabited his body and twisted his thoughts. She preferred remembering him as he was when they first married, and often, when gazing down into the water where the sun struck glancing, luminous shadows, she wondered where in the moving layers of water below her he might be, transformed, his limbs weightless, his eyes glowing, living another, mysterious existence.

She fished with new nets which George had made and she had paid for with medicine and fish. To ensure a good catch, she had made a small fire on the shore and burned tobacco before the nets and had also thrown tobacco into the water for the "boss" fish. All fall and summer her catches had been good, and she regularly gave fish to Uncle John, George, and Amy, besides drying her own.

Amy's friendship with Supaya had suffered no shock or interruption as it might have had Jess not given Reverend Crowell a ride home from the store one evening.

"He asked me," said Jess, "if I was on my way to your house, and I said I was. He said, 'Ah, well,' and coughed and cleared his throat—you know the way he does when he's embarrassed."

Supaya, leaning against Jess' knees as they sat by the fireplace, poked the fire and nodded.

"He said he thought you were a serious, hard-working young woman. I agreed—you were very serious." Supaya looked up, amused. "Then he raised his eyebrows at me and said he would not like to see *anyone* take advantage of you. I said certainly not! I would never permit anyone to do that. That anyone who tried to harm you would answer to me and would be very sorry indeed! Well, he couldn't object to that!"

"You," said Supaya, "are very clever. But he is a good man. He just doesn't understand."

"I don't understand you either. But I meant what I said. I notice Frank is back." Jess didn't put his question into words, but Supaya understood it.

"Frank would never harm *me*. Of course," she said mischievously, "he is not pleased with *you*."

Jess grinned. "If he comes after me, I'll have my wife, the doctor, put a spell on him."

"How do you know," asked Supaya laughing, "that I haven't put one on you?"

"I don't!" Leaning forward, Jess held her face between his hands and kissed her. "I think you put a spell on me years ago, with a pot of soup." He reached in his vest pocket. "I brought you something. It was my grandmother's. I want you to have it." He held out a gold ring with an intricate double knot, set in the center with a small, deep red stone.

"Ah, it is beautiful!" exclaimed Supaya, and held out her hand. Jess slipped the ring on her finger. "Now you see," said Supaya, "You have put a spell on me too."

Agatha Harris alone, of all Supaya's friends, tried just once to speak of Supaya's living with Jess. "Why?" she asked impatiently, as if dealing with an unreasonable child, "why can't you marry? Surely nothing is more important than the sanction of the church!"

Supaya refilled Agatha's tea cup, pouring from the flowered china teapot Lizzie had given her years before. "Miss Harris, please listen, for I will not speak of this again." She looked directly across the table at Agatha and spoke quietly, but her tone and the set of her face were subtly hostile. There was no humor in her smile. "Your church does not mean to me what it means to you. For me there are other things more important. I did it your way twice. The last time, I remember, you said being married in the church would prevent my husband's leaving me." Supaya paused that Agatha might remember. "It prevented nothing! This time I will do it *my* way. Please understand that I know what I want— my own house, my own land. I will never be bound in that way again. I will be bound only as *I* choose. I tell you my reasons not because I must, but for the sake of our many years of friendship."

Reprimanded thus, as she had been once long ago by Jules, Agatha was silenced. Jules himself seemed to look at her through Supaya's eyes and speak again in his quiet, decisive voice. Her cherished memory of him stirred within her. A sudden sharp awareness of the passage of time made her unsteady. She rose, putting a hand to her too-constricting collar. "I think I should go now. Thank you, Supaya, for the tea." She needed to be in the open, to feel fresh air on her forehead, but she had gone only a few steps beyond Supaya's door when she was overcome by an abysmal sense of loss. Abruptly she turned around, lips parted, wanting urgently to reach out, to say something. Supaya, standing in her doorway, seemed to be receding from her at the opposite end of a long, lengthening corridor. Dizzily, she took a deep breath and gripped her handbag, checking a crazy impulse to wave. Striving for solid ground, she said without thinking, "We *are* friends. Aren't we?"

Supaya, watching Agatha from the doorway, saw merely a brief moment of irresolution. Glad that the subject of marriage was settled between them, she smiled and said warmly, "Yes, Miss Harris, we are. Good friends."

CHAPTER TWENTY-NINE

Supaya was only partly prepared for meeting Jess' family. She remembered seeing them at Kirsten's funeral and thinking they were cold and falsely proud.

"They won't stay long," said Jess. "Victor will have arranged it that way. They're only coming out of curiosity. They want to see my wife."

"They will not like that you have married an Indian. You told them?"

"I told them I had a beautiful wife who heals people with one glance and if they aren't careful, she'll turn them all into toadstools."

"Jess, be serious!"

"All right. Seriously, you don't need to see them at all if you don't want to. I can tell them you're busy, or away, or anything."

"No. I want to meet them. I'll cook them dinner."

"If you want to. But I don't know why you'd want to."

Supaya shrugged. "We all have relatives we don't like. But they're yours, and I'm curious too."

Through the kitchen window. Supaya saw them drive up in Victor's Essex. The car had scarcely stopped when the rear door opened and a boy jumped out and raced for the verandah. Victor stepped out, inhaled deeply, and stood looking about, turning on his heels like a real estate dealer estimating the value of land. He paid no attention to the two women. Marietta, in a cloche hat and pleated skirt, stepped out gingerly, concerned for her silk stockings and flimsy shoes. She looked back impatiently at Hilda, who moved her stout, tightly girdled body out of the car in a series of short heaves.

When Jess opened the door, they had rearranged themselves, putting Hilda first. She entered stiffly, uneasy at setting her plump foot down in a home where she no longer knew what to expect. She had offered her powdered cheek for Jess to kiss when her glance fell on Supaya, standing to one side. Her eyes widened, and as Jess said, "This is Supaya, my wife," caught her breath (later she commended herself to her family for maintaining her composure) and, as she exhaled, murmured, "My dear."

"Welcome to our home," said Supaya smoothly, amused at her obvious shock. "Please come and sit down. You must be tired from your journey." As she spoke, the boy, whom Supaya recognized as the child at the funeral, ducked ahead of his mother and dashed past his aunt and Supaya.

"Eric!" Marietta reached, too late, to hold him back.

"I want to see the dolls!" exclaimed Eric impatiently, kneeling before a bookcase in the hall that held, besides books, several little Indian figures.

"He has talked of nothing else!" exclaimed Marietta, but her comment was automatic; her attention centered entirely on Supaya. She scarcely greeted her brother, so amazed was she at seeing an Indian woman standing beside him. Her fine arched eyebrows drew together in a frown at this affront to the family.

Behind her, Victor, more practiced at dissimulation, leaned forward and said in a deep, hearty voice. "Ah, and this is the bride!"

Jess laughed. "Well hardly a bride. It's been over two years now. Though it seems much less."

"Yes, well, we weren't invited to the wedding, so it seems like no time at all to us," said Marietta pertly. She sat down and leaned back, crossing her legs so her pleated skirt fell away from her silken knees. She let her arms hang over the sides of the chair like a bored princess and looked at Jess as if he owed her an explanation.

"It was a very simple ceremony, Marietta," said Jess, smiling. "It wouldn't have suited your taste at all."

"I don't see what is so funny," said Marietta, suspecting an implied criticism.

"Nor do I," said Hilda pompously. "You might have consulted us. After all, we are your family."

"Hilda," said Jess lightly, handing her a glass of wine, "you know better than that. Have I ever consulted you?"

341

"But marriage!" said Hilda glancing at Supaya, who was listening with an expression of polite interest. "Whom one marries is important to the whole family."

"Is it now! Well," said Jess, "Victor didn't consult me before he married you. Or Marietta before she married her traveling salesman."

"Really!" exclaimed Hilda, pursing her lips.

Marietta swung her foot in annoyance. "Jess, you're always so . . . so contrary."

"It's too bad," said Victor, sipping his wine, "that you didn't bring—Supaya, is it?— with you when you came last fall."

"I would have come," said Supaya, and they all turned to look at her, "but the children were in school."

"Oh!" said Hilda, raising her eyebrows. "You have children? You've been married before?"

"Yes, a boy fourteen and a girl thirteen," said Supaya.

"My, a ready-made family," said Hilda. "I suppose they're both quite dark?"

"Oh, *quite* dark," said Supaya solemnly, repressing an urge to laugh.

Marietta, sensitive to any hint of mockery, frowned. "Hilda! You say such silly things."

"But," went on Supaya affably, "perhaps I will be able to come with Jess the next time."

Hilda and Marietta were caught speechless. Victor standing with one hand hooked in his vest pocket, the other delicately holding his wine glass, beamed with good humor. "And we shall be delighted to have you! We can introduce you to some of Jess' old friends."

"I would like that," said Supaya, meeting his gaze blandly.

Going to the kitchen, Supaya found Eric sitting on the bottom step in the hall, his chin in his hands. Unlike the Fallons, he had straight, fair hair, but clear blue eyes like his mother's, like Jess'.

He looked up glumly at Supaya. "What's there to do here?"

"Come with me." He followed her down the hall, through a door at the far end, and into the store. From a box under the counter she took out a stick with a cup at one end and a ball attached to a string at the other. "See," said Supaya demonstrating, "you swing the ball and try to catch it in the cup. And here is a ball you can bounce outside against the house."

Eagerly, Eric took them both; then he caught sight of the

342

candy case. Following his glance, Supaya bagged some of the candy and handed it to him. "But that you put in your pocket until after you've eaten."

Smiling brightly, Eric nodded and did as she said. Then his eyes slid past her. Supaya turned quickly, expecting to see Marietta, but it was Victor who stood there watching them. Eric dodged past his uncle and ran outside. Almost at once they heard the thud of a ball being pitched against the house.

For a large man, tall as Jess but heavier, Victor moved very lightly. "An energetic boy. Quite wears his mother out," Victor commented. Supaya raised her eyebrows slightly and waited. His glance rested on her thoughtfully. He hadn't, Supaya was sure, followed her into the store away from the others to speak of Eric. "I forgot my tobacco pouch. Jess said you'd get me a tin."

Supaya smiled at his lie and moved ahead of him to the other side of the store. As she reached for the tobacco, his hand suddenly gripped her bare forearm. Without moving, she glanced at him, down at his hand, then up again. His eyes, she saw, were a paler blue than Jess', there were fine lines about his eyes and mouth and the flesh of his cheeks was going slack, but he had the assurance of a man used to admiration. He stared at Supaya, confident of his understanding of women, expecting she would falter, go limp in his grasp. But her expression of cold politeness as she waited for him to let go made him feel unexpectedly foolish. He removed his hand. She picked up the tobacco tin and held it out to him.

"Tell me," he asked, watching her intently, "are you and Jess really married?"

As she considered whether she should answer or not, Supaya studied him, her eyes opaque, long enough for him to feel the force of her scrutiny. "Yes," she said at last, "we are truly married."

"I thought you people married only with your own?"

"I marry whom I choose," Supaya said proudly and, smiling slightly, added in a tone that Agatha would have instantly recognized, "and I have answered your questions not because I must but only because you are my husband's brother."

"I see that I have been stupid," said Victor. "I'm sorry." He smiled charmingly.

"You can fill your pipe now."

"Oh yes. Yes, of course. Thank you." He saw a gleam of amusement in her eye, and tried again to put their conversation on a different level. "You are a very beautiful woman." Her amusement increased. Then he said, spontaneously, "But you speak like a man." At that Supaya laughed outright. Victor, uncertain of the reason for her amusement, asked, "Are you always so frank?"

"Like a man, I am frank when it suits my purpose. Now I must serve dinner."

Hilda sat down at the table looking as though she feared the food might attack her, but once she began eating, she ate with a concentration that suggested she had a certain area to fill and would fill it. Marietta pushed her food about her plate and ate very little. Pensively, she studied alternately Jess, then Supaya. She sensed a harmony between them that made her jealous and resentful. Worse, she felt she had worn the wrong dress or the wrong shoes. She was not comfortable. And Hilda was too fat and ate too much. And Victor could hardly eat at all for staring at Jess' wife. Their appearance, the impression they were making was all wrong!

"My husband," she suddenly threw at Jess, "is not a traveling salesman! Just because he's been away when you've come!"

"Isn't he? Sorry, I misunderstood."

"He has an office like anyone else. It's just that it's necessary for him to be on the road a great deal. You make it sound so . . . so cheap."

"Marietta, don't be sulky! Come, you're not eating. Supaya caught this fish herself."

"Herself!" exclaimed Hilda, pausing, fork in midair.

"Did you!" said Victor smoothly. "Then I must have some more. It's delicious." He smiled up at Supaya as she served him. "You're a most accomplished woman."

"You go fishing?" asked Eric, staring. "Could I go too sometime?"

"Eric, be quiet," said Marietta. "I notice you still wear your hair long. Everybody at home has cut theirs."

"I thought," said Hilda, whose hair, like Marietta's, was shingled, "you always wore braids."

"Sometimes I do," said Supaya.

"When it suits your purpose," interjected Victor, smiling, trying to build a hidden understanding between them.

Ignoring him, Supaya said to the women, "I like the way you wear your hair. It's very pretty."

As Jess had predicted, they did not stay long. Hilda complained of having eaten too much, and Marietta of a headache brought on by the constant thud of Eric's ball against the side of the house.

Walking toward the car, Marietta noticed that besides the cup and ball sticking out of one of Eric's pockets and the handball bulging in the other, he was holding something secretively in his hand. "What is that? What do you have?" she demanded.

Reluctantly, Eric opened his hand, showing her a little corn-husk doll. Its face had no features, but it was dressed as a man in bits of leather.

"You know you are not allowed to take things! Go put that back right now!"

Eric closed his fist and thrust it behind him. "But I *want* it! She told me I could have it!"

At his outcry, the others turned to look, and Marietta said low and angrily, "Oh all right! Get in the car!"

Victor, taking the opportunity to speak to Supaya apart from the others, tried still another tack. "I can see you've made my brother very happy," he said soberly, adding with an emphasis designed to flatter, "he has *not* been very happy in the past."

But Supaya would allow no implied comparison. "We have all had unhappy times. Now we make each other happy." Her smile was polite but cool, and when Victor, on an impulse, put out his hand, he wondered if she would take it.

She did, and her smile deepened, but grew no warmer.

"My brother," said Victor, now speaking honestly, "is to be envied."

When the car pulled away, Eric leaned out the back window, waved, and yelled good-bye until he was jerked back and the window rolled up.

CHAPTER THIRTY

When Bill graduated from high school, Rhea came for a visit. She had not seen her son since before he started high school. She had written Supaya brief, uninformative notes, giving her address and sometimes several well-creased dollar bills. Rhea's intention, though she did not say so immediately, was to take Bill back with her to Toronto.

"I'm married now, you know," she remarked, and held up her left hand, displaying her wedding ring as Bill displayed his diploma, a hard-earned certificate of achievement. "Oh yes. Just last year. My name's Hadley now, Mrs. Howard Hadley." She did not speak of the years she had worked as a waitress, living in one small, poorly furnished room and skimping that she might buy one stylish dress to wear when what she considered a "possibility" asked her out. Mr. Hadley, a short, spare man, some fifteen years older than Rhea, had been just such a "possibility," even though he had feebly tried, as had many others more aggressively, to get into her bed without resorting to such an extreme as marriage. But whereas others had cool-headedly found their freedom more seductive than Rhea and had settled for less demanding partners, Mr. Hadley had lost his head completely. The more Rhea denied him, the more irresistible she became. Whenever Rhea had been tempted, out of sheer loneliness, to relax in the ready arms of a more attractive man than Howard Hadley, she had only to remember the Indian women she knew in the city who had become prostitutes or who as maids in wealthy homes were vulnerable to the owner or the owner's son.

Seeing such unhappy women and knowing Howard to be the owner of a hardware store that did a good, steady business, Rhea was careful to be not only enticing but virtuous. When Howard began seeing Rhea in the faces of his customers and counted the hours and minutes until he could be with her instead of counting change, he begged her to marry him. She accepted him, demurely but firmly. Never had he any cause to repent, for Rhea gave him both the love he yearned for and the assistance in the store he badly needed.

But her city experience had taught Rhea to be a stern disciplinarian, far sterner than Miss Harris would ever have expected. She studied Bill not with the indulgence of a loving mother but with the sharply critical eye of a survivor. She would tolerate no lax behavior, no drinking, no chasing after women. He must be ready to work as hard, as single-mindedly as she worked.

They faced each other across the table, the son, by a strange alchemy of the blood, not only grasping immediately what his mother required of him and why, but, in the sharpness of his ambition, going beyond her.

"You could live with us, above the store. You'd have a room of your own, and Howard will pay you the same he would pay anyone. He promised me that," she added, softening for a moment as she looked at her son and remembered Jules. "But you'll have to work!"

"I will! I'm a good worker. Ask Jess when he comes. I worked for him after school and on weekends. And in Wellston I worked at a grocery store. You didn't know that." They eyed each other levelly. She absorbed his implied accusation of her neglect of him as well as the fact that he had been busy.

"No, I didn't," she answered calmly, refusing to take up any guilt. "Experience will help."

"I'm good at figures. I can keep his books too."

Thoughtfully Rhea agreed. She saw she would have no trouble with her son. They would work well together. "Who is Jess?" she asked, looking at Supaya.

"Jess Fallon, my husband. He owns the general store. See," said Supaya, playfully, holding out her hand. "I have a ring also."

Rhea nodded, having noticed the ring. "Then . . . how is it you still live here?"

"We married in the Indian way. I wanted to keep my house and land. I won't give up being an Indian."

"Oh that," said Rhea, shrugging indifferently. "I try to forget it. Your arrangement is fine for him, but he could leave you with nothing."

"I will always have my house and land. I don't need anything else. Besides," Supaya laughed, "all I want from him is himself, and I have that."

Rhea and Bill left the next day. Jess drove them into Wellston to the train station. Then he and Supaya had a short visit with Waboose, now in his second year at high school. He was staying with the same family Bill had stayed with, and when Supaya asked how he was, he gave the reply he always gave.

"I'm okay." He would not complain or say that he was often lonely and homesick. But Supaya observed that he came home eagerly whenever Jess could pick him up, and he rarely spoke of any friends. Supaya understood more than Waboose realized because she had spoken to Reverend Crowell about finding a home where Shooskonee could live if she were to go to Wellston high school.

"I am not sure," said Reverend Crowell carefully, "if Sally could stay with the same family as Walter. Apparently Walter hasn't, um, adjusted as well as Bill did. He doesn't seem to fit in. They were very pleased with Bill, you know. They *do* say that Walter works hard—though not as well as Bill. Do you want me to inquire if they would take Sally? Or perhaps find another family who would take her?"

Supaya was undecided what would be best for Shooskonee. But Shooskonee, now fifteen, knew exactly what she wanted to do. She wanted to get married and settle down on the reserve, as her mother and as Sarah had done. But Lizzie and Agatha Harris counseled Supaya differently.

"Sally is lovely," said Lizzie, "but she is just a child, much too young to marry."

"I was married at sixteen," said Supaya.

"But that was arranged for you. You had no choice. Sally does."

"Sally should certainly go to high school," said Agatha firmly. "If she doesn't, she is going to get into trouble. She's a very attractive girl. The boys flock around her. I've had to discipline them a number of times." Agatha's tart tone displeased Supaya, but she went on to say, "She's an intelligent girl with a distinct musical talent, and surely, Sophia, you want her to have all the education and training she can get," Supaya had to agree that she did.

Still uncertain, Supaya consulted Jess, who suggested a compromise. "Why not send her for a year or two. See how it goes. If she wants to continue, she can. If not, she can come home."

Remembering her own grief at leaving home and Kineu, Supaya asked Shooskonee, "There's no *one* young man, is there? One you especially don't want to leave?"

Shooskonee would not look at her mother. Sullenly, she shrugged one shoulder. "No."

So it was settled that Shooskonee should go to Wellston in the fall, and Reverend Crowell found another, more affluent family who would provide Sally with board and room in exchange for housework.

One afternoon in late summer Amy came to visit Supaya. Agitated and on the verge of tears, she pressed her clasped hands against her frail chest and tried several times to speak but could find no way to begin. Seeing she was troubled, Supaya made some tea and spoke admiringly of the flowers in Amy's garden, giving her time to think of what she wanted to say. But Amy grew no calmer and blurted out her news in a trembling voice. "Sophia, we're leaving! We're going back to England! Reverend Crowell's retiring! Just imagine! We're going home!"

"Amy!" exclaimed Supaya, "that's what you've wanted for so long!"

"I have! I have!" admitted Amy, as though acknowledging a dreadful fault. "But . . . I didn't . . . I never said . . . how did you know?"

Supaya smiled. "You told me without words."

Amy shook her head and made little whimpering noises. "When Reverend Crowell said, 'We're going home,' I didn't know . . . what he meant! I didn't know what to say! I thought . . ." Reliving the moment, she stopped, confused. "For so long," shaking her head again, "so long I've thought of England as home! But when he said . . . we're leaving . . . !" Her face began to crumple as she appealed to Supaya to understand. "Well, I thought . . . I couldn't . . . *this* is home! We *are* home! We've lived here so many years! All my friends . . . Oh, Sophia! You've been such a good friend! My best friend!"

Her old eyes filled with tears that spilled over and rolled

unnoticed down her soft, wrinkled cheeks. "Sophia!" Stricken, she leaned forward, her words for once coming in a rush. "It's too late! Don't you see? Too late! Our home is here after all! Everything there will be different! Our family, our old friends . . . they're all gone! We'll go all that way back just to be strangers again! I'll have to pretend to be happy, to sing in a strange church, make a home in a strange house where I won't know my way around in the dark! I'll have to, so *he'll* feel at home! He doesn't know what it will be like!" Her voice rose and thinned out. "When we're gone from here, it will be as if we never existed! Our lives will be forgotten! We'll die among strangers! Oh Sophia! I'm afraid! I'm too old to go back!"

For a long moment Supaya held Amy's agonized gaze. Then she rose, saying quietly, "I will get something for you." What she brought was a small birchbark box edged with sweet grass. Sitting close beside Amy, Supaya held it up for her to see.

"This box I made a long time ago of bark from the trees in the woods here. It is bound with sweet grass from that meadow just beyond the church. When you hold it in your hand and smell it, you will know that this land is still here. That the people who live on it are still your friends and will never forget you. That for them your spirit will always remain in your house and in the church. Now open it."

Amy did so, their heads bent together over it.

"This is for you only. Do not show it to anyone. At night, when you go to bed, put it near you and open it. You will see it glow in the dark. It will protect you, and you will know that no matter where you are or how far away you are, you will never be alone."

Her face filled with a childlike wonder and gratitude, Amy closed the box and held it in both hands. Supaya smiled and laid her hands lightly over Amy's. "Now, you see? You will not be afraid any more, or alone. You can go back to your old home with a calm heart."

The last funeral service Reverend Crowell read was for John Bruley, who died in his sleep, and the last wedding ceremony was for Louisa and Harry Black.

Harry, returned from World War I after a long convalescence, found his house empty and the garden overgrown with weeds. He had never received the letter Gerald had written him and his first thought was that Edna had left him. Then he saw her old carpetbag in a corner of the bedroom and her clothes still hanging on the pegs. He had gone at once to Gerald.

For Gerald the explanation had not been easy. He often had to give bad news but on this occasion he found it particularly painful. Harry, a young man, too thin for his large frame, his wide, strongly molded face still ashen from months in a hospital, sat opposite Gerald and listened impassively. His one stiff leg stuck straight out before him and he held his heavy staff across his lap. While Gerald spoke, Harry's eyes never left his face. Gerald saw them change and harden, his mouth set, and when he suddenly raised his staff, Gerald thought he was going to bring it crashing down on his desk. Instead, Harry brought it down on the floor with a force that jarred the room. He hoisted himself from his chair and stared out the window. Then he thanked Gerald for keeping his house and land for him and left, walking with a peculiar sideways lurch, swinging his stiff leg and thrusting his staff ahead at each step. Gerald accompanied him outside, offered to give him a ride home. But Harry preferred to walk. Gerald stood looking after him and saw him turn down the lane into the cemetery.

A week later Harry came back to see Gerald, to ask for a Soldier Settler's loan. Louisa, working on the ledgers, listened with a special interest when she heard Harry's name.

"I want to buy some cows," said Harry. "I want to build up a good dairy herd." There were a few cows on the reserve, but no herd that could supply milk in quantity. As the two men discussed the possibilities, Louisa kept silent, but she felt a shame and obligation toward this quiet-spoken man.

Several days later while working to clear his garden, Harry looked up to see Louisa. He had noticed her in Gerald's office, and thinking Gerald had sent her with a message, he straightened up, wondering how long she had been standing there watching his awkward struggle with the hoe.

Louisa stepped across where he had cleared the earth and faced him. "I'm Louisa Hagerstrom," she said and saw his head lift, his face darken. Her voice almost died, but she said what she had come to say. "I am sorry for what happened." Harry said nothing, hoping she would go. Louisa averted her gaze slightly. "My father was a bad man. I was glad when . . . when they got him. Afterward, I was alone and the Toomis' took me to live with them."

351

Harry, watching her, sensed the shame she felt and began to understand that somehow they each had a share in the same misfortune. "The Toomis' are good people," he commented.

"Yes," agreed Louisa, then, looking directly at him again, "you said you wanted to start a dairy herd, but you have no barn."

Harry was surprised she should point this out since it was no business of hers, and further surprised when she said firmly, "You must build one now."

Irritated and still wishing she would go away, Harry said brusquely, "Not until I get a loan. If I can't get a loan, I can't buy any cows."

"But you already have two cows. Three, pretty soon. One's ready to calve."

Harry frowned. "What do you mean?"

"I have two cows that are yours whenever you have a barn for them."

Harry gave an impatient snort. "I can't take your cows!"

Louisa straightened her thin shoulders, a gesture Harry was to come to know well. "Why not? If I choose to give them to you? Can't I do what I like with my own cows?"

"Yes, but . . ."

"Aren't they good enough for you?"

"Sure they are, but . . ."

She raised her head proudly, and though she appeared to be looking at him as she spoke, Harry saw that she was really looking inward. "It is *necessary* that you have them," she insisted.

Suddenly Harry remembered where he had seen such a look before. In his ward in the English hospital there had been a patient who sat all day, never talking, only staring. Day after day, staring inward. But at night he cried, muffling it with his pillow, thinking no one heard. But Harry had heard. Without further hesitation, Harry said, "All right. I will take them."

She didn't thank him, but her eyes, now clearly focused, were full of gratitude. "When you're ready, I'll bring them."

Gerald got Harry a government loan and Harry built the barn as Louisa said he must. Louisa came to check his progress and often stayed to watch, silent for the most part. But the silence was companionable, and over the weeks Harry began to anticipate her visits. Whenever several days passed without her coming, he missed her and found himself watching for her slim, straight figure to come down the lane. Once she offered to make him a pot of tea and soon she was familiar with his house and kitchen.

"Your house is bare," she told him. "You need cupboards."

"But I'm building a barn now."

"Yes, but after you finish the barn, you should make some cupboards. You'll have wood left over."

Round-eyed, Harry said, "I see. I must build a barn. Then cupboards. Is there nothing else?"

"Oh yes," she said at once. "You need more chairs. You haven't even got a rocker. Or a proper table. That one wobbles. Besides, it's too small. You need a larger one."

Harry stared at her comically, his eyebrows slightly raised. "I must build a barn, cupboards, chairs, table. I see I must become a carpenter. I thought I was going to raise dairy cows."

"You can do both," said Louisa with perfect assurance. She picked up their cups to carry them indoors, adding as if an after-thought, "you could get about faster if you did without that cane."

Instant anger flared up inside him. When Louisa returned he was nailing boards onto the barn frame, driving the nails in with smashing blows.

"I left some fresh bread on the table."

He went on as if he hadn't heard.

"I have to go now."

Then he glanced at her, his eyes cold with anger, intending she should know his displeasure. But Louisa, puzzled and question-ing, was waiting with such childlike openness for him to speak to her that he was disarmed. It came to Harry that she could easily be hurt. He forgot his anger, felt instead a protectiveness toward her, an impulse to put his arm around her shoulders. Surprised at himself, he took a firmer grip on the hammer, smiled, and thanked her for the bread.

Reassured, she smiled and inclined her head in a graceful little nod, pleased that he was pleased.

When she had gone, Harry gazed thoughtfully at his leg. He was lucky to have it at all, the doctors had said, though they had predicted he would never walk again. Horrified by such a prospect, he had driven himself to try, despite the pain, had failed and forced himself to try again, managing at last to walk with the help of his staff. Then they had said, never without a cane, and he had ac-cepted that limitation. Now this girl had challenged him. He leaned his staff against the barn, balanced himself, swung his leg forward, and trusted his weight to it. The leg slid sideways and back, pitching him forward, and he fell sprawling in the dirt, arms flung out. "You fool!" he said to himself, "you damn fool!"

But later, inside, he tried again, this time holding to the back of a chair and sliding it ahead of himself. He put weight on the leg a bit at a time, and tried to flex it. A muscle in his thigh began to twitch. Sweat beaded his forehead and a feeling of nausea rose in his throat. But he persisted until his good leg began to tremble, then he rested. Every day he practiced with the chair, and whenever he sat he tried flexing his knee, willing it to bend. For many days he detected no change, and went to bed exhausted and discouraged. Still, he persisted, saying nothing to Louisa of his attempts, until one day his knee flexed slightly. Gradually, as the leg became stronger, he was able to take one step before collapsing, then two.

On the day they had arranged that Louisa would bring the two cows and new calf, Harry waited outside the barn, sitting where he could see her coming up the lane. From a distance, Louisa waved and Harry raised his hand in greeting. But when she came within a certain precalculated range, Harry laid aside his staff, stood up, and began, slowly, carefully, to walk toward her. He was unsteady and had to extend his arms to balance himself, but he walked without his staff.

"Harry!" exclaimed Louisa. She stopped, staring in amazement. Halted unexpectedly, the cows bumped into each other and bobbed their heads. Dropping the tether, Louisa started toward him. Harry, grinning at her surprise, had almost reached her when his leg gave way. Stumbling, he flung his arms out toward her and Louisa ran forward, arms outstretched. He grabbed her shoulders, she caught him round his waist, and they stood grinning delightedly at each other as he caught his breath.

The head cow stepped forward, nudged Louisa and gave her a comradely swipe with her rough tongue. Louisa took up the tether and with one arm bracing Harry, they all moved in a halting, jerky procession toward the barn. Harry kept his arm firmly about her, and though he was breathing hard from his exertion, he tried not to lean too heavily on her.

"Louisa," he asked, taking pleasure in her name, "when I can walk up the church steps and to the altar, will you marry me?"

"Yes," said Louisa immediately, "I will." That was one question she didn't need to stop and consider.

CHAPTER THIRTY-ONE

Agatha had to walk with care. In her small house and in the schoolroom, though the furniture was blurred and the students' faces softened as if by fog, she managed well from long familiarity. But the road was difficult, and she occasionally stumbled. When she reached Supaya's, she sat in Nonen's rocker instead of on a straight chair at the table as always before, and rested her head back in a weary manner so uncharacteristic that Supaya looked at her sharply. In this unguarded moment there was a slackness about her, a despondency, that made Supaya think things had gone badly for her that day. But when she handed her a cup of tea and Agatha didn't see it and then, in taking it, miscalculated the distance, Supaya knew something was wrong.

". . . about Sally," Agatha was saying. "You haven't given me any news of her lately."

The question distracted Supaya's attention from Agatha, and she wished that Miss Harris had not asked. It had been she who insisted Sally go to high school, and although Supaya need not have taken her advice, she had been swayed by it. Deeply worried about Shooskonee, Supaya spoke bluntly.

"I have not heard from her since she left high school."

"Left . . . !" Agatha was instantly alarmed. "Why? Where did she go?"

"To Toronto. With the son of the family she was living with. They ran off together several weeks ago. I see you are shocked. So was I when Reverend Richards told me last Sunday after church."

"Oh, Sophia," groaned Agatha, "why would she have done such a thing! You must bring her back!"

"How can I bring her back when I don't know where she is! I hope she'll come back. Or write and tell me where she is. I should never have sent her away to school. I knew she didn't really want to go."

"But Sophia, think what might have happened had she stayed here!"

"Here!" exclaimed Supaya, impatient at Miss Harris' failure to perceive the greater danger. "Think what can happen in the city with only a boy to look after her!" Supaya moved about the room restlessly, angry with herself that her ambition for her daughter had allowed her to be influenced by anyone. "Here she would have been at home. I could have protected her. She would have married."

Agatha was stunned. "Sophia! I'm sorry if . . . perhaps I was wrong!" Increasingly agitated, she rose too quickly and in moving toward Supaya, stumbled and fell against the corner of the table.

Moving swiftly, Supaya caught and steadied her. "Miss Harris! What's wrong? Here, sit down!" She eased Agatha back into her chair.

Agatha gripped Supaya's arms and looked up at her through a blur of tears. "Sophia! You must believe me! I thought it was best for her that she go! I would never, never . . ."

But Supaya wasn't listening. Looking at Agatha closely with a practiced eye, Supaya saw that though Agatha was distraught, beyond that was a deeper trouble. "Miss Harris," said Supaya sternly, "you must tell me. What is wrong? Are you sick?"

Agatha leaned her head back and shut her eyes. Then, with something of her usual brisk manner, she took out a handkerchief, wiped her eyes, and said, "Yes, Sophia, I believe I am. Quite sick."

"Have you gone to a doctor? Jess would be glad to drive you into town."

"No. No, I haven't. I . . . it wouldn't do any good."

"How do you know!? Surely . . ."

Agatha smiled ruefully. "I've been wrong . . . often, I'm afraid. But not about this. There are lumps here," she touched her breasts, "and under my arms. And, as I'm sure you've noticed, my sight is not too clear. I've pain . . . especially at night, when I'm alone . . . and not occupied."

Supaya knelt beside her. "But you should rest, get some medicine! A doctor could . . ."

"But I don't want to rest! I want to teach as long as I can! It's my life! When I'm teaching, it . . . I can forget it then. The children, you see," she said, trying to laugh, "are a bigger help to me than I have ever been to them."

"Oh no!" exclaimed Supaya, "that is not true! You have been an example to us and have taught us all everything you could! We are all grateful! I am grateful!"

Agatha's mouth trembled. "I'm afraid I've given bad advice. Done harm where I meant to do good. Will you forgive me, Sophia? Will you come to see me when . . . when I can't get out?"

It soon became apparent to everyone that Miss Harris was ill. But she continued to teach, moving slowly and carefully about the classroom. Then she taught while seated at her desk, delegating various duties to the older students who were eager to help her. Her eyes seemed to sink into their sockets, her flesh to fade away. From hours of pain her face became set and tight, her skin stretched like parchment over the bones of her face. Even the youngest children sensed the effort she was making and tried to please her. Determined to finish the school year, Agatha devoted what strength and energy she could summon for teaching. Jess brought her groceries. Supaya, Lizzie, and Soos brought food already prepared. Sarah came with her three-year-old daughter, Josie, and as Agatha held the child on her lap and showed her picture books, Sarah swept and cleaned.

School closed three weeks early when Agatha could no longer leave her bed. Then Lizzie, Sarah, and Louisa, carrying her infant son, took turns coming during the days, kept the fires going, and brought food which Agatha could no longer eat. Supaya came in the evenings and stayed with her during the long, pain-filled nights.

"Miss Harris, would you like me to write to your brother or sister-in-law? Perhaps you'd like him to come? It's been a long time since you've seen him."

Agatha's mouth curved in a thin smile. Her dull eyes and emaciated face lighted in brief amusement. "Would you want to see him?"

Surprised at her reaction, Supaya said, "Well, no . . . but then . . ."

357

"Neither do I. He would only preach at me. Tell me I was paying for my sinful soul. Perhaps I am. We came to . . . disagree about many things. That is one reason I left Stone Island."

"There's no one else?"

"No one."

When Agatha's pain increased and gave her no breathing space, Supaya begged her, " Please, let me at least give you something for the pain! You need not suffer so!"

Agatha, her fingers gripping the blanket, her jaws clenched to keep from crying out, gasped, "All right . . . if you can."

Thereafter Agatha gladly and without question took the potion Supaya brought her. Several evenings later she asked Supaya about Sally. She looked piercingly at Supaya, her eyes glittering in the lamplight. "I must know," she said urgently. "She is so much in my thoughts."

Supaya lied without hesitation. "She's fine. I got a postcard from her. She's working as a waitress. She may come home this summer. You don't need to worry about her."

Agatha stared hard at Supaya to assure herself of the truth. Then, "I'm glad," she murmured, "so glad."

For several days thereafter, Agatha spoke very little. Except for rousing to take the pain-killer, she lay almost comatose. Then, the last night Supaya was there, Agatha remarked that she didn't need the medicine.

"I feel better, somehow." She lay quite still, her half-opened eyes turned inward, sorting over her memories. ". . . so clear, all so clear. You . . . such a pretty child . . . you and Kenneth Bruley. That necklace! What a rage he was in! That's when it happened, you know."

"When what happened, Miss Harris?"

A shadow of a smile crossed Agatha's face. "Your father . . . Jules . . ." She spoke in a whisper. "He was . . ." Her eyes widened slightly, her voice trailed off. Then, "He was so fine . . . wise . . . he understood. I had to leave." She was silent for a while, her sunken eyes nearly closed. "Sophia," she said, her voice barely audible. "You have been . . . I wish you had been *my* daughter." She moved her hand slightly. "Would you hold my hand. . . . I feel . . . so light. . . ."

Supaya clasped Agatha's hand and waited quietly to catch whatever else she might say. But she didn't speak again. Her lids closed and she sank into a deep sleep. Supaya too dozed off. Toward morning when a gray light filled the room, Supaya woke with a start. Agatha lay perfectly still under the blanket, her wasted body somehow diminished, her hand, resting in Supaya's, limp and indifferent.

The wake was held at the agent's house. Reverend Richards, the young man who had replaced Reverend Crowell, read a passage from the Bible, closed the book with a "There, that's done" snap, and led all those assembled in a brisk, businesslike prayer.

Old Alma, now unable to walk any distance, had come with Jess and Supaya and Waboose and his wife Betty in Jess' car, sitting in the middle of the back seat, serenely unperturbed by this new means of transportation. She listened attentively to the new preacher, her impassive face hiding the fine scorn she felt for his dry, impersonal tone. When he requested they sing a vigorous, militant hymn, she raised her old, mournful voice with such penetrating fervor that the young preacher cast a startled eye in her direction.

Agatha was accompanied by all those she had taught and their families to her burial in the newer part of the cemetery. Truly mourning her, they gathered around her grave, two and three generations to whom Agatha Harris had devoted her life. Among them all, Supaya had known her longer and better than anyone; even so, Agatha's last few puzzling words lingered in Supaya's mind. As the coffin was lowered and Reverend Richards asked them all to bow their heads, Supaya thought of Miss Harris as she had been on Stone Island, young, pretty, and, as Supaya now realized, undoubtedly lonely. And she thought of her father, Jules, strolling jauntily down the road, of his soft, penetrating eyes and enigmatic smile. Supaya knew Agatha had always had a special attachment for herself and her children, and had thought it stemmed from simple friendship for herself. Now, as the dirt thudded down on the coffin, Supaya's sorrow for her friend was deepened as she wondered what unsuspected longings, what lost love or vain regret were being buried with Agatha's slight, worn-out body.

Gerald wrote the necessary letters, to the government agency and Reverend Harris. Aside from her books, which she had left to the school, Agatha had almost no possessions of her own, and the two rooms she had lived in were soon made ready for the teacher who would take her place in the fall.

CHAPTER THIRTY-TWO

Supaya struck her hoe into the dry, cracked earth and turned over the soil with impatient, angry motions. For nearly two weeks no rain had fallen. If it did not come soon, she would have to start carrying water, a back-breaking job, but she could not risk losing the garden, not with three extra mouths to feed. And she knew she could expect no help, not from Shooskonee or her husband. Supaya had been working since early morning. It was now nearly noon, and still no sign that anyone was up. Lazy. They were both lazy. But they expected to be fed. And given a home.

Supaya's resentment was growing against them both. She could not excuse a man's refusing to work for his food, even a stranger; still less could she excuse her daughter, whose home it was and who knew the ways of her people. More deeply still, Supaya resented having to give up living in her own home. Neither she nor Jess were comfortable sharing the house with Shooskonee and Ed's jarring, uncongenial presence. Since the day when Supaya had surprised Ed entering her room, she and Jess had not slept in her house. She had moved her trunk to Jess', unable to abide the thought of Ed's curious, prying eyes, or his long, bony fingers handling her possessions.

Much of Supaya's anger was directed at herself for permitting such a situation to come about. But after seven years of thinking her daughter lost, she had been overjoyed to welcome Shooskonee and her little son Peter. Embracing her daughter, she'd seen over her shoulder a white man slouched against the doorjamb, his hands in his pockets, watching them. His head was cocked to one side and a strand of straw-colored hair fell across his forehead. The sly smile on his thin face cut through Supaya's emotion. She stepped back and Shooskonee introduced Ed Cassety, adding with only the slightest hesitation, "my husband." The man smiled at that and came forward.

He was a musician. He played the piano in the, another hesitation, establishment where Sal, as he called her, worked. Because of the Depression, they had both been fired. He was willing, he said, to take any job at all, and for a time had hung around the store. But he had not worked, preferring instead to engage the farmers in conversation. Waboose, who worked for a white farmer on a nearby farm, got him a job during fall harvest. After a week, Ed quit, saying it was too hard work for too little pay and bad for his hands. During the winter he had a few odd jobs, none lasting more than a day or so, and the little he made he spent on drink.

Speaking to Jess about him, Supaya had been vehement. "He's a no-good! Worthless! He refuses to work! I wonder Shooskonee puts up with him!"

Jess had rarely heard Supaya speak of anyone with such intense dislike. He sensed in her vehemence more than mere anger at Ed's laziness, and asked, "Has he done something bad, something to offend you? If you want him run off, I'll go and send him packing. You've only to say so. They don't have to live in your house. They can find somewhere else to live."

Supaya had been tempted, but thinking of her daughter and little Peter, had said, "No. I can't ask them to go. They need help."

But Ed *had* done something. One day on her way back from visiting a patient, Supaya had stopped at her house hoping to see Shooskonee. As she shook the snow off her jacket in the lean-to, Ed appeared in the doorway.

"Well! Just the one I'd most like to see on a snowy afternoon. Come in out of the storm and have a drink with me."

"No, thank you. Is Shooskonee here?"

"Old Sal? She's gone off. Took the kid and went to visit a friend. So she said. Can't blame her. Sure isn't anything else to do around here." He rested against the corner of the table, dangled one leg, and turned his glass round and round, his small, close-set eyes watching Supaya, who, at forty-eight, was still slim and lithe. She moved with the vigor of a woman used to much physical labor and, to Ed's shrewd eye, who was passionate and much loved. Her hair was still deep black and her mouth as sensuous as when Wenonga had first seen her.

Just now, as she fixed a pot of tea and cleaned a cup for herself from the pile of dirty dishes, her expression was stern and displeased. Since she had left her house in Shooskonee's care, it had become progressively dirtier. Every time Supaya entered it, her teeth were set on edge. She was coming to see her daughter as a slattern, who took no care of her home and little of her son. Ed Cassety she openly disliked and mistrusted. He was no true husband to Shooskonee, Supaya was certain. His eye was calculating, his excuses transparent. His calling Shooskonee "Old Sal" was to Supaya's ear not affectionate but thinly veiled contempt that filled her with anger.

The fire had burned low in the stove and there was no wood. Conscious of Ed's eye steadily on her, she said, without looking at him, "Bring in some wood. The fire is nearly out."

Ed raised his eyebrows. After a moment he set down his glass. "All right, sure. Sure, I will." With a great flurry and stamping of his feet, he brought in two pieces of wood, one in each hand, and dropped them by the stove. "Haven't seen much of you lately," he remarked, standing near Supaya as she thrust the wood into the stove. "And you're sure not much for conversation when you do come. But you're a woman of action. That's what I've got you figured as. Little talk, big action. Why don't we go in the other room and have a little action of our own, eh?"

Supaya straightened up and stared at him. His thin face had the unhealthy pallor of a man who spent all his days and long, restless nights inside. His sly, insolent expression was accentuated by an habitual quirk at one side of his mouth, the face of a man whose youthful cockiness had worn down to a mean cynicism. He reached out and put his arm comfortably around Supaya's waist. "Why so surprised? You're still a good-looking woman. Don't worry about old Sal. She won't care. That storekeeper you live with don't need to know. I won't tell him. That's one thing I like about you people, you're free and easy."

Seen up close, the irises of his eyes were a curious washed-out brown, a faded color with no depth. Were he to die, thought Supaya, there would be no spirit rise from him. His body would collapse like an empty sack. She smiled at the thought, and for a moment he thought she smiled at him, until, with a casual but firm gesture she picked up a kitchen knife and placed its edge against his throat.

"Hey!" His arm fell away. "You crazy bitch! You cut me!" He jerked backward in alarm.

Supaya advanced, still smiling and keeping the blade to his throat. He stood very still, his chin taut with fear. "No, I have not cut you, but I will if you ever come near me again. Or speak like that again. I see what you are. I let you live in my house only because of my daughter and her son. Do you understand? For her sake only. And you will not call her 'old Sal' again. Her name is Shooskonee."

Ed, thinking the danger past, gave a sickly grin. "Yeah? Well I'm not so good at those names. How about Indian Sally?" His grin turned into a leer. "That's what all her customers call her." The next moment he knew real fear, for Supaya's face went rigid with anger, her black eyes narrowed and she pressed the knife blade against his throat until the flesh welled up on either side.

Ed's eyes rolled wildly; afraid to move, he gave an inarticulate sound, half yell, half gasp. Supaya's arm trembled with her effort at restraint. Slowly her tension relaxed and she pulled the knife away. A thin red line appeared on Ed's throat.

Sick with disgust, Supaya said flatly, "While you live in my house and eat my food, you will speak of my daughter with respect. I have told you her name. You will learn to say it." When she left, he had still not moved.

That had been in the winter. Since then, Supaya had seldom gone to her house.

Shooskonee, whose face had lost its soft youthfulness and hardened into a sour discontent, avoided her mother. She refused to visit Sarah, whom she had once idolized. Sullen and short-tempered, she spent most of her time sitting about the house or out with unattached girlfriends. When Peter cried, she'd drop him off at the store, leaving him for Supaya. Her brother Waboose she resented and treated with contempt, remarking, "It was easy for you. Go to school, get married, settle down close to home, all easy, all simple."

Waboose had not found working his way through high school easy, nor finding a steady job simple. He worked long and hard on a farm near the reserve in exchange for a small farm building to live in and very little money. He found nothing to say to his sister, who scorned him and ignored his wife, Betty, an Indian girl he had met in high school. He, Betty, and their two small sons used to visit Supaya on Sundays; now they came to Jess' house, but less frequently.

Troubled by this disruption in her family and worried over Shooskonee's future, Supaya wielded her hoe energetically against the parched soil. Reaching the end of a row, she looked up to see Frank approaching and was glad to be diverted.

Frank was doing very well. With the help of a Soldier Settler's loan he had set up a lumber mill on the reserve which he'd operated successfully for several years. He had three or four men working for him and had offered to hire Ed, but Ed had refused. He had held up his hands, fingers outstretched.

"See these hands? They're a musician's hands. Have to be careful how I use them. Might cut myself. Then where'd I be?"

Ever since, Frank had referred solemnly to "the musician." This morning he greeted Supaya, then comically assumed a listening expression. "It's midmorning, but I hear no music," he remarked.

"That's because you're standing up," said Supaya seriously. "You have to be lying flat on your back to hear that music."

Frank sighed. "My ear is not keen enough."

"Nor is mine," said Supaya grimly.

A speculative gleam came into Frank's eye. "If you wish, I could persuade the musician to go and play somewhere else."

"No, thank you, Frank." That both Jess and Frank should offer to solve so easily a problem she found difficult was a source of irritation to Supaya. "The earth is dry," she remarked, giving a thrust with the hoe.

"Rain is coming," Frank assured her. "Soon. Maybe today."

"I suppose," said Supaya tartly, "you can smell it."

Frank rested his eyes on hers. "You are displeased with me. What have I done?"

"Oh Frank, it is myself I'm displeased with."

"Then let me help you! I long to make you happy."

"But Frank," protested Supaya in a lighter tone, "you have no time. You're much too busy making others happy. Your family has grown very large."

"Who says so!" exclaimed Frank with a fine show of indignation. "I have no family! And what friends I have are only to fill my loneliness without you!"

"Frank! If your 'friends' ever heard that! Don't worry. I won't tell. Come and have some tea and bread with Jess and me."

But Frank declined, a touch of sad reproach in his glance. Supaya thought he enjoyed playing the role of rejected suitor; still, although he and Jess were always civil to one another, he would accept an invitation to tea only if she were alone. He had, he said, to see the agent about a shipment of lumber, and went on down the road.

The agent, William Brent, was a newcomer, having been sent to the reserve three years before when Gerald Toomis retired. He was an efficient young man, and his wife, Natalie, was pleasant and friendly, but for Supaya they could never replace Gerald and Lizzie, who had gone to live in Wellston. For the first year or so Supaya had seen Gerald and Lizzie every week when they drove back to the reserve to visit Louisa and her family, but after Gerald's death, Lizzie was not able to come often.

As Supaya worked, thinking about Lizzie, living alone and working in Wellston, she noticed Ed come out of the house and saunter, hands in his pockets, toward the road. Deliberately she turned her back that she might not see him. She had worked only a little further along the row when Peter appeared at her elbow.

"Grandma, I'm hungry." Peter was six now and would be starting school in the fall, but he was small for his age. Standoffish and solemn, he had the face of a child, but his eyes were always sad. Looking down at him, Supaya's anger at Shooskonee flared up; taking Peter's hand, she went toward the house.

Shooskonee, half-dressed, hair uncombed, was sitting in Jules' rocker when she heard the back door open. Bending over, she picked up a stray shoe and threw it forcefully over her shoulder, saying as she turned, "You can just go . . . oh! it's you!"

"Yes, Shooskonee, it's me." Supaya picked up the shoe and handed it to her daughter, who took it petulantly, then tossed it under a chair. "What are you doing, just sitting there? Aren't you well?"

"Oh mother! If I don't work, work, work every minute you think I'm sick!"

"I have not seen you work since you returned home," said Supaya acidly. "If you are well, why don't you feed your son who says he's hungry?"

Shooskonee glanced at Peter, leaning against a chair, soberly watching her, her glance a mixture of fondness and impatience. "He's always hungry."

Her careless response angered Supaya further. She said sharply. "That's no answer. He is your son. You should care for him. And you should clean this house!"

"Mother, stop telling me what to do!"

"Someone must tell you! I think you are my daughter, but my daughter would not live in a dirty house or let her child go hungry. She would not sit here doing nothing while I work alone to get food for her and her family. My daughter would not so shame her parents. I no longer know you."

"No!" exclaimed Shooskonee, rising in a sudden fury. "You don't know me! You never did! What do you expect of me!?"

"I expect you to have self-respect!" said Supaya vehemently. "To keep a decent home for your husband and child! To have enough pride that you will work for your food and not be content to let others do it for you! Your husband is lazy but ignorant! For you—this is your home!"

Shooskonee listened, her head stretched forward on her slender neck. At the word "home" she suddenly interrupted, her words pouring out. "If this is my home, why did you send me away! Send me to live with whites who treated me like dirt! Send me off to clean their houses! Sarah didn't go! Oh no, not Sarah! She was allowed to stay! But then you always preferred her to me! Well, I went! Now I'm back you don't like what you see! Well don't think I'd have come back here if I'd had anyplace else to go!"

Shocked by her words, Supaya protested. "Sarah is not my daughter! With her I had no say. But you, Shooskonee, you I wanted to have an education! I sent you to learn! So you could live off the reserve and live well!"

"Oh yes," laughed Shooskonee bitterly, "that's what Miss Harris said!" Her laugh turned to a sneer. "She was just jealous because the boys liked me and she never had a man at all! Well, I found my place!"

"Shooskonee, that's not . . ."

"And I've had lots of men! Yes, lots!" Infuriated, she gripped the chair back and spit out her pain, fear, and rancor. "How else do you think I lived after Tim Riley deserted me! How else do you think I managed to have him," pointing a shaking finger at Peter, who sat on the floor, face hidden against his bent knees.

"You should have come home," said Supaya, aghast.

"Oh yes! Come home pregnant! With no husband!"

"You should have come home!" insisted Supaya, her face pinched with grief. "That would not have mattered!"

"I'm glad to hear that, because Ed's not my husband. You didn't really think he was, did you! I brought him along because he was kind to me. He gave me and my baby a place to live. And when I didn't have a paying customer I could sleep with him. You don't like to hear that, do you? But you see, I did learn! I've learned a lot, and," she taunted, "it's all your fault! All your doing!"

"Mine!" exclaimed Supaya, astounded, her horror overwhelmed by anger. "You dare accuse me! You could have come home from school whenever you wished! You did not have to stay there! You understood that! When you ran away you could have run home! You chose to do what you did! I am not at fault for the life you chose to lead!"

"Oh yes you are!" shrilled Shooskonee. "You just don't want to admit it! I'm a prostitute! That's what you made me! But why not? You live with a white man! You're no better than a prostitute yourself!" Shooskonee caught her breath and stared at her mother. Her rash words hung in the air between them. Despite her defiant rage, Shooskonee trembled with fear, expecting to be struck down.

Supaya stood as though turned to stone. After a long silence she spoke quietly, her face set, eyes fixed on her daughter as if she saw only empty space. "You and your man will get out of my house. You will go today before the sun sets. If you do not go I will have the agent put you out. You may leave the child if you wish."

Trying to shatter that implacable stare, to make herself acknowledged as a daughter once more, Shooskonee sneered, "Oh you'd like that, wouldn't you! Another child for you to educate! What talent would *he* have, I wonder!" But her words were wasted.

"Just as you wish," said Supaya coldly. "Only go."

And Shooskonee saw herself dead in her mother's eyes.

Supaya left and walked into the woods. She walked a long time without thought or direction. When she began to see where she was and found herself in a grove of cedars, she sank down on her knees and put her forehead to the ground. She had no prayer, but as she wept she found comfort in speaking her Grandfather's name over and over again.

That night the rain Frank had said would come poured down, straight and hard. Lying beside Jess, Supaya listened to it drumming on the roof close above them and smelled the fresh odor of wet pine carried in on the mist blown through the open window.

"Can you tell me now?" asked Jess. She had come home much later than usual, had fixed his supper but eaten nothing herself, sitting apart in a private, stricken silence. Jess, seeing she was herself unharmed, had waited, giving her time. Now, in the dark and within the protective circle of his arm, he knew she could speak.

"Today Shooskonee and I talked. *He* was not there. Only . . ." she hesitated, "only the boy." Not naming him lent more distance, made speaking easier. "I told her to go. This day just ended. I offered to keep the boy." She turned her face into the curve of his neck, muffling her voice. "You would not have minded?"

"No, no. Of course not."

"But she took him." Her voice shook. "They should be gone by now."

He held her closer. "It is better that they go. They were not happy here. He would never have found any work. He needs to be in a city. Besides, you've missed living in your own house. I've missed it too." He felt her nod in agreement, but she said nothing more.

The next morning Supaya walked to her house. Water lay in long irregular puddles along the road. Branches, heavy with rain, lifted in an occasional breeze to send down flurries of drops. The rain had stopped but the sky had not yet cleared. There was no sun, only a bright gray light.

She went around to the back door. Entering, she knew at once that they had left. The litter of clothes was gone. Dirty dishes were still piled in the basin and the remnants of a meal and an empty whiskey bottle had been left on the table.

Then she saw it. On the floor in front of the stove lay her prized china teapot, smashed into pieces. For a moment she was stunned. Then, skirting it, Supaya went to the front door, opened it wide, and stood on the threshold, feeling the freshened air blow against her and through the house. Leaving the door open, she turned back into the house and began carefully picking up the pieces of the broken teapot.

CHAPTER THIRTY-THREE

"Grandma, Jess wants you to come. He said to bring your bag." Supaya turned in alarm. "He's all right," said Charlie in his clear child's voice. "He's sitting in the storeroom. He said he didn't feel so good."

Supaya had been cutting up squash for drying. She laid down her knife. "I'll come right away."

She and Charlie, Waboose's younger son, walked to the store, Supaya striding ahead so rapidly that Charlie had to skip to keep up with her.

Jess was sitting on a crate, watching the door expectantly. When Supaya appeared, slightly out of breath, he smiled. "You didn't need to hurry so," he said.

But he would not have sent for her for nothing. It was unlike him to sit in the storeroom. She looked at him searchingly. "Did you hurt yourself?"

"No, no, nothing like that." He flexed his shoulders. "I just ache all over. Probably a touch of arthritis. I thought I'd go and rest a bit if you could help me upstairs."

Taking as much of his weight as she could, Supaya helped him move slowly down the hall. From his sharp intake of breath and tightening grip on her shoulders, she realized that moving caused him pain. Halfway up the stairs he had to stop. "Just . . . just a minute," he said. They waited, his head hanging forward, his chest heaving. Then, smiling sideways at her, he nodded and they started up again. He was able to reach the bed, where he sank down, exhausted by his effort. Turning, he fell back with his head on the pillow. Supaya removed his shoes and carefully lifted his legs onto the bed.

"Jess, where does it hurt?"

He opened his eyes, still vividly blue and sparked with humor. "Everywhere!" he said, grinning.

"I'll call the doctor."

Jess caught her arm. "No, I don't want you to do that. You're my doctor. Besides, this is nothing. Just cold settled in the joints. It'll be gone in a day or two. Give me something for the pain and I'll be fine."

"But Jess, shouldn't I . . ."

He tugged at her arm. "Give me a kiss." Supaya shook her head in mock exasperation, but bent down and kissed him. "There. You see, I feel better already. Don't fret about a doctor. He'd just haul me off to a hospital, and I don't want to go. Now, brew me a potion, you witch."

Supaya gave him a medicine, and for several days Jess felt better. He seldom got out of bed, but he sat up and ate the meals Supaya brought him. Charlie and his older brother, Tom, lived with Supaya from fall through spring so they could attend the reserve school. They delighted in carrying messages between her and Jess, and with their help, Supaya managed to keep the store open. But she found it hard to wait on customers, for her thoughts were constantly on Jess. He was cheerful and insisted he felt better, but he continued to ask for her medicine and drank it down rapidly, eager for the relief it brought him.

One evening she had brought his supper on a tray and was going for more tea when, halfway down the stairs, she heard the crash of tray and dishes hitting the floor. Running back she was horrified to see Jess fallen sideways, his body shaken by tremors, his head and arm hanging helplessly over the side of the bed. Crying out his name, Supaya pulled him back onto the bed. She cradled his head against her and gripped his shoulders, striving to hold him firm. As suddenly as they began, the spasms stopped. He lay inert, his face ashen, eyes closed, his mouth slack.

"Jess, Jess!" she whispered imploringly. She stroked his forehead, and finding it wet and clammy, gently laid him back on the pillow and got a towel to dry his head. Trying not to weep, she stroked his face and begged him to open his eyes. She massaged his limp hands and pressed them to her face. After an agonizing wait, his lids moved slightly. "Jess, look at me! Please, Jess! Open your eyes!"

Slowly, heavily, his eyes opened, but he stared straight ahead. She had to put herself in line with his gaze.

"Jess, let me call a doctor!"

He half closed his eyes and his lips moved slightly, forming a soundless "no." As his eyes rested on her, they gradually opened a bit wider. His color improved and there appeared the faintest suggestion of a smile about his mouth. For a long time he gazed at her and then gradually seemed to fall asleep. But once she moved slightly and his hand instantly tightened.

"I'm here, Jess," she whispered, "I'm here." Without letting go his hand, she twisted around so she could lie beside him. She stared into the dark, trying to control the tight core of fear inside her that threatened to burst into panic. It was not arthritis Jess had, not just cold settled in his joints. He was seriously ill, she knew. If only her father were there to advise her. Or Wenonga. If only there were someone who could help! Should she call a doctor against Jess' wishes? Or should she get Frank to drive Jess into Wellston to the hospital even though she knew he did not want to go? Soos would care for the boys. She could close the store and go with him. But that would be a betrayal. Finally, emotionally exhausted, she fell into a troubled sleep.

She started awake with a feeling of dread before she was even fully conscious. Early morning light filled the room. Turning, she saw that Jess' eyes were open. Leaning over, she kissed him and was encouraged to feel him respond. "I'll clean up here, then go down and put the teapot on and come right back."

Jess blinked his eyes to show he understood. He made no attempt to speak, and she tried not to think about that as she made up a fire in the stove and put on the pot. He was watching for her when she returned with the tray, and he made an effort to lift himself but could could not raise his head. Supaya propped him up with pillows and a blanket. He could not move his left arm at all, his right only slowly and shakily. Supaya gave him his tea by spoonfuls. When he had drunk about half a cup, Jess moved his hand to indicate he didn't want any more. He cleared his throat.

"Supaya." His voice was hoarse and faint, and he spoke hesitantly, finding it difficult to shape his mouth to the words. "Call . . . my brother. Victor. I want . . . to see him."

"I will, Jess, I will. But let me call the doctor in Wellston too! Please!"

He moved his hand again. "No . . . no. I want . . . to stay here. Call Victor . . . now." As Supaya rose to go, Jess added, "Tell him . . . come soon." Jess had willed the store and all his possessions to Supaya, but he wanted to ask Victor to ensure she never wanted for anything, and to say that he wished to be buried here, in the Indian cemetery, where Supaya would one day be buried. He watched her go, wishing he had the strength to explain all that, hoping he would be able to by the time Victor came.

Supaya called Victor on the store telephone, the first long-distance call she had ever made. She spoke to the operator in Wellston; the phone crackled, she heard a distant ringing, then a faraway masculine voice. Victor said he would come at once.

That day Soos came. After one look at Supaya's face, she put her basket down, folded her shawl over it, and stayed. She kept the kettle hot and busied herself in the kitchen. Sarah came, and after speaking briefly with Supaya and her mother, took Tom and Charlie back home with her.

William Brent, the agent, came. He stood just inside the door and held his hat in both hands. "I'm sorry to hear your husband is ill, Sophia. His brother just called and asked me to see that everything possible is being done. Has he seen a doctor?"

Stiffly erect, Supaya answered, her lips trembling. "No, he doesn't want to see a doctor."

The agent frowned. "But surely . . ."

"He has refused to see a doctor!" said Supaya sharply.

Seeing her distress and knowing Victor was coming, Brent said simply, "If there is anything I can do, please let me know," and left.

All that day Jess remained the same. Supaya stayed close to him, resting beside him when he slept. Whenever he roused, which seemed to her to be at longer and longer intervals, she spoke to him and coaxed him to take a few mouthfuls of soup. At the sound of her voice, his eyes would focus on her and rest there as if he had returned from wandering. He would obediently open his mouth and swallow until he could make no further effort. Then she would gently wipe his chin, stroke his hair, and kiss him, while his gaze never left her face.

That night while Jess was sleeping, Supaya went outside. She left the lamp burning in the kitchen. Its light fell through the window, casting long shadows through the slatted back of the bench across the porch. She went beyond the reach of the soft, yellow light into the woods. A cool night wind touched her face and stirred the trees. Not for many years had Supaya prayed to her guardian, not since Kineu had rejected her and she had put the stone bear in the bottom of her trunk. Even when she had driven her daughter from her, she had not prayed. Now, in her extremity of grief and fear, like a repentant child, she addressed her Grandfather, finding relief and comfort in whispering the old, loved words that came naturally to her lips, bridging the years of silence as if they had never been. Scattering tobacco into the wind, she spoke.

"Oh Grandfather! Hear me! I am weak and helpless and bowed with grief! Help me!

"Oh Great Spirit Bear! Hear me! You who have always granted others your strength when I asked it! Now grant strength to me! For I shake with fear! Death is waiting to enter and I am powerless to keep him out!

"Oh Great Spirit Father! You whose heart beats with life eternal! I cannot save the one I love! Give me your courage! For my courage is gone! My heart cries out in dread! Oh help me! For I cannot face the morning!"

Victor and Marietta arrived at dusk the next day. Solemn and imposing, his hair now entirely white, Victor stood by the bedside looking down at his sleeping brother. Marietta, after one brief glance, demanded that Jess be moved at once.

"He certainly hasn't gotten the care he should have! He should be in a hospital! With doctors who could help him!" Marietta, now a matron, spoke aggressively, knowing she was right.

"I would have called a doctor but he refused to see one. He wants to stay here," said Supaya stiffly.

"A sick man is in no condition to know what he wants! We should . . ."

"Please, Marietta," said Victor, "don't make it harder." He turned to Supaya. "He should be in a hospital. We must move him. With proper treatment . . ."

373

"But not now! Not tonight! He's asleep! Wait until morning, when you can speak to him! Please!" Only for Jess would she have so begged of these people. Her dark eyes were anguished, her face worn and ashen. Looking at her, Victor agreed.

"It's probably wise not to move him tonight. But tomorrow we must. I'll call the agent in the morning."

Lying close beside Jess, Supaya slept not at all. They would take him away from her. She could not stop them. The agent would come and she would be pushed aside. Jess' wishes, now that he was helpless, would be ignored. He would die in a strange place among strange people. Clasping his nerveless hand, she stared with aching, burning eyes into the dark, dreading the coming of dawn.

Victor wakened early, having spent a restless night on the sofa. Soos had returned and was already working in the kitchen. When he appeared in the doorway, rumpled and rather irritable, Soos offered him a cup of hot tea which he gratefully accepted.

"I'll send Supaya down," he told Soos, but Supaya would not leave Jess' side. She stood close by as Victor leaned over him. Marietta, who had slept across the hall in Kirsten's room, entered in her robe and stood on the far side of the bed.

"Hello, Jess. You're awake, I see. Marietta and I arrived last night, but you were asleep."

The brothers had not seen each other since Jess had gone to Hilda's funeral, a few years earlier. Jess looked at Victor and made a slight motion with his right hand. "I want . . . you to . . ."

"Don't try to talk," admonished Victor. "Save your strength. We're going to take you into Wellston, to the hospital. We'll get you all fixed up!"

Jess was instantly alarmed and his reaction was violent. His face twitched. His eyes widened frantically as he struggled to speak. "No! No! Here! . . . . I want . . . Supaya! . . . Supaya! I . . ." His right arm suddenly flung out, his body, seized by a powerful spasm, arched upward, his chest straining painfully in one last convulsion. Marietta screamed.

"Jess!" cried Supaya. Pushing Victor aside she caught Jess in her arms. His head fell against her shoulder, his eyes shut. Through his parted lips came only the faintest breath. "Jess! Jess!" Supaya eased his head back onto the pillow. "Jess, speak to me, open your eyes! Jess!" She stroked his face, his arms, called his name, but he gave no sign of hearing. Her arm thrust protectively across his body, Supaya pressed her head against his side and wailed softly.

"He's still breathing," said Victor, leaning above her. "Here! Get up! We'll take him at once!"

But when he touched Supaya's shoulder, she sprang up, furious, tears streaming down her face. "You! You killed him!"

Victor drew back, shocked.

"What a dreadful, ridiculous thing to say!" exclaimed Marietta.

"You did! Now get out! Both of you!" Supaya raised her fists threateningly. "Get out!"

Victor frowned. "He's still breathing. We won't waste time arguing. I'll make arrangements immediately. Marietta! Get dressed!"

Supaya shut the door behind them and turned the key. Jess lay still, his lips slightly parted. Once more she rubbed his hands and arms, stroked his face, beseeched him softly to hear her. But there was no response, only a barely perceptible, irregular heartbeat.

"Ahhh, Jess!" she reproached him, weeping. "You no longer hear me! You have gone and left me here, alone!" Getting a comb from the dresser, she sat beside him and carefully combed his black hair, touched with gray at the temples. She straightened his pillows and smoothed the blanket. Then she searched through the dresser until she found his old watch and chain, at the back of a drawer behind his folded shirts. As she lifted them out, she caught sight of something—a small birchbark box with quill embroidery. She turned it over, removed the lid. It was empty but she recognized the pattern. It was one of the first she had made after coming to Two Bluffs, one of the first she had brought to the store for Jess to sell. Blinded by tears, she stood holding the box until her paroxysm of grief had passed. Then she put the watch, fob, and chain into the box. She turned again to Jess. Bending down, she took his face in both her hands, gazed at him, then gently kissed him.

Unlocking the door, Supaya went downstairs and into the kitchen. Soos, sitting at the table, looked up questioningly, but Supaya went to the window and stood there, her back turned.

"Why are they taking so long to get here?" fussed Marietta. She had come down and found Victor waiting in the living room.

"The agent will be here shortly," said Victor. "You go and wait in the car."

Supaya heard the agent arrive with another man. She heard their footsteps overhead, their brief comments to each other as they carried Jess downstairs and out to the car. She heard Victor come

375

and stand behind her and saw his white hair reflected in the window.

"You are welcome to come with us, Supaya." He paused for an answer, but she said nothing, only raised her head higher. "Of course you understand that . . . should he not recover, he will be buried in our family plot."

Supaya stared at his image in the glass, refusing to turn around or acknowledge he had spoken. After a moment, his face disappeared, and she heard the door shut behind him.

When the sound of both cars had faded away, Supaya reached up and undid her hair. She stared at the unreality of her own image in the glass, a woman with long hair, dark shadows for eyes, and a blurred, ghostly gray face.

As Soos silently watched, Supaya cut off her hair, cut it off fiercely, as close to her scalp as she could. She gathered the cut hair and wrapped it up in a bundle. With her shawl over her shorn head and carrying the bundle, her medicine bag, and the little birch box, she said in a tight voice, "Come, Soos. It is time to go."

She locked the door behind them, and together the two women walked off down the road.

PART FIVE
1946–1967

CHAPTER
THIRTY-FOUR

Supaya liked to go fishing early. She enjoyed having her tea alone, before Tom and Charlie were up, and walking through the cool, damp woods as the mist was lifting. She took pleasure in the sound of the water slapping against the boat and in seeing the sun rise out of the lake, its red brilliance reflected in the shining, ever-moving surface of the water. Sometimes when the mist clung along the shoreline and only the green woods above stood out in the early light, she was reminded of the view from her dreaming place on Stone Island.

How she had longed to be there when Jess had gone! To hide among the rocks and weep out her sorrow to the eternal, listening earth. Instead she had knelt on the floor of her room, clasped the blue stone, and imagined herself there, kneeling on the dry, pebbly earth, with only the luminous sky high above her. So transported, she had prayed.

"Great Spirit Bear! You who shake the earth with your tread! Help me! I am lost and cannot find my way! All paths are the same to me! Teach me where to walk!

"Great Father! You who have power over the earth and all creatures! Hear me! I am weak and filled with despair! All joy has fled from my heart and I tremble, here alone! Give me strength that I may lift my head!

"Great Spirit Father! You who raise the sun and the
     moon! You who bring life and warmth to all things!
     Help me! For I move in cold and darkness! I see
     only ashes of dead fires! Open my eyes that I may
     see your light! Warm my soul with your fire! For
     without your help I cannot live!"
She had filled her days helping Waboose and Betty raise their sons,
Tom and Charlie, storing food for winter, and treating her patients.
In healing, Supaya had found the greatest consolation. She spent
hours preparing medicines and during the long dark winter trudged
endless miles to visit her patients, forgetting her own loss in comforting others.

That fall, winter, and spring, terrible for Supaya in its aching
loneliness, had been for the reserve, as well as for her, a time of
change. Patterns of living were broken and came to resemble those
that had long existed off the reserve. Age-old habits fell away like
worn-out garments. The band council voted to bring electricity onto
the reserve. Poles and wires appeared along the dirt roads. At night
houses were illuminated not with soft lamplight but the glare of the
electric bulb. Electric stoves and heaters began displacing black iron
stoves. Pumps were installed and radios blared. Rusted, second-
hand cars, coaxed into life, raised clouds of dust and became a
familiar part of the landscape, parked alongside houses and barns,
their owners' heads hidden under their raised hoods.

But Supaya, disillusioned in her hopes for her children, had
returned more and more to the old ways, narrowed her activities
and resisted change. When William Brent told her Jess had left her
all his property, the building comprising house and store and everything in it, she had handed him the keys and asked him to sell it for
her. When she had locked the door and walked away, it was final.
She refused to go there again. Whenever she needed supplies, she
sent Tom or Charlie or asked Soos or Sarah to bring what little she
required.

Brent had had no difficulty selling the store, but when he
placed the cash in Supaya's lap, she looked down at it with horror
and could hardly bring herself to touch it. She spent half of it at
once, to help her family and friends. For Waboose she bought a car,
for Betty an electric stove. For Soos, Sarah, and Louisa she bought
an electric iron each. Spending half the money eased the aversion
she felt for it, and she was able, against some future need, to put the
remainder in her trunk.

That fall she had not gone to the fair, where competitions of all sorts were held—in art, writing, cooking, gardening—and money prizes were given. She listened with detached, amused tolerance to endless debates over the judges' decisions. Sarah's daughter Josie had won the spelling prize and Soos the cooking. All agreed those were fair decisions, but certainly Louisa's quilting was superior to that of Emma Smith's, who got the prize.

She had withdrawn from the church women's group, having no further interest in their meetings. She stopped attending Sunday service, although the boys went of their own accord to Mrs. Richards' Sunday school. Reverend Richards always thought, a trifle guiltily, that she had stopped coming because he referred to Jess as her "friend" when he had called to offer his sympathy. But he mistook her. At the time she had not even heard what he said. It was later, sitting in her usual place in a back pew, that she had wondered what she was doing there, listening to a service that was suddenly as alien and unsatisfying as it had been when as a child she had gone with her father. She never went again and it was as if all her years of attendance had never been.

She had no interest for anything beyond Waboose and his family, her few friends, and her work. She first heard of World War II from George, who lamented he could not go because of his wooden leg. Then from Sarah, who rejoiced that Caleb would not be taken, and from her patients whose lives were changed when their husbands and sons left home. Waboose came to tell her he was going too. Supaya would have stopped him if she could. "Think of Betty, of your sons! At least wait until you are called!"

But like his father, Waboose had wanted to go—partly because of his father. He was unable to explain, afraid of reviving memories painful to his mother. Even to himself he could not explain his strange but urgent desire to follow where his father had gone, hoping by so doing to find him again. Or at least find understanding of him.

Rowing back to shore with her catch, Supaya thought of Kineu, remembering how proudly he'd held their newborn son and named him Waboose, Little Rabbit. Now Waboose too had gone to a distant country to fight in a war, and Supaya prayed he would not return as Kineu had returned, changed and unapproachable, a stranger to his wife and children.

She thought too of Frank. For months after Jess had gone, Frank, still unmarried, had hovered about, but always at a tactful distance. He would raise his hand in greeting as he passed by the house or, seeing her coming toward him on the road, he would tip his hat and strike off in another direction. He did not intrude on her but inquired constantly and closely of her friends as to her welfare. Not until the following spring had he come to the house and spoken directly to her.

"I have come," he had said, rather stiffly, "to tell you I'm enlisting in the army again. I go tomorrow."

Supaya had insisted he come inside and have some tea and bread. "You went once, Frank. Must you go again?"

"I must," he had said, pleased that she'd rather he didn't go.

"What will happen to the mill while you're gone?"

"Caleb will run it for me. They won't take him again." Nor would they take Harry, thought Supaya. He still walked with a halt.

"You . . ." Frank hesitated. "You will be all right?" He felt foolish, awkward. He wished to say more but would not allow himself. It was still too soon. Supaya's hair had just reached her shoulders, not even long enough to tie back, much less braid.

"Of course, Frank. I have the boys. And my work."

As he left, he had looked back to say, "You will be here when I return?" He wanted assurance, a promise even.

Supaya sighed. Like a great, stubborn child, Frank was always asking her to say what she could never say. "Yes, Frank. I will be here." And he had gone off, satisfied.

On her way home Supaya stopped at Louisa's and gave her some fish. Harry, always busy with his dairy cows, had no time for fishing. Approaching her own house through the woods, Supaya saw a strange car parked in her lane. That it might be Victor struck her like a blow. She felt suddenly faint and sat down to recover. She would not see him, not if she had to sit in the woods all night. But as she watched the house, a man stepped out of the back door, gazed around, then strolled over and leaned on the pigpen. He reached down and scratched the pig's back, and from his stance and gesture, Supaya knew him.

"Wagash!" Supaya greeted him with pleasure. "You have stayed away far too long! Come in and . . ."

"Bill," he said, smiling but firm, and at her glance, insisted, "my name is Bill."

"Ah yes. I forgot. Well, come in Bill, and . . ."

"Don't you want to see my car first?" he asked, with the same sort of pride with which he used to show her the money Jess paid him for helping in the store. "It was Mr. Hadley's, but he got a new one and sold me his old one. Not bad, eh?" Supaya followed him as he walked admiringly around the car. "It's all mine! Of course, the next one I get will be new. Well? What do you think of it? Why are you smiling?"

"You have just gotten this one and already you think of the next one! But," she added, not wanting to disappoint him, "it's a fine car, a very fine car."

Gratified, Bill nodded agreement, his attention still on the shiny black car. His face was thinner, thought Supaya, watching him, and though just now it was flushed with pride, there were tired lines around his eyes, and an underlying tenseness in his face. His black hair was cut short and neat. His suit looked new.

"Bill, how is your mother?"

"Rhea? Oh, she's inside. She drove up with me. Anything for a change . . . no, she really did want to see you."

Rhea was drinking tea when they entered. "I got tired of waiting, so I made myself at home." Rhea had put on weight. Her face was rounder, her waist a tight line between breast and hips. In the hardware store men still eyed her appreciatively and, drawn by the subtle, incorrigible lure in her dark eyes, exchanged banter with her, knowing they could safely do so without risking entanglement. Her brisk replies and sure manner with the cash register assured them of that.

"I looked for your fancy teapot but couldn't find it."

"It was broken," said Supaya, preparing to fry some fish, "years ago."

"Oh, too bad." Rhea paused and put down her cup. She perceived a change in Supaya. Puzzled, she came close to her. "Supaya, what . . . you look . . . Your hair is different."

"It's not long enough yet to wear as I used to." Unable to look up, Supaya stared at her hand holding the frying pan. "Jess . . ." she still had difficulty saying the word, ". . . died."

Rhea was shocked. "But it's so sudden! He was no older than Howard!"

"How is Howard?" asked Supaya, turning the conversation back to Rhea's interests.

"Fine. Going to retire soon, I think." Rhea shrugged. "He's older of course. But then, so am I. What about the store, Supaya? It was open when we came by."

"The agent sold it for me. Some man and his wife and daughter run it now." Supaya shrugged. "I never go there."

"Never . . . . You mean he left it to you and you sold it?!" Rhea exclaimed incredulously.

"Sold it! Why'd you do that?" demanded Bill. "He did a good business there!" He had a sudden stunning vision of himself as owner of two stores, a vision now lost because of Supaya's thoughtlessness. "You had no right to do that!" Standing up, he slammed his chair angrily under the table.

"Bill, Bill!" chided Rhea, but softly, understanding his train of thought.

Supaya turned from the stove to stare at him, resenting his words and his tone. "How is it you feel free to tell me I had no right! It was left to me. I sold it because I didn't want it!"

"But *I* would have wanted it! *I*, your brother! You thought only of yourself! You should have thought of me!"

"You have been away too long and forget yourself!" said Supaya. She spoke quietly but fiercely, and Rhea, remembering Supaya's anger, kept silent. "You forget that I cared for you as a mother, that this was once your home. It has been many years since you troubled to return and now it is only, as you said, 'for a change'! Can it be that while you have taken no interest in your family we should have been thinking only of you! You think your wants are important? You are too puffed up! You are no true brother! You shame your father's spirit by looking only for money that you may buy new cars to replace old cars!"

Bill waved his hand angrily. "I only know that I work hard, six days a week, to get ahead! Here I am, sweating to make a place for myself and you sell a store that could have been mine without having to say, 'Yes, sir,' and 'No, sir,' until I'm sick at my stomach! Or wait for old . . . ." he glanced swiftly at his mother and finished weakly, ". . . for him to retire!" His anger suddenly deflated. He turned away, saying with a mixture of disgust and self-pity, "Can't be sure he'll leave it to me anyway!"

There was a vibrating silence. Hidden nerves had been shamefully exposed. Studiously Rhea and Bill looked away from each other. Supaya, scornful, turned back to the stove. Her action and the homey, ordinary sounds and smells of cooking gradually eased the tension.

Rhea wanted to ask Supaya about the money she'd received

383

from the sale, but seeing the stiffness of her back and the anger in her face, thought better of it. Instead she straightened her plump shoulders and said in a dry voice intended to reduce large problems to small ones, "I am sure Howard will do as we expect. He as good as promised me."

"He'd say that just to get the work out of us," grumbled Bill. Irritated with her son, Rhea made an impatient sound, and Bill, brought round by her assurance and his own hopes, said, "Yeah. I guess he will. He's only got that nephew and he doesn't see much of him." He glanced at Supaya. "I'm sorry. I shouldn't have said what I did."

"It no longer matters," said Supaya. "The fish is ready. Please sit and eat."

They ate with relish. Supaya ate little. Studying Wagash, she could see nothing of his father in him. He had his mother's willfullness and her temper, but he was weak. He didn't have her stamina. Sadly, Supaya perceived he had paid too high a price for that old car.

Rhea, as hungry for the companionship of her own people as for food, talked to Supaya of her work in the store and of life in the city. "Sometimes," said Rhea, in a rare moment of confession, "I feel so alone. There's no one I can talk to, no woman, that is," she hastened to add out of pride. "You should come and visit us. Howard wouldn't mind. You could come back with us now. The change would do you good."

"Thank you, Rhea, but I can't go now. Waboose's boys, Tom and Charlie, live with me. They'll be home from school soon. Besides, I don't need a change. I'm content here. This is my home."

"You always did love this house," commented Rhea, as if at a loss to understand why. "But I couldn't live here, not after the freedom of the city."

Supaya, thinking of Shooskonee, remarked, "Sometimes the city is not a place of freedom."

Rhea glanced sharply at Supaya, wondering what she implied. But she answered truthfully, according to her own experience. "You're right. It's necessary for a woman to be married."

"But then," Supaya reminded her, "you give up your rights as an Indian."

"By marrying a white man, I provided well for myself. And for my son," said Rhea defensively. "What have I lost?"

"I enfranchised," said Bill, "just this winter. I got two

hundred dollars, my share of the band funds. Do you know what I did with it?'' His tense face lit up with satisfaction. "I bought a government bond! It's only one, but it's a start! I'm going to be a rich man some day!'' he exclaimed in a burst of renewed confidence. "You wait and see!''

When he and Rhea drove away, they passed two young boys as they turned out of the lane onto the road. Bill honked his horn and waved.

The boys stared after the car, partly obscured by the dust rolling up behind its tires. When it passed out of sight, they raced to the house, bursting in breathless and excited.

"Grandma! Who was that man? He waved at us!''

Supaya almost said, "No one I know.'' Instead she said, "That was my half-brother and his mother. Your half-uncle. They live in Toronto.''

"That was some car!'' exclaimed Tom. "He must be rich!''

"No!'' said Supaya sternly. "He is *not* rich! *Your* father has a car too, remember.''

"Yeah, but not one like that!''

"How come he's got a big car like that if he's not rich?'' asked Charlie.

By saying, "Yes, sir,'' and "No, sir,'' thought Supaya, flipping fish for their dinner. But she said, "He worked very hard for it.''

"We should have come home sooner,'' said Tom to Charlie. "I bet he'd have given us a ride in that car!''

CHAPTER THIRTY–FIVE

"Aunt Suppy!" Where, wondered Sarah irritably, could she have gone! Just when they were in a hurry! She knocked again and called through the partly opened lean-to door, "Aunt Suppy!"

"I'm here, Sarah. What is it?" asked Supaya, coming out of the shed.

Surprised, Sarah turned. "Oh, there you are! I've been knocking and calling."

"I heard you. What is it?"

Sarah started to answer, then broke off to ask, "What were you doing in the shed?"

Supaya smiled. "Sarah, you come and knock on my door to find out what I'm doing in the shed?"

"Well, what were you doing?"

"Sarah," said Supaya testily, "I don't have to tell you what I'm doing! What is it you want?"

Sarah made an impatient gesture. "I wanted to ask if you'd like to go with us to Wellston to see Mother. Caleb said we'd drive in this morning and come back late afternoon."

"No, I can't. Thank you for asking me. But I can't. Not this time."

"Why not? You wouldn't come last time either."

"I'm busy, Sarah. I have things to do."

"What things?"

Supaya looked thoughtfully at Sarah.

"Oh all right, I won't ask. But Mother misses you. She'd like to see you."

"I miss her too. You tell her that. And tell her I will come to see her. Some time. When I can."

Riding into town, Sarah remarked pensively to Caleb, "I don't think Aunt Suppy will ever visit Mother. She always has an excuse. She said she had things to do!"

"Well, she does," said Caleb reasonably. "She has lots of patients, she works her garden."

"She's not that busy! She wouldn't even tell me what she was doing in the shed!"

Caleb laughed. "She's an independent woman. Always has been. You shouldn't be so nosy."

"Well I don't think she ought to be living there alone. She's sixty-nine and forgetful. And getting short-tempered. I worry about her."

"Stop it, Sarah! You know she's able to take care of herself. And if she needs any help there's always Frank."

"Yes, but Mother will be so disappointed."

Supaya watched Sarah go off, then went back into the shed, got down a basket, and started off toward the meadows. Blueberries were at their peak and she knew where the largest, sweetest ones grew. Her intention was to pick them early, before the sun grew hot and before anyone else discovered them. Frank was fond of blueberries. She had not wanted to say to Sarah, "I cannot come because I am going to pick blueberries for Frank." Besides, that would not be true. She had not gone because she didn't want to see Soos sitting useless in a strange room being treated by strangers. Supaya shied from even imagining it. Some day she would bring herself to go, but not until . . . She popped an especially plump berry into her mouth and thought about Sarah.

Supaya had begun to worry about Sarah. She was only fifty-six, too young to be fussy and short-tempered. She was always asking questions. Of course Soos' falling downstairs and losing the use of both legs had been a shock. And Sarah worried about Soos' being in a nursing home, Supaya knew, because Sarah was always harder to get along with after returning from a visit.

Her basket full, Supaya started home. There had been a time

when she'd expected Sarah would be her apprentice. She remembered Sarah, ten, twelve years old, learning to make salves, medicines, and poultices, going with her on her rounds. But after Sarah married and had Josie, she lost all interest in healing. Since then Supaya had worked alone. She thought of Beedaubun, who had passed on to herself all she knew, but for her, as for Jules and Wenonga, there was no one. What she knew, what Beedaubun had known, and what someone before Beedaubun had known, would all be lost.

Supaya emerged from the woods behind Wenonga's old house. The roof had partially fallen in. Weeds crowded the doorway where Nonen had once stood to welcome her. When she got home, Supaya made up the fire and sprinkled tobacco on it for the pleasure and comfort of Jules, Beedaubun, and Wenonga.

Frank came early, as he always did, bringing fish for their dinner. He sat at her table like a mannerly bear, burly and hungry, but waiting patiently. He enjoyed watching Supaya cook. She worked efficiently, with a minimum of fuss. Her body had grown thicker, but her carriage was erect and her graying hair, combed straight back and knotted above the nape of her neck, set off her fine forehead and facial bones, more prominent now that her face had lost its fullness.

She surprised him with the blueberries and the soft cheese Louisa had given her. The way he glanced up at her when she served him and the obvious pleasure he took in the berries brought a flashing memory of a cold, windy spring day, a crackling fire, the smell of tobacco, and herself placing before Wenonga a dish of berries. He had glanced up just so, expectantly, his large eyes lingering on her face. Her nerves still remembered the shock of that look, his wide, dark face and wild hair.

"You're not eating," commented Frank. "Why don't you eat?"

"I ate as I picked."

Frank squinted at her. "What are you thinking about?"

Why did everyone question her so! Sarah, now Frank! "I was wondering," she said deliberately, getting back at him, "why you never married. Why didn't you, Frank?"

Frank studied her a moment in silence. He saw that he had piqued her. She had not been thinking of him at all. But she was never more appealing than when she was pert. He put on a soft, sad smile. "Because the one I chose has a heart of stone and will not listen. That is why I spend my days alone."

"Ah, Frank, not alone, surely. I see young Franks everywhere I go! The school has been filled by your efforts!"

"A man can't refuse what comfort is offered him. Because he is treated cruelly is no reason for him to treat others so. You would not have me trample . . ."

"Oh never, Frank, never!"

Pushed too far, Frank was suddenly serious. "I have been faithful!"

She knew he had, and relented. Quick to see her change of mood, he leaned across the table. "If you would marry me today, tomorrow . . ."

Supaya smiled at him. He was endearing, handsome, and vigorous, his strong face softened by a wide, humorous mouth, his thick gray hair springing back from his broad forehead. On impulse she put out her hand to him and he clasped it in his.

"I can't marry again, Frank. But you will always be my friend, my very dear friend."

"But I want to be more. . . ."

"Please, Frank! Here, have some more blueberries. And don't ask me any more questions!"

Supaya walked through the woods on a path of brown leaves. Above her, bare branches swung and tossed in a fall wind. At seventy-two she found the seasons flowed past like a stream. It seemed to her spring had just come, but the heat of summer had come and gone, and already the days were growing chilly. She was going to Kineu's little house at the head of the inlet, taking Waboose and Betty a pot of soup. They lived there now, part of the year. Since returning from the war, Waboose had been working as a migrant farm worker in season, returning to the reserve in the fall to fish for winter and remaining until spring. This was the path where she had confronted Wenonga, the path that had led her back to Kineu. Now his son, Waboose, lived in the house where he'd been conceived, and *his* sons were grown. One, Tom, was married and had two daughters, Theresa and Maggie, Kineu's great-granddaughters.

Coming down from the shelter of the trees onto the beach,

Supaya felt the cold wind more sharply. In pulling her shawl closer, she fumbled the pot and nearly dropped it. Swift as thought, a tall man in a fancy vest bent over her, laughing, his eyes a piercing blue under his wide-brimmed black hat. And in that instant, with the emptiness of the cold, rocky shore before her, a pang so sharp struck her that tears filled her eyes and she paused half bent over to recover.

Waboose, seeing her from the window, rushed out to help. As she lifted her head, he suddenly saw, for the first time, that his mother had grown old.

"Mother, are you all right?"

"Yes, yes. I just stumbled and nearly dropped this pot."

"But you're crying! Are you hurt?"

She shook her head impatiently. Would they never stop asking her questions! "I am not crying! The wind cuts my eyes. Just take this pot and let's go in!"

Waboose looked anxiously at his mother. He had never thought of her as old, never considered that she, like Auntie Soos, might one day go to the old people's home or even die. "Here, Mother, sit here."

"Don't fuss over me, Waboose. I'm all right."

But he was disturbed. He felt strange, as if something were slipping from his grasp, something—he wasn't sure what—that he should hang onto. "Mother, do you ever . . . well . . . wish the old times back?"

Another question. Supaya looked at her son. There was no gray in his hair, but his face, similar in feature to her own, was tired. His shoulders sagged. He was forty-eight, but the war had aged him. And the rootless life of a migratory worker was wearing to his spirit, that she knew. But not knowing exactly what was in his mind, Supaya answered cautiously.

"Just like now, old times were good and bad."

"But weren't they more good than bad?" he persisted. "Weren't we happier, before father went to war, than now? Weren't our lives more . . . I don't know, fuller, happier, at least for the men?" Supaya was considering how best to answer when he suddenly burst out, "I went to school, got an education. I've got a wife and sons, but half the time I don't know why I'm doing what I do. Oh, we got to eat, so I work, but it never comes to anything! I've got no purpose! Hell! I've got two names, but I don't even know who I am!"

Supaya was shocked, then indignant. "Since you have forgotten," she said sternly, "I will tell you who you are! You are Waboose Bruley, son of Kineu Bruley, a strong man who could run like the wind! A man who dreamed and was blessed with a powerful guardian! A man who understood the ways of animals and the winds and the currents. There was no finer hunter or fisherman than your father, and he fished and hunted on the land where his father and his grandfather and his great-grandfather fished and hunted. And your mother is the daughter of a powerful doctor whose name was known and respected on reserves far distant from his own. And his father was a great doctor before him! Their flesh is your flesh! The blood of all of them flows in your veins and in your sons!" Erect in her chair, Supaya's old hands grasped the arm rests firmly. She frowned intently at her son as if to impress her words indelibly on his consciousness. "You are an Indian, that's who you are, and they are your heritage! You should remember them and walk with pride!"

Waboose was struck silent. He had not expected such an answer or such vehemence. "But what," he asked, after a moment, "of the man *Walter* Bruley?"

Supaya smiled proudly. "There is only one man— Waboose. Walter is like a coat that Waboose wears when he goes among white men. Because we live in a white world, you have to live and work with white people. That is why I sent you to school, so you could learn to be part of this world. But you are still Indian!"

Waboose heated a pot of tea for his mother. Betty, he said, was taking care of Tom's little girls while Tom and Charlie went into Wolcott Harbor.

"They want to buy a garage that's for sale. It's the second time they've gone to look at it. Don't know why. Even between them, they haven't got enough money."

Supaya was grateful for the tea. She felt unusually tired and cold. "Is it a good business?"

"Sure. It's in a good location. Lots of tourists, lots of cars."

"You think Tom and Charlie could do it?"

"They'd be good at it. They're both mechanics. Charlie knows more about fixing cars than anybody around here. But there's no chance."

Supaya frowned, nettled by her son's hopeless tone. "Waboose, I have some money they can have. You tell them. Tell them to come and I'll give it to them." She finished her tea and got up to go, brushing aside Waboose's amazement and gratitude. All she asked was that he stay and help them. "They'll need you," she said, putting on her shawl. "Then you can stay here and work."

"Why don't you wait, Mother, and have some soup with Betty and me?"

"No, no, I have to go home."

"Why? There's nobody there."

Supaya looked at him. "Waboose," she said distinctly, "I have things to do."

She had climbed up the hill from the beach and was halfway home when her right arm went numb. Further on she felt dizzy and had to sit down. Through the trees she could look down the slope and see the shed with its now empty pigpen and the back of her house. As she rested, she thought sadly of her son who had no purpose, of her lost daughter, of Wagash, who had sold his heritage for a government bond. They had all of them, despite her efforts, taken a wrong turning, and she knew, sitting there in the raw wind, amid the bare trees, that they had done so because they had not had a vision. They had no direction and no guardian to lend them strength and courage. They had received no blessings at all.

She sat quietly, pensively, and waited while the numbness gradually left her arm. The gray fall sky had darkened imperceptibly. The outline of her house and shed had faded into the dusk. Still she sat on until suddenly through the woods came the long, drawn-out, mournful cry of a wolf. Startled, she raised her head and listened, her whole spirit intent. But all she heard was the soft soughing of the wind.

CHAPTER THIRTY-SIX

The sign on the front lawn read in large black letters on white, Sunset Haven, and below, in smaller letters, County Home for the Aged. Supaya squinted at it, the only visible sign of her aversion which she allowed herself. She knew Sarah was watching her, as she had done all the way to town, and since she had asked Sarah and Caleb to bring her, Supaya was determined not to be disagreeable.

As Caleb turned into the driveway, she had a view of the building, once the home of a well-to-do merchant. Its siding was painted a bilious yellow and the straight-hung curtains at the long narrow windows were an antiseptic white. A brick extension had been built onto the back of the original building; it had small, square windows, also white-curtained.

"Let us out near the entrance, Caleb," said Sarah. "Aunt Suppy won't have as far to walk."

"I can walk as well as you, Sarah," said Supaya tartly. Her apprehension over seeing Soos and Lizzie again after so many years was causing her patience to wear thin.

Sarah had been greatly surprised when Supaya had asked to come along. Her mother, now eighty-seven, had been living at the home for ten years, Lizzie, who was eighty-nine, for twelve, and this was the first time Supaya had asked to visit them, a request so unusual that Sarah instantly thought Supaya was ill.

"No, no! I am not sick!" Supaya had said impatiently. "If I were sick, I'd stay home! I told you I would come when I had time.

Now I do." But for once Supaya had not been altogether honest. She did have time, but she was not sure how much, and she wanted to see Soos and Lizzie once more.

Soos and Lizzie's room was on the second floor. Lizzie met them at the door, and Sarah tactfully left them alone. The room had once been a corner bedroom. Now there were four wrought-iron beds, painted white, two on each side, sticking out into the middle of the floor that was covered in a slick brown Congoleum. Light reflected from its surface into Supaya's eyes and at first she did not recognize the old woman with one hunched shoulder who caught her arm and stared at her with pale, watery eyes.

"Sophia! You finally came! Here, come sit over here." She tugged at Supaya's arm, leading her to two padded white wicker chairs at the far corner of the room, between the windows and a bed. "Here, sit here." They sat just as a fierce-eyed old woman in a wheelchair spun herself forward from the opposite corner and rolled rapidly down the center of the room. "I'm so glad you've come, Sophia! We've so much to tell you, haven't we, Soos?" Lizzie leaned close. Too close. Her wizened face shocked Supaya. Turning away, she was shocked again to see that the old woman propped up in the bed was Soos, smiling and nodding.

They both talked at her excitedly, of the food, the nurses, their bickerings with other patients, their words overlapping. Supaya, hemmed in, was distracted by their interrupting and contradicting each other, each bent on pursuing her own thought. Looking from one to the other—as they spoke more to each other than to her—she was stifled by the sense that these two old women were not her lifelong friends but strangers. She had waited too long to come.

Lizzie, spritely, upright Lizzie, was lost in this old woman humped forward in her chair, whose thin, wispy hair scarcely covered her skull and whose bony hand, still gripping Supaya's arm, shook with a persistent tremor. And Soos, robust and strong enough to swing herself about on crutches when Supaya last saw her, was painfully shrunken. Her long braided hair, which had always been coiled about her head and framed her face, had been cut off short and square like a child's, incongruous with her gaunt face. Her large eyes had sunk deep in their sockets. Her gown hung over her wasted chest, and under the blanket her useless legs made two parallel ridges.

Supaya heard only snatches of what they said. Her ears felt numbed. Sarah, having put away the clean clothes she brought for Soos and Lizzie, was standing near the door, conferring with a woman and glancing back now and then at her mother.

"They used to let me have a wheelchair after they took my crutches away," said Soos, "and I went everywhere, even down that ramp into the new section. Now they won't let me. She," glancing scornfully at the woman in the wheelchair, "never goes anywhere."

Catching Soos' glance, the woman wheeled herself rapidly straight at Lizzie and Supaya, stopping just short of banging into their knees. Stretching her head forward, she stared at them balefully, her eyes shouting silent abuse. Abruptly, she spun around and wheeled to the opposite corner where she sat with her back to the room.

"She should be in another room," said Lizzie critically. "Things are not well run here." Caleb, who'd been standing about, strolled out of the room. "He knows that's true," said Lizzie, following him with her eyes. "They need someone here like Gerald. *He* would run things properly!"

Across the room an old woman began to whimper. One of her emaciated legs protruded from under the blanket, suspended in midair like a withered branch from a frame attached to the bed.

"Pay no attention," said Lizzie. "It doesn't hurt. She just wants attention."

A woman in a starched white dress came in and scolded the old woman cheerfully, as she would a child. Then she handed out pills all around.

"They give us these to keep us quiet," Lizzie declared.

"Now, Mrs. Toomis, you know that's not true," chided the nurse, flashing a quick smile at Supaya. "You'll give your friend the wrong impression," she said and turned briskly away.

"Have you seen Nathan and Ralph? Louisa's boys?" asked Lizzie. "They came, just last week. They're fine boys. Nathan's wife's going to have another baby."

"Josie and her family live in my house now," said Soos. "She has a garden larger than mine used to be."

Supaya only nodded, dismayed that they should tell her about people she saw every week.

"Gerald ran the agency very well for many years, all by

himself. Then Louisa helped him. Well," Lizzie hesitated, her tone uncertain, "maybe you remember."

Then Supaya realized she too had become a stranger, that they were looking at her like old, disappointed children.

"Sarah says you live alone," remarked Soos, but before Supaya could answer her, her attention returned to herself. "If I hadn't fallen, I would still . . ."

"Please, Mother," said Sarah, patting her arm. Caleb returned, nodded at Sarah to indicate they should go. "We have to go now, Mother." They went, leaving Supaya to say good-bye.

Supaya rose. Until this moment her visit had appalled and confused her, made her wish she had not come. Now, knowing she would never come again, Supaya wanted one last time to greet her oldest, dearest friends. She gazed intently into their eyes, striving with all her will to break through to them, to cut through the mask of old age and illness to the Soos and Lizzie she knew were there, recall to them who and what they were, and what they had shared. She wished, once more, to touch their consciousness with her own. Slowly, as Soos returned Supaya's look, a smile illuminated her face. Her eyes grew warm with remembrance. With no need for words, she pressed Supaya's hand. Lizzie, her moist eyes bright with recognition, said soundlessly, "Supaya." For one moment they shared an awareness of their past and put a final seal upon their friendship.

"Mother looked better than last time, didn't she? Lizzie, too. I asked the matron to move that woman to another room. She's going to hurt someone with that chair. They were both so glad to see you, Aunt Suppy. Oh, Caleb, she's fallen asleep. All that talking tired her out."

Supaya heard Sarah's remarks but being full of her own, more interesting thoughts, didn't bother to correct her. She was glad, after all, that she had gone, and now she was remembering the first time she had traveled from Wellston to Two Bluffs. It had been a long, bumpy ride on the bare boards of a wagon bed. She had sat hunched in the corner behind a strange man named Eli who was to be her husband, and the stars had gradually appeared in the darkening night sky. The horse, she remembered, had stomped impatiently when they'd stopped to buy a comb. . . .

The agent, William Brent, occasionally dropped by to see Supaya. Any eighty-one-year-old woman living alone needed to be looked in on. He tried to catch her when she was outside so he could more easily avoid her invariable invitation to have a cup of tea.

"Come in, Mr. Brent." Supaya smiled mischievously. "Come and have a cup of tea." She knew he was ill at ease in her house. He fidgeted like a boy, and Supaya delighted in teasing him.

"Thank you, Sophia, but I can't stop today." From the way she looked at him, her impenetrable stare and slight smile, he felt she constantly compared him with his predecessor and always to his own disadvantage.

And he was right. Supaya's private opinion was that William Brent had never measured up to Gerald Toomis. What Gerald understood baffled William. Gerald would have been glad for a rest and a cup of tea. He would have put his hat on the floor beside his chair and talked as a friend, now and then running his fingers through his red hair. Remembering Gerald, Supaya squinted at William Brent and said, "You work too hard."

Immediately William felt he stood accused of idleness. He swallowed hard and said, "I heard you went to Wellston to visit old friends." Supaya said nothing, not liking to be spied on. "You'll have to go there too before long." Now why had he blurted that out! Look at her, going stiff all over!

"What do you mean?" asked Supaya.

"Well, it's difficult to live alone . . . when one reaches . . . a certain age. It's better," he finished in a rush, "it's better to be where people can take care of you."

Supaya gave him a withering look. No one, not Quayo, Aunt Theresa, Auntie Em, Nonen, Uncle John, Alma, no one had ever found it necessary to go to an old people's home! Not until William Brent became agent! Not until then had Soos and others been taken there. That he should speak so to her, presume to order her, made her furious. William Brent was truly a fool and not worth teasing.

"Young man, understand me! This is my home and here I will stay! I can take care of myself!"

Nodding and tipping his hat, William retreated down the lane, Supaya following after him.

"I will stay here until I die! And I don't need you coming to see if I'm still alive!" She let him go, but then, remembering Waboose, she called out and hurried after him. Pointing a finger at him imperiously, she said, "Just you remember! Waboose . . . Walter Bruley gets my house when I'm gone! Only my son, Walter Bruley! You write that in your ledger!"

Supaya, getting herself a cup of tea, got out two more cups for her great-granddaughters, Theresa and Maggie. She wished they hadn't come so early. She had awakened with the now familiar pain in her arms and had stayed in bed until it eased. She wanted to sit in her rocker and have her tea peacefully, alone. Maggie, sixteen, always fussed at her about the old stove, why didn't she get an electric one like everybody else's, and the lights, nobody uses those old lamps any more. Maggie was a loud girl and feeling self-important because she had just graduated from the reserve school and in the fall would go to high school in Wellston.

"You want to go?" asked Supaya.

Maggie laughed. "Sure I want to go, Grandma. I can get a job in Wellston. Maybe even go to Toronto! There's nothing to do here!"

Supaya squinted at her. Wagash still lived in Toronto. Charlie had gone to see him once when he was in Toronto getting supplies for the garage. Wagash was still a clerk in the Hadley hardware store. Howard had outlived Rhea and had given the store to his nephew. Wagash lived in a room by himself somewhere. Charlie said he hadn't talked much.

"But it's true, Grandma," insisted Maggie. "All those things you did when you were a girl nobody does anymore. I can't spend my life making baskets and telling tales of the old days. Besides, nobody's interested!"

Supaya's hand shook. She set down her cup. The pain was coming back and she didn't want them to know.

"Grandma," said Theresa, leaning toward Supaya, "Grandma, Dad thought maybe one of us should come and live with you, you know, help you with the housework and the garden. Grandma! You're not listening."

"She's daydreaming again," said Maggie.

Supaya was not dreaming. She had heard. And she saw them both clearly, their youthful, untouched faces and dark, restless eyes. But she saw them from a distance. She could no longer help them. She needed all her remaining strength to follow her own path. They would have to find their own way, and it would be hard, for they had not dreamed. They had no vision. There was so much she could have told them if they had only listened, and the pain in her chest may have been for the loss of what they would never hear.

"Grandma, did you hear me? I asked you if . . ."

Supaya held up her hand. "I hear you. No. No. I don't need any help with the house. And Frank helps me with the garden."

Theresa felt put off. "But Grandma, at night, you're all alone!"

Alone! Supaya smiled. "I'm never alone! My house is full of people!" She saw them glance at each other and almost laughed thinking what they would tell their father. Suddenly impatient, she stood up, wanting them gone, gone to whatever future they imagined they wanted. It had nothing anymore to do with her.

"You girls go along now!" She made a sweeping gesture, the pain in her arms spurring her to action. "I've things to do, and my house is crowded with people!"

Driving by early one morning, Frank saw there was no smoke rising from Supaya's chimney, and he had thought to stop by for a cup of tea. Like himself, Supaya was an early riser, and he wondered if she were sick. Recently he had begun to suspect she did not feel well. Not that she said anything. But she'd stop working and sit down with a distant, preoccupied expression. It was not like her and it made him uneasy.

As he pulled up alongside the house, he saw that the front door stood wide open. His hand raised to knock, he paused, struck by a sense of emptiness. In the fireplace the ashes were cold. There was a log left lying on the hearth, and at the far end of the house the lean-to door stood ajar.

She was gone! Gone without a word! She had escaped him again, and his heart contracted painfully in his chest. He spoke her name aloud and then, though he knew it was no use, he went upstairs. Her bed was smooth but the dress she'd worn yesterday lay in a heap and her trunk stood open, empty except for some old postcards and letters and a bundle of hair. He stared at the glossy black coils, touched them gently. He would have taken them, kept them, but he knew he had no right to what had been cut off in sorrow for another man.

He went to the back door and looked out. There were no fish hanging on the drying frame, and the pigpen was overgrown with weeds. She'd said she wanted no pig this year. Carefully he latched the back door. When he came to this house again, it would be to return the body of a woman he had long loved, a woman with real blessings, gifts from her Grandfather, a woman of real power.

He shut the front door. He would wait one full day. Tomorrow he would hunt for her.

EPILOGUE

Dressed in her long black skirt and her blouse with the quill embroidery that Auntie Em had given her, Supaya stepped out into a cool, gray dawn. Her gray hair, combed straight back like her mother's, hung in one thick braid down her back. Around her neck was the bear claw necklace, and on her feet the beaded moccasins Quayo had sewn for her. Carrying her medicine bag, Supaya started up the slope behind her house. Never had the distance up to the edge of the woods seemed so long or so steep. She remembered fleetingly Alma telling the children about the four hills. This, Supaya thought, was as far as she would ever climb on the fourth hill. Slowly, leaning forward and bracing her hand against her thigh at each step, she made her way up the slope. Pain burned across her chest and down her arms. Each breath was a kind of moan. When her legs threatened to buckle under her, she paused to rest, not looking to see how far she had yet to go, but only at the slope before her, and she held tight the blue stone of her necklace to give her strength.

When she reached the trees at the top, she wasted no time in looking back, as always in the past, but went on, a little faster now that the ground had leveled off, toward the cedar grove where she'd been attacked by the great white dog and had seen the footprint and the power of the Great Bear.

The gloom of night still lingered in the quiet, damp woods. The only sound was her own labored breathing. Reaching the cedar grove, she sank down on her knees beside a fallen log and rested her head against its rough bark. Exhausted, she closed her eyes, then opened them, afraid that if she once gave in, she could not again summon up the strength she needed.

With a broken branch, she began digging a hole beneath the log, scraping away the dirt with her hands. When the hole was deep enough, she laid in it her black velvet medicine bag, the bag of Negik, her great-grandfather, a wise man and a great healer, that held the stone bear, Jess' watch and chain, the beaded skin amulet of her father, and her medicines, hers and Quayo's and Beedaubun's. She covered the bag over with earth and pressed it firm, brushing back the leaf mold and hiding all trace of the burial.

Her task finished, Supaya's last strength drained away, leaving only a fierce, engulfing pain. The earth tilted under her. Fainting, she slumped back against the log. Then, beyond the pain, as in a dream, she saw a meadow flooded with sunlight, and heard the sound of women's voices. Their soft laughter and the still vivid memory of her dream aroused her. Filled with sudden elation, Supaya struggled to raise herself, knowing He was there! "Grandfather!" she whispered, reaching out her arms. For a moment her vision cleared and she saw him once more, looming over her, the Great Bear, vibrant and luminous, saw him with piercing clarity before he enveloped her in his all-powerful, eternal embrace.

GLOSSARY

ahnee: a greeting, "welcome"

blessings: knowledge and power acquired during dreams from *manitos* and/or the Great Spirit

"boss" fish: each species of plant and animal has a chief in every locality; these "bosses" are always larger than normal specimens

"glowing powder": a compound medicine containing, among other ingredients, wild ginger root, sweet flag root, wild leeks, and ground, dried fluorescent fungus; this powder protects against evil wishes and can bring about success in any venture upon which it is carried

guardian spirits: young Ojibwa fasted and prayed until experiencing a vision; the spirit or *manito* appearing in this vision became the dreamer's lifelong guardian

helper spirits: in addition to guardian spirits, shamans had one or more "helper" spirits, upon whom they called during ceremonies

k'neu or kineu: eagle

maheengun: wolf

manito or manitou: nonhuman beings with supernatural power, associated with plants, animals, places; often called "spirits;" intermediaries between man and *Kitchi Manito,* the Great Spirit, source of all power *midé:* a shortened form of *midewiwin,* the name of the Grand Medicine Society of the Ojibwa; this is a secret society, with a number of grades of membership. At one time a form of this society existed among the Georgian Bay-Lake Huron Ojibwa. Both Jules and Wenonga, in addition to being shamans, were *midé (midewiwin)* brothers

mukwah: bear

nimepin: wild ginger *(Asarum canadense),* a root, dried and used as flavoring in stews and as a tea to treat heart trouble; is also carried as a protection against witches and is one of the ingredients in Quayo's "glowing powder"

nishnabeg: a colloquial form of *Anicinabek,* the Ojibwa word for human beings, used to refer to all people who speak languages related to Ojibwa

noshan: aunt

Nzagima: chief of the water serpents; fights the thunder and helps the Ojibwa; if he feels insulted, he will cause misfortune to the offender

Pay Day: the day upon which the Canadian Government annuity was distributed to the Indians; the amount varied from five to fifteen dollars per person, depending upon the particular treaty involved. On some reserves, there were two annual Pay Days, on others, only one

scone and bannock: a form of baking powder bread that was usually either baked or fried in lard; it could also be cooked in the hot ashes of an open fire

sweet grass: picked in late July or early August and dried out of the direct sun but in a warm and constant draft, then wrapped up to preserve scent; used for mats and to trim birchbark boxes

weekan: sweet flag root *(Acorus calamus)* gathered in the late summer, dried, and chewed as a general tonic or a remedy for sore throat and colds, and also carried as a charm against evil spirits and evil wishes